INDIANA STATE SERIES

PRIMARY LESSONS

IN

HUMAN PHYSIOLOGY

BY

OLIVER P. JENKINS, Ph.D.

PROFESSOR OF PHYSIOLOGY AND HISTOLOGY IN LELAND STANFORD JR. UNIVERSITY

INDIANA SCHOOL BOOK COMPANY
INDIANAPOLIS, IND.

A WORD TO THE TEACHER.

THESE lessons have been prepared as a guide to the study of the human body ; and while, no doubt, the teacher who undertakes to teach the subject of this little book is fully competent to do so, yet the writer may be pardoned for giving expression to his views in regard to the true place of such a book.

The writer would insist that the book be used only as a guide to such study and not the sole object to be studied. The human body itself should be the object studied. To supplement this, abundant materials from the bodies of lower animals should be used as a means to give true conceptions of the parts of the human body and its actions. If the teacher had sufficient time to give complete individual direction, a book would be of questionable use in this connection.

If this or any other elementary text-book in physiology is used simply as a book to be learned and recited, the time spent on it is worse than wasted. The terms used in the description of the parts of the body and their actions can not have their proper meanings unless the real objects are seen. To attempt to cram children's minds with terms which to them stand either for nothing, or for vague conceptions wholly different from those for which the terms have been chosen, is doing the children a great injury.

This procedure is not only harmful but unnecessary. Many of the parts of the body can be put under study and their operations carefully observed and analyzed. The lower animals can furnish the rest of the illustrations. A bone is a bone, the animal kingdom through. The same may be said for muscles, tendons, ligaments, nerves, and all other parts that make up the body.

Charts and drawings have also their place in teaching, but they should come after the objects, and never before, and certainly should not stand for them. If the charts and models prevent finding true materials for illustration, they have done harm.

The illustrations from the lower animals need have nothing unpleasant about them, and certainly nothing disgusting about them.

The subjects treated of in this book can all be illustrated by the bodies of some small animal, the dissection of which, if neatly done, will not disgust any one.

A chicken or a frog will answer admirably, and certainly its preparation for class study need be no more objectionable than its preparation for dinner.

The human body and the bodies of the lower animals should also be studied in action, each in its own natural surrounding, as organisms adapted to these surroundings. It is only by constantly seeing the organisms in their true relations to other things that even elementary conceptions of physiological facts can be obtained.

The teacher need not feel discouraged if not provided with charts or other apparatus, he can make use of the living world around him to illustrate the study of the most interesting of living organisms. The work thus pursued will be of a real value beyond the interesting knowledge gained, and will bring the reward of a satisfaction of having accomplished something of worth.

In the second book of this series the writer has introduced directions for the practical demonstration of many anatomical and physiological facts, which might well be suggestive to the teacher of this book. For these directions and for a fuller discussion of many of the subjects treated here reference may be made to the second book. There are now published many hand-books for the dissection of many of the groups of the lower animals, any one of which will be helpful in preparing illustrations for the study of the human body.

But illustrations of the work, or subjects for study, will be numerous enough and more vital if they come from his own observation and experience with the objects of study.

O. P. JENKINS.

GREENCASTLE, INDIANA.
May, 1891.

CONTENTS.

6 *CONTENTS.*

LIST OF ILLUSTRATIONS.

PRIMARY PHYSIOLOGY.

CHAPTER I.

HOW MOTIONS IN THE BODY ARE PRODUCED.

The Study of the Human Body.—The human body is made up of a great number of parts, which may be called so many pieces of machinery. They work together so harmoniously that they all help each other. When, for example, a boy climbs a tree, almost every part of his body is contributing to this action. Many parts of his arms, his legs, the muscles and bones of the rest of the body, the eye, the touch organs, the nerves, the lungs, the heart, and indeed almost all the organs must act together to get the boy's body up the tree.

To study out how these actions are performed, and how such a large number of separate parts come to be so well controlled as to accomplish any thing the body can do, is well worth the trouble it takes. To understand more clearly the parts of the wonderful machine which is our constant servant, and to learn how to keep it in the best order, is certainly very important knowledge.

Study of the Hand and Arm.—One may well

begin the study of the human body by observing the common movements of his own arm and hand. Let him pick up an object from the table and raise it toward his mouth, and observe closely what takes place. First, the arm is straightened—that is, the part below the elbow, the fore-arm, is carried away from the part above. The whole arm may also be moved away from the body. The hand is carried toward the object, and just as it reaches it, the fingers and thumb are stretched out. The thumb and one or more fingers close together over the object to hold it firmly, when the fore-arm is carried toward the upper arm, and the hand with the object is carried toward the mouth. This is a very common action, and is repeated here to observe just what happens. Let us look at the actions separately, and attempt to see how they are accomplished.

Let us first examine the fingers and the thumb, and their actions. It is easy to determine that each finger has running through its central portion a row of three hard pieces, which are known well enough to be bones. These bones form two joints in the fingers, and the one next to the hand forms a joint with another bone at the knuckle. These joints allow the fingers to fold toward the palm of the hand, and to unfold again until straight, or even curved slightly backward. It is plain that if it were not for the rigid parts and the joints the fingers could not be extended with much force.

Now let us examine what is the action by which the bones of the finger are bent or straightened. If, while one is moving the fore-finger rapidly by extending and bending it, he places the finger of the other hand on the back of the hand just back of the moving finger, he can detect a firm cord crossing the knuckle and running toward the wrist. This becomes rigid every time the finger is extended. By causing each of the other fingers to move in the same manner, a similar cord for each one can be felt just under the skin. These cords can be traced even past the wrist into the fore-arm, where they are lost to the touch.

The skin of the palm is thicker than that on the back of the hand, so it is more difficult to detect the cords running from the palm side of the fingers at this place. But if we examine the region of the palm side of the fore-arm just above the wrist while the fingers are in motion, it is easy to show that there is a number of cords here which are moved every time the fingers are bent.

It is plain from this that the fingers are moved backward and forward by these strings pulling, first the one set, then the other. What pulls on the strings? If while the thumb and finger are closed and opened, as before observed, the other hand be made to grasp around the fore-arm just below the elbow, it will be found that this part of the arm shows great activity beneath the skin. This is due to the action of the parts that pull on the cords. These parts are the *muscles*. The cords are the *tendons*.

What the Muscles are like.—Not only are the fingers extended and bent by muscles pulling on the tendons which are tied to the finger bones, but when **the arm is bent at the elbow,** the action is accomplished by a muscle in the upper arm pulling on a tendon attached to a long bone in the fore-arm.

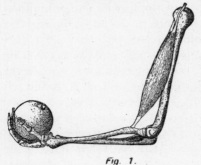

Fig. 1.

BICEPS MUSCLE ATTACHED TO THE RADIUS.

If with your left hand you grasp the right upper arm while the arm is b e i n g bent, the flesh on the front side of the arm will be felt to swell up greatly.

If the fingers be held at the front side of the elbow while the arm is being bent, a very large cord, the tendon, can be felt. The swelling flesh is a large muscle. Fig. 1 shows the arm with all the parts removed except the bones of the arm and this muscle and its tendons which bend the arm. Fig. 2 shows the same muscle removed, so as to better show its appearance.

Appearance of a Muscle.—As seen in the figure, this muscle, which is called the *biceps*, has a thick body, tapering off at each end to the *tendons*. The thick body is composed of a reddish mass. The lean part of the flesh of an animal, which is familiar to every one, is muscle.

Fig. 2.

BICEPS.

The muscle is surrounded by a tough membrane, which holds all of its parts together, and runs off toward the ends of the muscle and continues into the tendon. The tendon runs to the bone, where it is continuous with a membranous covering of the bone. Thus the muscle comes to be firmly attached to the bone.

Action of the Muscle.—It has already been seen that when the hand clasps the arm over the *biceps* muscle during the bending of the arm, it is felt to swell up to a considerable thickness. If, when the muscle is in action, it could be examined with the covering of the arm removed, one could see it shorten as well as thicken. It is this power of shortening and thickening, or *contracting*, as it is called, which enables the muscle to pull the bone and cause the motion of the arm.

The cause of the motions of the fingers which we observed is also the *contraction of the muscles*. In the part of the arm just below the elbow is a number of muscles. Each one is smaller than the biceps, but it is shaped very much like it. Each one ends in a tendon at each extremity, the one toward the elbow being short and attached to some one of the bones at points near the elbow joint. At the end toward the hand the tendons are long, some passing to the wrist, some to the hand, but most of them passing on to the different joints of the fingers. Some run along the back of the hand, as we observed, and some on the palm side.

A Review of these Points.—To bend a finger, we contract a muscle in the fore-arm ; to straighten it, we contract another. To straighten more than one finger, as in reaching for an object, we contract several muscles in the fore-arm ; to bring them together on the object, we contract several others in the same position. To bend the arm at the elbow, we contract the biceps. We may, by clasping the upper arm, find that when we straighten the arm, muscles on the opposite side from the biceps contract and pull on tendons attached to the fore-arm, and bring it back to its extended position.

Muscles that produce other Motions of the Arm.—If one place his hand at different positions around his shoulder while he lifts his whole arm up, brings it forward, backward, downward, or in any other direction, he will find that the muscles of the breast, of the top of the shoulder, or of the back, or just below the shoulder, are acting. These muscles are very large and make up most of the flesh in these regions. Those parts which lie just beneath the skin are shown in Fig. 3, but still others lie beneath these.

Other Muscles in the Body.—Whenever any motion of the parts of the body is made, it is by the contraction of the muscles. To produce the very many motions that the body performs, it is furnished with about five hundred muscles. Figs. 3 and 4 show where many of these muscles are placed, but a very large number lie deeper than these and many are small, so that all can not be represented at once.

Number of Motions.—The five hundred muscles can produce more than five hundred motions, for each one can produce a motion acting alone, a still different one when acting with another muscle, or even with several other muscles. For example, we may carry the whole arm in many hundreds of different positions with but a limited number of muscles, by combining their contractions in different ways.

Contractile Power of Muscles.—*The power of contractility* which the living muscle has is the source of the force which the body can exert. The contractile muscular substance is to the machinery of the human body what the steam is to the engine. It is well known that hot steam presses against the walls of the vessels containing it. It will lift the lid of a kettle, or may push so hard as to burst the walls of a steam-boiler. Men take advantage of this great power, and let the steam push against a piston, and by its connections turn a crank which makes all the motions in a great machine-shop.

In the body, the muscular substance, instead of pushing, as does steam, pulls on the ends of the vessels which contain it, and thus, by means of strings (tendons), pulls on the bones and makes the motions of the body.

Muscles in the Lower Animals.—The muscles in the common animals, such as horses, dogs, cats, rabbits, and the like, are of the same form, and are attached to bones in the same way as those in man. They have the same power of contracting and are in every respect like those of the human body.

The motions of all animals, except certain forms, chiefly microscopic, are produced by muscles. The muscles of the higher animals are arranged in about the same number and order on the limbs and the remainder of the body as in man. The examination of the muscles of the body of some small animal would teach very clearly how the muscles appear and how they are arranged in man, and how the tendons attach them to the bones.

What causes the Muscles to Contract.—We know that we can cause the muscles to contract whenever we wish to do so. The arm can be moved at the exact moment and with just the force we desire. It is said, for example, that the muscles of the arm are under the control of the will. If the arm could be laid open for examination, there could be seen some other things beside muscles and tendons.

Among these latter would be seen some white cords, which divide into many branches, one going to each muscle. They penetrate the sheath of the muscle and are lost in its substance. These cords, dividing up into fine threads, are *nerves*. If they are traced from the muscles, they are found to run up the arm, through the shoulder, across to the backbone, and into its center. Here they connect with a large nerve cord, the spinal cord, which runs to the brain. These we will study later, but mention them here to show that the muscles are connected with the brain, through which the *will* acts.

Now, if a nerve going to a muscle be cut in two, then no power of the will can make it contract. It is only when the nerve connects the muscle with the brain that we can move the muscle when we wish. The brain can send some influence that the nerve is able to conduct, which, when it reaches the muscle substance, makes it contract. The exact nature of this influence is unknown, nor is it known how it

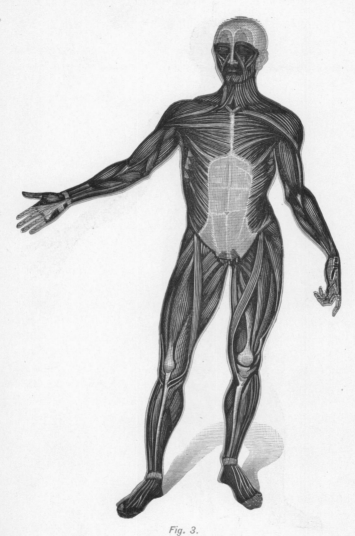

Fig. 3.

FRONT VIEW OF THE SUPERFICIAL MUSCLES OF THE BODY.

PR.—17

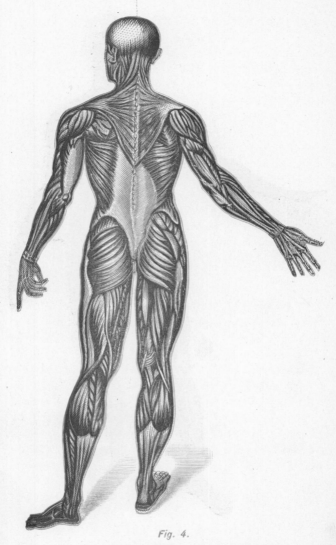

Fig. 4.

BACK VIEW OF THE SUPERFICIAL MUSCLES OF THE BODY.
PR.—18

makes the muscle contract. This influence is called a *nervous impulse*.

When a nervous impulse comes to a muscle to contract it, it is said to *stimulate* the muscle. Other things will stimulate a muscle to contraction beside the nervous impulse. For example, if a living muscle is touched with a hot wire, or pinched, or struck, or has applied to it some chemical substance or electricity, it will contract ; but in the bodies of men and the lower animals only the nervous impulse is made use of to move the muscles.

Voluntary and Involuntary Muscles.—All those muscles whose action may be controlled by the will are called *voluntary* muscles. They are the great majority of the muscles in the body. The muscles of the heart and of the stomach, and of some of the other organs, are stimulated to action from some other source than the *will*, and the will can not control them. Consequently, they are called *involuntary* muscles.

Some of the most important actions of the body, such as those in the circulation of the blood, in breathing, and in the digestion of food, are carried on by involuntary muscles. The arrangement by which certain muscles may act independently of our care and attention allows important actions to go on while we are asleep, and when the mind is so occupied that they would be forgotten or neglected.

Further, these operations are so complex, and make use of processes that we know so little of, that, if they depended on our will alone for direction and control, they would surely go wrong in a very short time. The involuntary muscles relieve us of the responsibility and trouble of these operations, and give us time to accomplish other motions.

Questions for Review.

1. What makes up the body?
2. How do the parts work in any action?
3. Show what is meant by the eye and foot working in harmony.
4. What takes place in the arm and hand in picking up some thing from the table?
5. What forms the hard parts of the fingers?
6. What are found fastened to them?
7. Describe the action of the joints.
8. Describe the course of the strings which are attached to the bones of the fingers.
9. What are these cords called?
10. What pull on them?
11. Describe a muscle.
12. How does a muscle act?
13. Where are the muscles that move the fingers?
14. Where are the muscles which extend the arm?
15. Where the muscles that bend the arm?
16. Where are their tendons?
17. Show in your own hand and arm all these parts.
18. Where are the muscles that lift, lower, and produce other motions of the whole arm?
19. Point out these muscles in Figs. 3 and 4.
20. How many muscles are there in the body?
21. Where are they placed?

22. What of the number of motions which they can produce?

23. How can two muscles produce more than two motions?

24. What is the source of the force which produces the motions of the body?

25. How may muscle substance be compared to steam?

26. What of the muscles in the lower animals?

27. What are the nerves?

28. With what do they connect the muscles?

29. What makes the muscles contract?

30. How do we know that a nervous impulse passes along a nerve?

31. What is meant by *stimulate?*

32. What are voluntary and what are involuntary muscles? Give examples.

33. What advantage is gained by having certain muscles act involuntarily?

CHAPTER II.

SKELETON OF THE UPPER EXTREMITIES.

General View.—Since the bones of the arm and hand are so easily traced, and their uses can be so clearly made out, we will study them in some detail. The bones of the arm illustrate many facts about bones in general. They are generally grouped as bones of the *hand*, the *fore-arm*, and the *arm*, and are attached to the body by the *shoulder girdle*, the whole group being sometimes referred to as the bones of the upper extremities.

The Bones of the Hand.—We have just seen that the fingers have each three bones and the thumb has two—fourteen in all. They are called the *phalanges*, a single one a phalanx. The five bones which we traced in the palm of the hand, and whose outer ends are the knuckles, are called the *metacarpals*.

Notice that the metacarpal of the thumb is free to move in many directions, while those of the fingers are firmly bound together. This arrangement allows the thumb to be brought opposite to any one of the fingers or to most points on the palm. This power of moving the thumb so freely increases very greatly the usefulness of the hand.

To convince one's self of this, let him attempt to use the hand without using the thumb in picking up objects, and in handling them, and then in contrast repeat the operations with the help of the thumb. While the fingers without the thumb may become very expert, yet the thumb wonderfully increases the usefulness of the whole hand.

If we attempt to trace the metacarpals back toward the arm by feeling them under the skin, we soon lose them in the flesh that surrounds them.

Immediately under the skin and flesh in the wrist we can feel a solid portion. This is a bunch of small bones, eight in number, arranged in two rows of four in each row. They

Fig. 5.

BONES OF THE HAND.

are the bones of the wrist and are called the *carpals.* Compare your own hand with the picture of the bones of the hand shown in Fig. 5.

Bones of the Fore-arm.—That part of the arm between the wrist and the elbow joint is called the fore-arm. Immediately back of the wrist joint the ends of the two bones may be felt under the skin. The end of one makes the little round knob which shows under the skin on the little-finger side of the arm.

This is the end of the *ulna.* The bone may be traced for its whole length, when it will be found to extend to the elbow joint. It makes the point of the elbow where it is very close to the skin.

By the side of this bony knob of the ulna, near the wrist, lies the end of the *radius.* The broad end of this bone fills up the space from the knob of the ulna to the edge of the arm on the thumb side.

It is this broad end of the radius to which the hand is joined to make up the wrist joint. Thus the radius carries the hand. The radius may also be traced to the elbow joint.

Movements of the Radius.—If the hand be held out with the palm turned upward, it will be found that the radius and ulna lie side by side. Now, while the arm is in this position, turn the hand over, so as to bring the palm down, and during this motion watch the motion of the two bones of the fore-arm. It will be seen that the radius turns over the ulna until it comes to lie across it.

Radius. Ulna.

Fig. 6.

BONES OF THE FORE-ARM.

It ends at the elbow in a little shallow cup about three fourths of an inch across, which fits on a knob on the large bone of the arm. This cup-shaped end of the radius allows it to turn on this knob as on a point.

A groove in the side of the wrist end of the bone allows it to slide over the knob of the ulna. Now, muscles are so arranged that they can quickly pull the radius over the rigid ulna; and as the radius carries the hand, of course the hand is turned over. This arrangement is for turning the hand over.

The same bones in a dog's fore-leg are bound firmly together, and, consequently, it can not turn its fore-paw over; but in the cat's fore-leg the radius has a little motion, and it may be seen while the kitten is playing with a ball, it will often turn its fore-paw slightly.

Now examine carefully the figures of the ulna and radius given here, and determine which parts of them you can make out in your own arm. It may be remembered from the lesson on muscles that it is to the radius that the biceps muscle is attached.

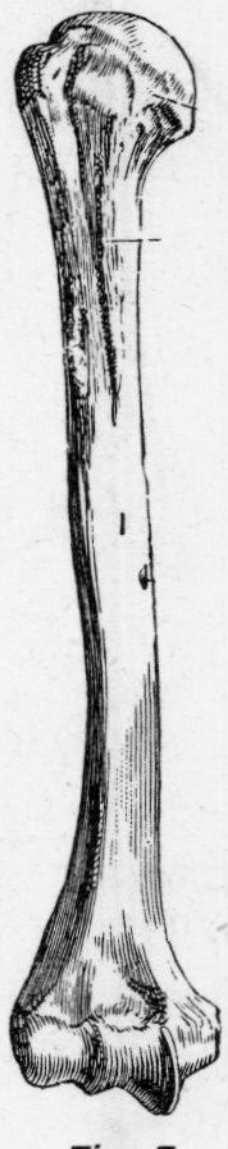

The Humerus.—In the part of the arm between the elbow and the shoulder is a very large bone called the *humerus.* A picture of this bone is shown in Fig. 7.

Fig. 7.
THE HUMERUS.

The elbow end has grooves and a knob for the ulna and radius to fit into. The shoulder end is formed into one large, smooth, round end to fit into a cup-shaped part of a bone at the shoulder, called the shoulder blade.

The sides of the broad end of the humerus are very prominent at the elbow, but the shoulder end, called the head of the humerus, is so deeply buried in the large muscles which move the arm that it can not be so well examined.

Scapula and Clavicle.—As was said, the round head of the humerus is fitted to a part of the shoulder blade, the *scapula* (seen in Fig. 8). One can not well make out the whole outline of this bone in his own shoulder, but he may easily trace it in that of another person.

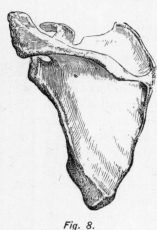

Fig. 8.

THE SCAPULA.

The prominent hard part felt just at the top of the shoulder is the upper end of the ridge which runs across the bone. This ridge lies near the skin, and can be traced across the bone to its posterior edge, where it ends. The edges of the scapula can also be made out. It is a flat, triangular bone fitted to the upper part of the back. Besides acting as a support to the humerus, it serves also as a place to which are fastened many of the muscles that move the arm.

The *clavicle* is the collar bone. It is very near the skin at the front part of the base of the neck, and can be traced from the shoulder to a point at the top of the front part of the chest. Its use is to hold the shoulders and arms back from the chest.

The Pectoral Arch.—The clavicle and scapula together make a firm brace to support the arm and attach it to the body.

Often the arm is called upon to lift a heavy weight,

or push with great force against an object. These actions would be impossible if the arm were not thoroughly braced against the body. The scapula and clavicle make this brace, and are called the *pectoral arch*, or *pectoral girdle*.

Levers.—If at your desk you use a lead pencil to pry up one book by letting the side of the pencil rest on another, the lead pencil is used as a *lever*.

In the lever three points are named : the point to which the weight is attached, generally called *W;* the point to which the power is applied to lift the weight, called *P;* and the point where the lever is supported, called the fulcrum, whose sign is *F*. The point *F* is stationary, while the remainder of the lever turns on this.

Now, in the use of the pencil described, the point *F* was between *P* and *W*. When a lever is used in this way it is said to be a lever of the *first class*.

Now push one end of the pencil under one of the books for a short distance, and raise the other end of the pencil. It will be seen that now *F* is at one end of the pencil, while *W* is between *P* and *F*. The pencil so used is called a lever of the *second class*.

Now hold one end of the pencil down on the table, and after placing a book across the other end, raise the book by grasping some point on the middle portion of the pencil. In this case note that the point *P* is between *W* and *F*. The pencil so used is a lever of the *third class*.

The Rule of Levers.—In all of these cases the power required to lift the weight will be as much less or greater than the weight as the distance of the weight from the fulcrum is less or greater than the distance of the power from the fulcrum. This is expressed in the following proportion: $P : W :: WF : PF$.

By levers of the first and second classes one can lift stones heavier than he is able to lift without them; but with a lever of the third class, since the weight and fulcrum are separated by the whole length of the lever, the weight lifted will always be less than the power required to lift it.

In regard to the velocity of the motion, the case is reversed. Whenever a lever gains an advantage in the amount of weight lifted, it loses proportionately in the velocity of the motion of the weight, and where it loses in the amount of weight, it gains in velocity.

Verification of these Rules.—These facts can be made very clear by using a rod of wood of two or three feet in length, measured off in inches. Known weights may be used as weights, and the lifting power of the hand may be measured by a spring balance placed between the hand and the lever.

The Bones of the Arm as Levers.—In applying our knowledge of levers to the action of the bones of the arm, we learn that when the biceps acts on the radius, it uses the bones bound together as a lever of the third class.

The tendon of the muscle is attached very near the fulcrum of the lever, which is in this case at the elbow, while the weight at the hand is at a much greater distance. In order to lift a weight of ten pounds in the hand, the muscle will have to exert a force which, applied directly, would raise sixty pounds, but with the advantage of lifting the ten pounds with six times the velocity of the sixty pounds.

Each one of the phalanges, the hand used as a whole, and the humerus, are all levers of the third class.

The Uses of the Bones of the Arm and Hand.— Our study of the arm has shown that the uses of the bones of the arm and hand are three :

1. To act as levers.
2. To serve as fulcrums.
3. To furnish places for the attachment of muscles.

Each of these uses is concerned with the movements of the arm.

The Fore-limbs of the Lower Animals.—The bones of the fore-limbs of animals which have backbones—that is, mammals, birds, reptiles, frogs, and fishes—correspond to those of our own arm and hand.

The bones in the fore-leg of a cat are very much like our own. The clavicle is very small, and there are but seven carpals; otherwise they are all present, and of nearly the same shape.

As different as the fore-leg of a horse or of a cow appears from our own arm and hand, a comparison of the bones of each would show them to be remarkably alike.

The wrist bones of these animals are at the joint usually known as the "knee." The hand is very narrow, consisting of but one strong bone and two slender rudiments of bones to represent the metacarpals, and with but one finger in the horse, and four fingers in the cow—two being fully developed, and two only rudiments.

Of course, we call these the feet of these animals, but they correspond exactly to the last joint of our fingers, the hoofs being the nails.

The fore-limbs of animals differ greatly in order to fit them to the different conditions of life in which we find them. If you will examine why this is true in the case of several animals, such as those just mentioned, and also of others, such as a bird, a mole, a squirrel, a rabbit, a sunfish, or a frog, the study will make the knowledge of our own arm much clearer.

Questions for Review.

1. What are the bones of the hand?

2. Point out each in your own hand.

3. How do those of the thumb differ from those of the finger?

4. Show what advantages are gained by having the thumb attached as it is.

5. Trace the outline of the bones of the fore-arm.

6. To which is the wrist attached?

7. Which one makes the point of the elbow?

8. How does the radius join the humerus?

9. Describe the action of the two bones in turning the hand over.

10. Does the knob at the wrist end of the ulna move in this action, or remain stationary?

11. How does the radius act in some of the lower animals?

12. Show all these points in the figures of the ulna and radius given in this book.

13. Give the position of the humerus and describe its form.

14. How do its two ends differ?

15. To what is each attached?

16. Describe the scapula and give its uses.

17. Locate the clavicle and state its use.

18. What is meant by the pectoral arch?

19. Explain the important use of the arch.

20. Show with a pencil and books (or with similar objects) what is meant by a lever.

21. Define the terms *power*, *weight*, and *fulcrum*.

22. Arrange the levers as one of the first, one of the second, and as one of the third class.

23. What is the rule for the levers in regard to the relation of the amount of power to the weight?

24. What is the rule in regard to the velocity of each, the weight and power?

25. Name each bone of the whole arm and show for each case: 1st, whether it is used as a lever; and 2d, of what class.

26. What are the advantages and disadvantages gained in the arrangement of the biceps muscles and the radius?

27. What are the uses of the bones of the arm?

28. How do the bones of the arm compare with those of the fore-limb of the lower animals?

29. Compare the bones of the human arm with those of the fore-leg of a cow or horse.

30. Show how the fore-limbs of several different animals are adapted to the actions they perform.

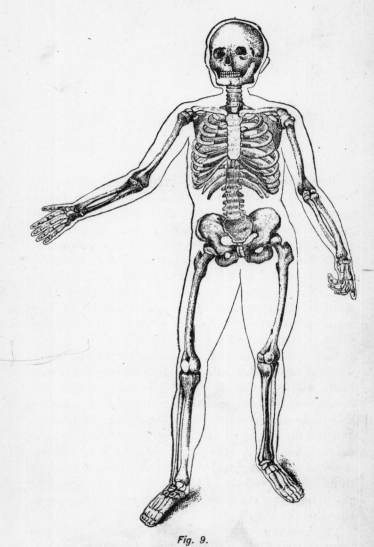

Fig. 9.

THE SKELETON.

CHAPTER III.

THE SKELETON.

The Bones of the Leg.—The bones of the leg correspond very nearly to those of the arm. In the toes the number is the same, and they are called by the same name, the *phalanges*. There are five *metatarsals*, in place of the metacarpals, and seven *tarsals* in the instep, which corresponds with the wrist.

The tarsals are of larger size than the carpals, while the phalanges of the foot are smaller than those of the hand. In Fig. 10 the bones of the foot are shown as sawed through. This shows the large tarsal which makes the heel bone.

Just above this bone is the next largest tarsal, which forms a joint with the bone of the lower part of the leg. In this figure we may see also how the tarsals with the metatarsals form an arch of bones on which the weight of the body rests in standing.

The large bone of the lower leg resting on the tarsal bone is the *tibia*. It extends from the instep to the knee, where, with the bone above, it forms the knee joint. By the side of the tibia lies the *fibula*, a long, slender bone firmly attached to the tibia.

The bone in the thigh is the *femur*. It is the largest bone in the body. The end at the knee is

broad and has a deep groove in it, while at the
upper part there is a turn in the bone which then
ends in a smooth ball.

This ball of the femur fits closely into a cup-shaped
surface on the hip bone, to make the hip joint. The
hip bone, or *os innominatum*, as it is named, is a large,
irregularly shaped bone. It comes out from the
central line of the body, its posterior edge joining
firmly to the backbone, and the front edge being also

Fig. 10.

SECTION THROUGH THE BONES AND LIGAMENTS OF THE FOOT. THE PARTS OF
THE JOINTS ARE WELL SHOWN.

firmly joined to the corresponding edge of the hip
bone of the opposite side. Thus we see that the hip
bone acts as a strong brace on the arch for the femur
to press against, which bears to it the same relation
as the pectoral arch does to the humerus. The hip
bone makes the *pelvic arch*, or *pelvic girdle*.

The pelvic arch is a stronger one than the pectoral
arch, as it must, during walking, bear the whole
weight of the body, and often very heavy weights
besides, which one may carry. If the leg be straightened, there can be easily detected at the knee a disk-

shaped bone which is known as the *patella*, or knee-cap.

This bone is imbedded in a large tendon which passes over the knee to join the tibia. The patella, by fitting into a groove on the end of the femur, helps the tendon work over the bend of the knee.

Uses of the Bones of the Leg.— The bones of the leg are, like the bones of the arm, mostly used as levers. When the muscles of the front part of the thigh contract, they pull upon the tibia and extend the leg; when those on the opposite side contract, they bend the leg. Muscles at the hip, by acting on the femur, may pull the leg in various directions.

A large muscle in the calf of the leg is attached by a very large tendon to the heel bone. This is shown in Fig. 11, and can easily be felt under the skin at the heel.

When this muscle contracts it acts on the bones of the foot, which are bound firmly together. It is a lever of the second class, to pry up the body resting on it by the tibia. These muscles are all used in the leg in standing, walking, and running. The limbs should be studied in these actions.

Fig. 11.

Muscles and Tendons of the Back Part of the Leg.

The Divisions of the Body.—The evident parts of the body are the *head*, the *neck*, the *trunk*, and the *limbs.* The limbs—the arms and the legs—are to be thought of as mere appendages of the body to serve its demands. The legs carry the body about, and the arms carry to it what it needs, defend it, and in a hundred ways attend to its wants.

Fig. 12.
SPINAL COLUMN.

That the limbs may thus act, they must have a firm support to push against. The bony arches which carry them find this support in the skeleton of the rest of the body.

The Axial Skeleton.—The main foundation of this skeleton is the *central axis,* made up of the spinal column and the skull.

The Spinal Column.—The spinal column consists of twenty-six bones very firmly bound together into one firm beam. Its bones are twenty-four vertebræ, the sacrum, and the coccyx.

The vertebræ are divided into three groups : seven in the neck, the *cervical* vertebræ; twelve to which the ribs are attached, the *dorsal* vertebræ; and five in the loins, the *lumbar* vertebræ. The sacrum is the base on which the column of vertebræ stands, and serves as the place for the pelvic arch to brace against.

A Vertebra.—Each vertebra (Figs. 13 and 14) has a central part from which extend seven projections, called processes. These serve for the attachment of ligaments by which the vertebræ are joined in one mass. They also serve for the attachment of many muscles which move the limbs and the head, and ac complish other motions. Each vertebra has an open ing in its posterior part. When the vertebræ are brought into line these openings make a canal, called

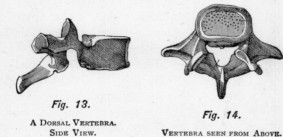

Fig. 13.

A DORSAL VERTEBRA.
SIDE VIEW.

Fig. 14.

VERTEBRA SEEN FROM ABOVE.

the *spinal canal*, in the upper part of which is the *spinal cord*, and in the lower portion are many *nerves*.

Bones of the Thorax.—The walls of the chest are supported by the twelve ribs on each side, the ster num or breast bone in front, and the dorsal vertebræ behind. The ribs end in cartilages in front. The cartilages of the first seven are joined to the sternum; those of the next three are joined together and to the seventh, and the last two are free in front.

The Skull.—The skull, the skeleton of the head, is placed on the upper vertebra. It consists of the *cranium* and the *bones of the face*. The cranium is the part that incloses the brain. If it is examined by feeling it under the scalp, it will seem to be one spherical bone, but it is really made of plates which are so nicely joined together that the joints can not be detected until the bones are exposed. The whole eight make a box, with several holes in the floor.

The bone in the forehead is the *frontal;* the *occipital* is at the back, the two *parietals* at the top, the two *temporals* at the sides and bottom, in the region of the ear. The opening of the ear tunnels into it.

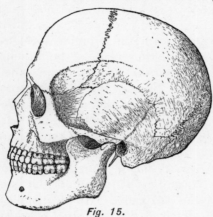

Fig. 15.

BONES OF THE HEAD.

The *ethmoid* helps form the floor in front, and continues into the face back of the upper part of the nose. The *sphenoid* is at the bottom of the box, and is very irregular in shape; its edges touch each of the other seven bones of the cranium, beside some bones of the face.

Bones of the Face.—These are fourteen in number. The only one free to move is the lower jaw bone, called the *lower maxillary*. This bone bears the lower teeth. It forms a joint with the temporal bone. It is drawn upward in closing the mouth by muscles which can be felt in the cheeks, and is drawn down by muscles in the neck.

Determine what kind of lever it forms in these motions.

The *superior maxillaries* are those which carry the upper teeth. They meet in front and extend up on each side of the nose as far as the eyes. Two small bones, the *nasals*, form the bridge of the nose just beneath the eyes.

The two *malar* bones form the prominent ridges, one under each eye. A thin plate of bone helps form the partition between the nostrils, and is called the *vomer*. Two curved bones project into the passages of the nostrils. They are the *inferior turbinated* bones. Two very thin bones which form a part of the inner lower surface of the orbit of the eye are called the *lachrymal* bones.

The *hyoid* bone is a U-shaped bone in the front part of the neck. It can be felt just under the skin, immediately above the part called "Adam's Apple." Many muscles are attached to it, the chief of which is one in the tongue.

Identify these bones in the figure of the skull, and attempt to trace as many of them in your own head as come near the surface.

The Uses of Bones.—We have already seen that the main uses of the bones of the *arm* and *leg* are for levers, or for the attachment of muscles to produce motions.

The *shoulder and pelvic girdles* are for the attachment of muscles, and to serve as braces for the limbs to push against. Many of the *bones* of the *head* serve

for the attachment of muscles, which make it possible to carry the head erect, and to move it about.

Some of the bones of the head are the necessary
place of attachment of muscles to move the lower
jaw, the bone of the lower jaw being itself a lever
with motion as its chief purpose.

The *spinal column* is the main region for the
attachment of the great muscles of the body, and is
at the same time constantly acting as a lever. The
ribs make rigid walls to a part of the body to act as
the sides of a bellows in breathing. They also act
as levers, both in taking in the air and in expelling
it from the lungs.

The skeleton, then, has two chief functions: to act
as levers, and to furnish surface for the attachment
of muscles to work these levers.

Secondary Uses of the Bones.—Some of the
bones are incidentally used for protecting parts from
outside injuries, as in the case of the bones of the
skull, guarding the brain, and the bones of the chest,
guarding the heart, while they perform their more
important functions as well.

Different Kinds of Skeletons.—All those animals
which have a spinal column are called *vertebrates.*
They all have more or less developed hard parts,
composed of bone or *cartilage* (to be described presently), imbedded in their bodies, to act as does the
skeleton of man. Because this kind of a skeleton is
so placed it is called an *endoskeleton*—that is, an inside skeleton.

But in animals like the crawfish, which performs
vigorous motions by means of muscles, the same

necessity exists for hard parts to act as levers, and for the attachment of muscles. In this animal, the skin, by becoming a rigid crust, only flexible at the joints, furnishes this means. The muscles inside the limbs and the body are attached to this hard crust, and its divisions serve the same purpose as the bones of man. This kind of a skeleton is called an *exoskeleton*—that is, an outside skeleton. In vertebrates there is also an exoskeleton represented in the nails, hairs, and epidermis of man, but in vertebrates it does not serve as an organ of motion. The insects, crawfishes, and crabs have the exoskeleton greatly developed for the purpose of motion.

An examination of the crawfish or some large insect will allow the arrangement of the muscles and of the exoskeleton to be much better understood.

Animals without a Skeleton.—There are animals without a skeleton of any kind, but they are not able to accomplish very powerful motions. Most of them live in water, where they are partly or wholly held up by the water and have only slow motions. Most of these animals are very small and can be seen only by the microscope.

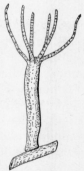

As they have no skeleton, they generally have no muscles. Consequently they are wholly unable to accomplish a very great number of motions, and these must be very indefinite.

Fig. 16.

A FRESH-WATER HYDRA. MAGNIFIED.

One such animal is found growing on sticks and

leaves in our ponds and ditches, and is called the
Fresh-water Hydra. Fig. 16 is a drawing of one.
This represents the animal magnified. The animal
is only about half as large as one of the six arms
shown in the picture.

It can swing itself about, stretch out its six arms,
and if a small animal comes within its arms, it can
close them down on it and pull it into the hydra's
mouth, which is in the center of the end bearing the
arms.

This it does by contracting the whole substance
of its arms and body. We can readily see the great
advantage of an arm like our own over such an arm.
Our arm has part of its substance contractile, the
muscular substance, and part of it resisting, the
bones, so that we can get muscles and levers. What
a very great number of kinds of motions such an
arm can accomplish above those of a soft mass of
flesh having the power to contract, but not being
rigid enough to be extended except when floating in
water !

This little animal will serve to emphasize more
strongly the advantage of a *skeleton*.

Structure of a Bone.—A living or fresh bone consists of a hard portion whose sides are covered with a
membrane of the same substance as that of the tendons. The ends are covered with layers of cartilage.
In the central portion of the long bones, like the
femur, the hollow space is filled with a fatty substance called *marrow*. The hard part is thickened
at the central portion of the bone.

In the ends of the bone the hard substance is arranged like the fibers of a sponge, the spaces being filled with a substance called *red marrow*. The bones generally have near their extremities rough places, or even projections, called *processes*, to furnish surface for the attachment of tendons and ligaments.

Articulations.—The word *articulation*, in the study of the bodies of animals, is applied to the joining of two bones. We have had occasion to refer to these, in the study of the muscles, as *joints*. The word joints, however, is generally applied to the joining of two bones in such a way as to allow motion, such as exists between the bones of the fingers. These joints are sometimes called *movable articulations.*

An *immovable articulation* is one where the ends or edges of the bones are so firmly joined together as to allow of no motion. Examples of joints of this class are found between the surfaces of the bones of the head.

The edges of the bones of the cranium are very irregular in outline, and lock into each other and make the

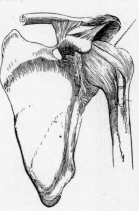

Fig. 17.

SHOULDER JOINT, WITH SOME OF ITS LIGAMENTS.

whole one covering of the brain. These lines of junctions of the two bones are called *sutures*, and can be seen in the figure.

This arrangement in the skull allows the whole to

act as a firm covering, yet if any part should become fractured, the fracture might be checked at the junction of the bone.

The movable articulations, such as the joints in the fingers, are formed especially to allow the easiest motion.   Each joint is formed on the same plan.

The ends of the two bones fit together very nicely, and are covered with *cartilage*, which is a very smooth and a very elastic substance.   Over the layers of cartilage, fastened firmly to it, is a membrane which secretes a liquid which keeps the surfaces of the joints moist.

This arrangement allows motion with the least friction.   The elasticity of the cartilage lessens the jarring effects of the motions of the body.

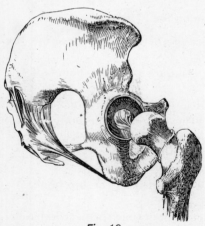

The bones are held firmly to their places by very strong bands known as *ligaments*. These are shown in the figures of the joints given. These bands are of the same substance as the tendons.   They are woven into the sheath of the bone.

Fig. 18.

Hip Joint, with Ligaments removed, except the one on the Head of the Femur.

Classes of Joints.—When one end of the bone

forms a round surface which fits into a cup, the joint is known as a *ball and socket* joint, an example of which is seen in the hip joint. This sort of a joint allows motion in all directions.

A *hinge joint* is one in which the motion is, as at the elbow, in but two ways.

A *pivot* joint allows motion around an axis. This kind of a joint is found between the first and second cervical vertebræ. By its means the head can be turned in all directions.

Determine what kinds of joints are in the other parts of the body.

Questions for Review.

1. Name the bones of the foot, and describe the position of each.

2. How do these compare with the bones of the hand?

3. How is the arch of the foot formed?

4. On which does the weight of the body rest?

5. Describe the position of the tibia.

6. Where is the fibula?

7. Where is the femur? Describe it.

8. Give the position and use of the hip bone.

9. What is the pelvic arch?

10. Why must it be stronger than the pectoral arch?

11. What is the patella and what is its use?

12. How are the bones of the leg used?

13. Describe the motions of standing, walking, and running, as you may observe them by observation of the actions.

14. What are the divisions of the body?

15. How are the limbs to be regarded?

16. What is necessary in the structure of the body that the limbs may act?

17. What is the main part of the skeleton?

18. Of what is the spinal column made up?

19. Give the groups of vertebræ with the number and location of each.

20. Describe a vertebra.

21. What are the processes for?

22. What is the spinal column, and how is it formed?

23. What is placed in it?

24. What bones support the walls of the thorax?

25. Give the number and position of the ribs.

26. How are they connected?

27. What are the divisions of the skull?

28. Describe the location of each of the bones of the cranium.

29. Point out the positions of as many as you can on your own head.

30. Give the positions of the bones of the face.

31. What kind of a lever is the lower maxillary?

32. Point out each of these bones in the picture of the skull.

33. Point them out as far as you can in your own face.

34. What are the functions of the bones?

35. Show this to be the case in the different parts of the skeleton.

36. What are some of the secondary uses of the bones?

37. Give as many examples as you can of these.

38. Which are the vertebrate animals?

39. What are the two kinds of skeletons among animals?

40. Describe the skeleton of the crawfish.

41. How are its muscles attached?

42. What constitutes the exoskeleton in man?

43. What common animals, beside the crawfish, have well-developed exoskeletons?

44. What of animals with a skeleton?

45. How do they move?

46. What advantages arise from the possession of a skeleton?

TABLE OF THE BONES.

I. AXIAL SKELETON.
 A. Skull, 28.
  1. Cranium, 8.
   a. Frontal, forehead, ... **1**
   b. Parietal, ... **2**
   c. Temporals, temples, . . . **2**
   d. Occipital, ... **1**
   e. Sphenoid, ... **1**
   f. Ethmoid, ... **1**
  2. Face, 14.
   a. Inferior Maxillary, lower jaw, . **1**
   b. Superior Maxillaries, upper jaw, . **2**
   c. Palatine, palate, . . . **2**
   d. Nasal Bones, bridge of nose, . **2**
   e. Vomer, ... **1**
   f. Inferior Turbinated, . . . **2**
   g. Lachrymals, . . . **2**
   h. Malars, cheek bones, . . **2**
  3. Bones of the Ear, 6.
   a. Malleus, ... **2**

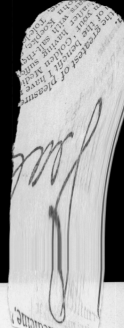

b. Incus,	. . . . . .	2
c. Stapes,	. . . . . .	2

B. Spinal Column, 26.

1. Cervical, or neck vertebræ,	. . .	7
2. Dorsal, or thoracic vertebræ,	. . .	12
3. Lumbar vertebræ,	. . . .	5
4. Sacrum, . . .	. . . .	1
5. Coccyx, . . .	. . . .	1

C. Ribs, 24.	. . . . . .	24
D. Sternum, 1. . . .	. . . .	1
E. Hyoid, 1. . .	. . . .	1

II. APPENDICULAR SKELETON.

A. Shoulder Girdle, 4.

1. Clavicle, collar-bone,	. . . .	2
2. Scapula, shoulder-blade, .	. . .	2

B. Upper Extremities, 60.

1. Humerus,	. . . . .	2
2. Radius, . .	. . . .	2
3. Ulna, . . .	. . . .	2
4. Carpals, wrist bones,	. . .	16
5. Metacarpals, . .	. . .	10
6. Phalanges, . .	. . .	28

C. Pelvic Girdle 2.

1. Os innominatum, .	. . . .	2

D. Lower Extremities, 60.

1. Femur, thigh bone, .	. . . .	2
2. Tibia, . . .	. . . .	2
3. Fibula, . . .	. . . .	2
4. Patella, knee-cap, .	. . . .	2
5. Tarsals, ankle bones,	. . .	14
6. Metatarsals, bones of the instep,	. .	10
7. Phalanges, bones of the toes, .	. .	28

CHAPTER IV.

THE STUDY OF THE HUMAN BODY.

Divisions of the Subject.—Having now become familiar with many of the objects in the study of the human body, some time may be taken to learn how the subject is divided and what its divisions are called.

In the first chapter, in making a study of the hand and arm, we learned many facts which we can separate into two classes.

The Study of the Structure of the Body.—One class includes all those facts in regard to the form and position of each part, together with the name of each. These facts teach us how the arm is constructed. All such facts—that is, those that pertain to the structure of the human body—are put under the subject of *Anatomy*. *Anatomy* is the science which treats of the structure of the body.

The Study of the Uses and Properties of the Parts of the Body.—The second class of facts is those pertaining to the uses and properties of the parts of the arm; for example, what muscles do in general and what each muscle does in particular; how bones act as levers, the tendons as strings; and what are the properties of each which make it fit for these actions. All such facts—that is, such as pertain to the uses and properties of parts of the body—

are included under the subject of *Physiology*. *Physiology* is the science which treats of the uses and properties of the parts of the body.

The Study of the Health.—In learning how to keep the parts of the body in healthy action, how to avoid injuries and disease, we are studying a third subject, known as *Hygiene*. *Hygiene* is the science which treats of the health of the body.

The Relations of these Sciences to Biology.— These sciences are but small divisions of a subject including many others, which is known as *Biology*, the meaning of which science we should know. The human body is only one among thousands of living forms that are on the earth.

The forms are the plants and animals and they appear to be very different from each other. An oak tree does not seem in many ways like a turnip, but in reality they are very much alike. The differences are mainly in form and size. All plants have a great deal in common. It is the same with animals. All have much in common, as widely different as they are in form and size.

They could be thrown into a few groups, in which all the animals of a group would be alike in very many respects; as, for example, the birds. Nearly all the parts of an elephant are found in a mouse.

Bones, muscles, nerves, and all in considerable detail are present in each and arranged on just the same plan, so that the same names can be given to most of the parts.

Even animals and plants are alike in a great number of ways. This similarity that exists among all these organisms has led to the grouping of all the sciences which treat of plants and animals under one head, called *Biology*.

If, while we are studying these lessons on the human body, we should constantly observe the lower animals in their habits, in their methods of motion, how they use the parts which correspond to those in man, much pleasure would be derived from such study. It would also add greatly to our knowledge of living beings in general and of the human body in particular. And, better than either of these, in this exercise we should learn to see and to think with greater skill.

The divisions of Biology are numerous and need not be discussed here, but they are all connected with the study of animals or plants. From this fact arise two great divisions of Biology, which are *Zoology* and *Botany*, used in the widest sense of the terms. The anatomy and physiology of the human body is but a part of the general subjects of anatomy and physiology of all animals.

In the study of the human body we are learning many facts which are true of a great number of the lower animals. In studying many of the lower animals we should learn many facts that are also true of the human body.

The knowledge of any one animal or plant gives us some knowledge of the whole living world, a knowledge which is becoming rapidly extended and more and more interesting as it progresses.

The Meaning of Different Forms of Living Beings.—The wonderful number of forms among plants and animals are to fit each to the particular set of surroundings in which the animal or plant is found.

For example, every part of the crow helps it in the life it lives. Every part of a blackberry bush is also suited to its kind of life. The same may be said of every plant and animal, no matter how large or how small or of what shape.

The human body is also in all its parts fitted to the life of a human being.

––––––

Questions for Review.

1. What is Anatomy?

2. What is meant by the term structure?

3. Give an example of the study of the anatomy of a part.

4. What is Physiology?

5. Illustrate the definition from the study of the arm.

6. What is Hygiene?

7. Of what general science are all these a division?

8. What is said of the similarity of all living things?

9. What of the similarity between the oak and other plants?

10. What is Biology?

11. What connection is there between the study of the human body and that of other animals?

12. What are the two great divisions of Biology?

13. What advantages have animals in their different forms?

14. Illustrate this from your own observations.

CHAPTER V.

TISSUES, ORGANS, AND SYSTEMS.

Tissues.—In the study of the muscles and bones it was seen that a muscle or a bone is not composed of a single substance, but of several different materials. For example, the muscle has in it a part that will contract, and a part which ties it to the bone—the tendon. The bone has in it a hard part, but at the end there is the elastic cartilage, and also fastened to it are the ligaments.

These materials which make up the parts are called *tissues*.

The tendon is made up of *connective tissue.* It is used to make the ligaments for tying bones together. It is a strong, flexible material, and is well fitted for fastening the parts together, or for making a framework and support for other parts. There are two kinds of connective tissue : one is *elastic* and the other *inelastic.* The inelastic variety is used in tendons and ligaments, for it is plain that if the parts which hold the bones together in a joint were elastic, the joints would constantly be giving way. If the muscles were fastened to the bones with cords that would stretch, they would work at a disadvantage. and could not lift heavy weights at all. Elastic india rubber would not be good material for the harness of a horse.

In the muscle, the substance which contracts is called *muscular tissue*. This contractile material is placed wherever motions are to be produced. It is held together by connective tissue.

The hard material of a bone is called *osseous tissue*. It is used wherever a rigid rod for a lever, or a strong post for the attachment of muscles, or a hard plate is needed. It has in it some mineral substances of the same composition as *gypsum*, a kind of stone, and common lime stone. Osseous tissue could be spoken of as tissue partly petrified.

Cartilaginous tissue is a very elastic material, yet very firm. It is used on the ends of the bones at the joints, as we have seen, and in other positions where a certain amount of rigidity and elasticity is required.

The other materials of the body are *nerve-fiber* tissue, placed in the nerves; *nerve-cell* tissue, in parts of the brain and spinal cord; *fatty tissue*, found in various parts of the body; *epidermal tissue*, the material for the nails and outer thin layer of the skin; and the *epithelial tissue*, the thin layer of the alimentary canal. The principal substance of the glands is called *glandular tissue*. In every part devoted to the use of the senses, such as the eye, ear, etc., is a special tissue that is affected by the light, sounds, etc. This is called *sense-organ tissue*.

These few kinds of materials are used in making up the parts of the body, each being just where its peculiar property recommends it.

If one intends to build a house, a ship, or a wagon, he selects materials, each piece of which will be suited for what it is to do in the thing made. These materials are iron, ropes, wood, stone, brass, glass, and so on. In the same manner in nature, in the formation of the different animals certain materials are used. These materials, in all but the lowest in the scale, are about the same as those found in man, and used for the same purposes just given above.

As the only tissues which we can examine in our own bodies are the epidermal tissues on the outside of the skin and the epithelial tissue lining the mouth, we should examine the others in the lower animals to understand what is meant by them. Most of these materials can be seen in their natural positions in the leg of some small animal. A piece of meat prepared for cooking would, of course, show some of these tissues.

Organs.—A part of the body like the brain, liver, or eye, which is somewhat separate from the parts around it, and which performs some special operation, is called an *organ*.

An organ itself is usually made up of several tissues. For example, in the eye there are epidermal, nervous, muscular, and sense-organ tissues, all held together by connective tissue.

Systems.—When all the parts of one kind of the body—for example, the bones—are considered together as one large group apart from the others, it is called a *system*. Thus we have the *bony system* (the skeleton), and the *muscular system*, which were treated in former chapters. Besides these we have the *nervous system*, the *circulatory system*, and the *digestive system*, to be studied later.

The separation of the body into organs and systems helps us to see the whole body more clearly, but we must not forget that in reality these parts are mingled together, as seen in the arm. They are so closely connected that they can work together in harmony and not in confusion.

Organization.—A school is organized when its members are divided up into groups or classes, and each group taught what to do and when to do it. By this arrangement the whole school can accomplish a great deal more work than if no such arrangement existed.

It is only by organization that a large manufacturing establishment can accomplish its work. In a machine shop there may be employed hundreds of men. These men are divided into groups and put into different parts of the building, each group and even each man is instructed in just what is to be done. His duty is to work on some one part of a machine that is being made. When the work of all is put together the product may be a very large and fine engine, which it would be impossible for any one man to make if he spent his whole life at it.

Division of Labor.—Dividing the work required to make an engine among different workmen is called " *division of labor.*"

This principle is practiced in every home and in every shop where more than one person is working. It is at the foundation of all our life in communities.

Almost every thing we have in the house, that we wear, that we use in school or elsewhere, is the result of the advantage of the division of labor.

Determine for yourself how this is true of the bread

*you eat, the pencils you use, or of any other object in
common use.*

Now, the bodies of animals are formed in accord-
ance with the principle of the " division of labor."
The life of a single day requires many motions, also
seeing, hearing, smelling, tasting, feeling, circulation
of the blood, breathing, digesting, secreting, the
making of heat, and many other processes.

These processes are given out to different groups
of tissues in the body called organs, each of which
performs its own work without attempting any other
or interfering with any other.

This is *organization* in the body, and as all plants
and animals show this in a greater or less degree,
they are called *organisms*.

There is a great difference in animals in the degree
to which the principle of the division of labor is carried out.

In a former chapter this was shown in the comparison of the arm of a hydra with that of a human
being. The comparison may now be extended. The
hydra's body is of a single tube made of two layers
of substance of the same material as that of the arms
around the mouth. These tubes can move, digest,
secrete, and perform many processes. It differs from
the parts of a larger animal in not having the labor
of these processes so completely divided among its
different parts.

And when we compare what the hydra can do with
what a squirrel, a bird, or a man can do, we can see
of what very great advantage the principle of the
division of labor is.

Plan of the Body.—The systems in the body mentioned above are arranged in a certain definite way, which is the same in all animals which have a backbone. It may be remembered that the plan of the bony skeleton is a central axis from which all other parts are extended. In this lies the central axis of the nervous system, from which its branches also extend.

Just in front of this lies the central axis of the blood vessels, from which its divisions are given off. **This is in a cavity,** divided into two parts in man, one for the lungs—the thorax; another for the stomach, intestines, etc.,—the abdomen. Extending through the body is the tube of the alimentary canal. The whole of the body is covered with the skin, which is continuous with the lining of the alimentary canal.

Fig. 19 is a diagram which shows the position of

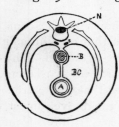

Fig. 19.

PLAN OF THE BODY IN CROSS-SECTION.

The explanation is given in the text.

these parts. It represents the positions which would be shown by cutting through the trunk of the body. The upper part is at the back of the body, the lower part at the front.

The outside ring represents the skin. The figure at the top with three parts is the spinal column; the black spot marked N is the spinal cord, the nervous axis; B is the aorta, the axis of the circulatory system; A is the alimentary canal; BC is in the space which represents the cavity of the thorax or of the abdomen, according to the place of the section. Between the cavity *BC* and the skin are the bones and muscles of the body.

Now, a slice across any vertebrate—that is, mammal, bird, reptile, frog, or fish—would show just the same arrangement. Consequently this may be called the plan of a cross-section of the vertebrates.

Questions for Review.

1. What are tissues?
2. Of what kind of tissue is a tendon?
3. What are the properties of this tissue?
4. In what other positions is it used?
5. What are the varieties of connective tissue?
6. What is muscular tissue?
7. What is its peculiar property?
8. Of what tissue is the hard part of a bone composed?
9. What is its composition?
10. In what positions is this tissue used?
11. What is cartilaginous tissue?
12. Where is it used in the body?
13. Give examples of other tissues.
14. To what are the tissues in the body compared?
15. What is an organ?
16. Of what is it composed?
17. Give three examples.
18. How is a system made up?
19. Illustrate this.
20. What is meant by the term organization?
21. How does a school illustrate this

22. How is it shown in the management of a large machine shop?

23. What is meant by the term division of labor?

24. Illustrate this.

25. Show how the principle of the division of labor is made use of in the body.

26. What differences are seen in animals in the degree to which this principle is carried out?

27. What advantages arise in the body in making use of this principle?

28. Illustrate this by comparison of the hydra to a squirrel.

29. What is said of the plan of the body?

30. Draw a diagram illustrating the plan of a section of the body.

31. Which of the lower animals possess this same plan?

CHAPTER VI.

ANATOMY OF THE CIRCULATORY ORGANS.

The Use of Blood.—We have long known that we require food every day, and that water is also an absolute necessity, and that we must have air every moment.

The more active we are the hungrier and thirstier we become, and the more food do we actually take. We may not notice that we use more air, yet it is true.

What is the cause of these demands? Just for our present purpose we may say that in work the body consumes the food, water, and air, and, in consequence, there must be a further supply of these substances. When we say that the body needs these, we mean nothing more than that the parts of the body need them—that is, the muscles, the bones, the nerves, and the like. Further, since work causes an increased demand, it must be the parts that are working most that are in need of the food most. Those organs are the muscles, but, of course, many other parts work with them.

Now, we know that the food we eat does not go to the muscles in the form in which we see it. The food of the muscles and of the other parts of the body is the blood.

They live upon the blood, which is formed from the food, the water, and a part of the air, the gas oxygen. The muscles, the nerves, and indeed every tissue in the body, gets its food, drink, and oxygen from the blood. When, then, we take more food or drink, or breathe faster, it is to add more food, water, or air to the blood to take the place of what the tissues of the body have used in the work.

How the blood receives the supply of food and drink we take, and how its supply from the air is obtained, we shall study later in the chapters on Digestion and Respiration. At this place we shall study the blood and its motion through the body.

The Blood in the Hand.—The hand may answer again as a beginning point for our study. Many accidents have taught every one that the hand is full of blood. If it is pierced at any point, even with a very fine needle, the blood will flow from it, the only exceptions being the very thin outer layer of the skin, the epidermis, and the nails.

How does the Blood exist in the Hand?—It might be supposed from the experiments with the needle that the blood is in the hand as water may be in a sponge, but it can easily be shown that such is not the case. If the hand is allowed to hang down quietly for a short time, and the back is observed, a network of ridges of a bluish color will appear under the skin, and the whole hand will be of a deeper pink color. Now, if the hand be held above the head, it will be observed that this network will become very much less prominent, if, indeed, it does not entirely disappear. The network of ridges consists of tubes which are carrying the blood from the hand. When the hand is held down the blood in them has to flow up-hill, and consequently the tubes all become well filled with the liquid. The pink color shows that the rest of the hand has more blood in it.

Now, when the hand is held up the blood runs out of these tubes better, and they are left nearly empty. There is less blood left in the rest of the hand also. To show that the blood is flowing from the hand toward the shoulder, one can press the blood out of the tubes of the back of the hand and watch it fill again. It will always be seen to fill from the direction of the fingers.

How does the blood get into the hand? Find the place above the wrist where you can feel the beating of the pulse. It is just between the skin and the end of the radius. This beating is in one of the tubes which bring blood to the hand. That the blood is coming from the shoulder to the hand can be proved by pressing firmly on the tube until it is closed, and then it will be found that the stroke of the beat is on the shoulder side of the wrist.

The Names of the Tubes.—The blood is running along this and other tubes deeper in the arm, on its way to the hand. These tubes are called *arteries*.

As it goes to the hand, the arteries divide into many branches which become smaller as they branch. These go to the muscles, bones, and skin, which they penetrate, and in which they finally branch until they are so minute that they can not be seen without a microscope. These very fine divisions of the tubes are the *capillaries.* They are very numerous, making an extremely fine network, which brings the blood to even the minutest divisions of the muscles, bones, etc.

This network of capillaries soon unites its vessels into larger and larger ones, which leave each muscle, bone, and other parts in the same way that the arteries enter them.

These returning tubes are the *veins.* The smaller

Fig. 20.

RELATIONS OF ARTERY, VEIN, AND
CAPILLARIES.

veins join into larger and larger ones, some of which we have observed on the back of the hand. Fig. 20 shows how they appear in some tissues. The picture represents them with all the tissues removed from the blood vessel. The largest white vessel may represent the smallest artery, which is divided up to form the network of capillaries, and the dark vessel the small vein with the returning blood. To sum up what has just been learned of the hand, it may be said that the blood comes into it by arteries which divide until they finally become capillaries, which are in every part except the nails and the outside layer of the skin, and from these it returns by means of veins.

The Blood in other Parts of the Body.—What has just been learned of the hand is true for every other part of the body. To every part arteries are distributed, ending in capillaries which join to form veins.

When the hand hangs down, the blood must be forced up-hill the length of the arm. When the hand is held above the head, the same must be done in the arteries. In either case it must be pushed along with great force. If the arteries ar.d veins were exposed to view, we could see them running up the arm, past the shoulder, across the upper part of the chest, and finally ending in the *heart.* The general view of the arteries is shown in Fig. 23.

The Heart.—The heart is a force-pump which night and day pumps the blood into the arteries with enough force to send it on through the capillaries and back to itself through the veins.

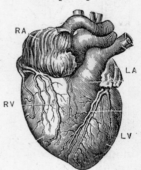

The heart is in the lower part of the cavity of the chest. It is somewhat of the shape of a cone, with the point turned down and a little to the left, with the broad end turned toward the right shoulder. One's heart is about the size of his fist.

Fig. 21.

THE HEART.

RA, right auricle; *RV*, right ventricle; *LA*, left auricle; *LV*, left ventricle.

The position of the point or apex of the heart is easily determined by the beats it makes against the side of the chest, between the fifth and sixth ribs, a little to the left of the central line.

If the open hand be laid on the chest, so that the

tip of the middle finger is at the point where the beats are felt, and the wrist is turned toward the right shoulder, the hand will be over the heart.

The Interior of the Heart.—The heart is divided into four rooms, two at the broad (upper) end, the *auricles* (Fig. 22), and two below these, in the narrower end, the *ventricles*. There is a partition between the auricles, and one between the ventricles. The auricles and ventricles are distinguished as *right* and *left*.

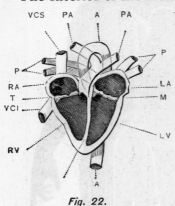

Fig. 22.

DIAGRAM OF THE HEART.

A, aorta ; *PA*, pulmonary artery ; *VCI* and *VCS*, vena cava inferior and vena cava superior ; *T*, tricuspid, and *M*, mitral valve. The other letters same as in preceding figure.

Between each auricle and the ventricle below it are flaps composed of a strong membrane. These flaps are arranged as *valves*, which lie against the ventricles when the blood passes from the auricles to the ventricles ; but on an attempt of the blood to return to the auricles, these valves are closed by the current. They are shown closed in Fig. 22. The one on the right side, the *tricuspid* valve, consists of three flaps ; the one on the left, the *mitral* valve, consists of two flaps. There are also valves at the origin of each of the large vessels leaving the heart, called *semilunar* valves.

The Vessels Connecting with the Heart.—From

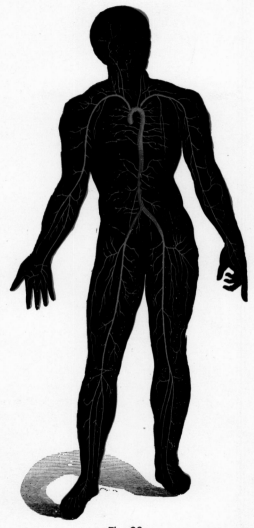

Fig. 23.

DISTRIBUTION OF THE ARTERIES.

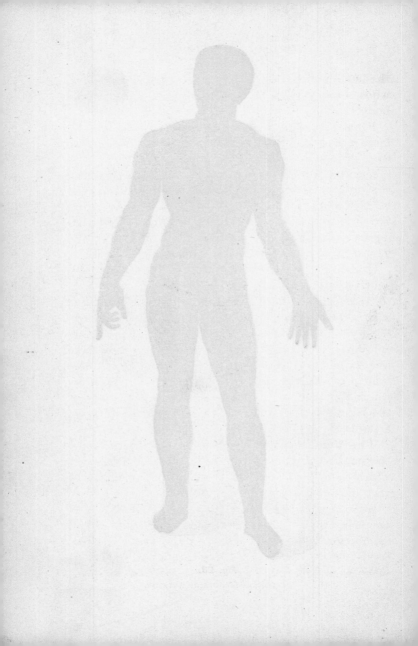

the left ventricle there arises a large artery, the *aorta*, whose branches are distributed to all parts of the body.

From the right ventricle there arises an equally large vessel, the *pulmonary* artery. Its divisions go to the lungs.

Opening into the right auricle are three large veins : the *superior vena cava*, which receives blood from the veins coming from the head, the neck, and the arms ; the *inferior vena cava*, which receives the blood coming from the legs and most of the trunk ; and the vein from the heart itself, the *coronary* vein.

Opening into the left auricle are four *pulmonary* veins, bringing blood from the lungs.

The Aorta and its Divisions.—The aorta, as soon as it leaves the heart, makes a turn called the *arch of the aorta*, and passes down just in front of the spinal column. It gives off branches at the very start from the heart, and along its whole course. These branches subdivide and go to each part of the body, where they end, as we have learned in the study of the hand. Trace them in the figure representing the arteries.

The Veins.—After the blood is gathered up by the small veins it returns by a number of larger veins, which correspond in their distribution generally in each part of the body to the arteries.

Structure of the Heart.—The walls of the heart are made up of muscular tissue. The valves are of connective tissue. There is a connective-tissue layer covering the heart. A sac called the *pericardium* surrounds the heart. Between it and the heart is a liquid known as the *pericardial liquid.* This arrangement allows the heart to beat with as little friction as possible. The walls of the ventricles are much thicker than those of the auricles, those of the left ventricle being thicker than those of the right. The greater amount of work done by the left ventricle requires this.

Structure of the Blood Vessels.—The *arteries* have strong walls of connective tissue, with some muscular fibers, especially in the small arteries. The connective tissue is largely of the *elastic* variety, so that the walls of the arteries will stretch like rubber.

Fig. 24.

A VEIN LAID OPEN, SHOWING ITS VALVES.

The *veins* have much thinner walls, which are mainly of *inelastic* connective tissue, and consequently they will not stretch. The small veins have some muscular fibers in their walls. Many of the veins have valves in them, formed by pouches of connective tissue, which allow blood to pass toward the heart but prevent it from going the other way.

The capillaries have extremely thin walls.

The Divisions of the Circulatory System.—The aorta, its branches and their subdivisions, the capillaries into which they empty, and the returning veins that empty into the right auricle, are known as the vessels of the *systemic circulation.* The pulmonary arteries, the capillaries of the lungs, with the pulmonary veins, are the vessels of the *pulmonary circula-tion.*

_____

Questions for Review.

1. What is the cause of hunger and thirst?
2. Where are the substances called for needed?
3. How does work cause an increased demand?
4. What is the food of the tissues?
5. In what part of the hand is the blood?
6. How does the blood pass through the hand?
7. Prove it in the case of your own hand.
8. How does the blood come to the hand?
9. How does it leave the hand?
10. What are the names of the blood tubes?
11. How are they arranged with respect to each other?
12. Draw a diagram showing this arrangement.
13. Sum up what has just been learned of the course of the blood through the hand.
14. How do the parts of the body compare with the hand in this respect?
15. What in the circulation through the arm shows that the blood goes with considerable force?
16. What sends the blood out with this force?
17. Give the position of the heart.
18. Describe the heart.
19. Describe the interior of the heart.
20. Draw a diagram of a section of the heart, and locate the parts in it.
21. What vessels are connected with each room in the heart?
22. What is the position of the aorta?

23. What of its branches?

24. How are the veins distributed?

25. Of what tissues is the heart composed?

26. What is the pericardium and what is its use?

27. Describe the structure of the arteries.

28. The structure of the veins. Of the capillaries.

29. What constitutes the systemic circulation?

30. What constitutes the pulmonary circulation?

CHAPTER VII.

THE PHYSIOLOGY OF THE CIRCULATORY ORGANS—THE BLOOD.

The Course of the Blood in Circulation.—The course of the blood in circulation is represented in the diagram in Fig. 25. This shows how the heart is a double pump, one portion being placed in each of the systems of circulation, the pulmonary and systemic.

As the valves are shown, the blood can flow but one way, and before completing the circuit must pass through the heart twice. It must also pass through at least two sets of capillaries—those of the lungs (pulmonary capillaries), and those of some other part of the body (systemic capillaries). That portion of the systemic circulation which carries the blood to the stomach, intestines, and spleen, and from them through the liver to the inferior vena cava, is called the portal circulation.

We may now consider the action of each part of the circulatory system.

The Action of the Heart.—The blood flows gently from the large veins into the auricles, and they throw the blood into the ventricles with enough force to dash it up their sides, as water does up the sides of a glass when poured into it. This not only fills the ventricles, but closes the valves between the auricles and ventricles.

Then the ventricles immediately contract and force the blood past the semilunar valves, the right ventricle into the pulmonary artery, and the left ventricle into the aorta. The heart is a very active pump, making about seventy-two strokes a minute.

The Blood in the Arteries.—The pulse felt near the wrist is caused by the shock given to the blood in the arteries by the beat of the left ventricle.

The capillaries are so small and numerous that their walls make a very large surface for the blood to flow over. The friction from this surface is great enough to hold the

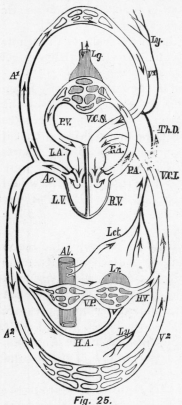

Fig. 25.

DIAGRAM OF THE COURSE OF THE BLOOD.

RA, right auricle; *RV*, right ventricle; *LV* and *LA*, left auricle and left ventricle; *VCI* and *VCS*, vena cava inferior and superior; *Ao*, aorta; *Lg*, lungs; *Al*, alimentary canal; *Lr*, liver; *VP*, portal vein; *Ly*, lymphatics; *Th D*, thoracic duct; *Lct*, lacteals; *HA* and *HV*, hepatic artery and vein.

blood back. As the heart keeps up the pumping, the arteries become so full of blood that their elastic walls are stretched to give it room.

Every time the heart beats the walls of the whole system of arteries spring out. It is this that we feel in the pulse.

Pressure of the Blood in the Arteries.—By being held back at the capillaries and forced on at the heart, the walls of the arteries stretching to receive it, the arteries become so crowded with blood that if an artery is accidentally opened the blood spurts from it with great force. If an opened artery were connected with a perpendicular tube the blood would rise five or six feet in it. This condition of the blood in the arteries is like that of water in a reservoir; it is under *pressure*.

The Blood in the Veins.—In the veins the blood flows by a steady stream, very slowly in the smallest veins, and gradually quickening toward the heart. If a vein be opened the blood flows from it, but with little force. It is not under very much pressure in the veins.

The Use of the Blood Pressure in the Arteries.—The advantages of the arrangement just discussed are :

First.—While the blood is thrown out from the heart in jerks, it will flow into the capillaries in a steady stream. The pulse gradually decreases in force from the heart to the capillaries, where it disappears. This is a very important advantage. The walls of the capillaries must be thin to allow the blood to soak through them to the tissues. Thin walls could not endure a stream of strong jets without breaking.

Second.—As the blood is under pressure on the arterial side, and under little or no pressure on the venous side, the amount of blood going to any organ may be regulated by widening or narrowing the arteries going to it. The muscular substance in the walls of the small arteries do this by contracting or relaxing.

This advantage is just as important as the first given, for without it there would be no means of regulating the supply of blood to each of the organs. All parts would receive blood equally at all times, whether they needed it or not.

The Action of the Capillaries.—It may be recalled that the blood is to supply the tissues with food, water, and oxygen from the air; but this is not all that the blood does. It also takes away from the tissues certain substances which they in their activity are constantly making, and which, if they remained in the tissues, would be very injurious to them.

Now, the changes between the blood and the tissues can take place only through the very thin walls of the capillaries. The liquid part of the blood, and whatever may be dissolved in it, can soak through the thin walls of the capillaries, and the substances dissolved in the liquid part of the tissues may soak through in some way to the blood, which carries them along in its current to be disposed of elsewhere by processes to be described in other chapters.

Then it may be said that all the changes between

the blood and the tissues take place in the capillaries, and that the object of the other parts of the circulatory system is to drive the blood continually through the capillaries.

Regulation of the Actions of the Circulatory Organs.—The heart is composed of involuntary muscles and can not be influenced by the will, but its rate of beating is often changed to suit the needs of the body. If one counts his pulse before performing some vigorous exercise, and again in a short time after he has begun it he will find the pulse in the latter case more frequent. The heart has been stimulated by its nerves to greater action.

At the same time, in the parts of the body that are in action the small arteries dilate a little by their muscular walls relaxing. This allows a greater amount of blood to flow into them. When any part is not in vigorous action, small arteries which furnish it with blood contract their walls and lessen the supply.

These actions are regulated by nerves in a way to be studied when we come to the nervous system.

Properties of the Blood.—The blood is familiar to every one as a bright red liquid. The shade of red varies in the body from the bright red to a very dark red. Seen through the thin walls of the veins, it appears blue.

The microscope shows that the blood is composed of a nearly transparent liquid, in which is suspended a cloud of immense numbers of little particles.

The liquid is *plasma*, and the particles are *blood corpuscles*.

Blood Corpuscles.—There are two kinds of blood corpuscles—the *red* and the *white*.

The red corpuscles, when very greatly magnified,

are seen to be thin round disks with slightly concave sides. They are about $\frac{1}{3200}$ of an inch in diameter. Although they are called red corpuscles, their color is but a faint yellow. It is only in great numbers that they give the mass the appearance of red.

Fig. 26.

HUMAN RED BLOOD COR-PUSCLES. HIGHLY MAGNIFIED.

They differ some in shape and size in different animals. Fig. 26 shows the appearance of the red corpuscles from the human blood, and Fig. 27 those from the blood of a frog. The white corpuscles are few in number compared with the red. They are colorless and of irregular shape.

The Use of the Red Corpuscles.—The red cor-

puscles in the lungs take up oxygen, one of the gases of which the air is composed, and carry it to the tissues, which require oxygen constantly.

Fig. 27.

BLOOD CORPUSCLES OF A FROG. HIGHLY MAGNIFIED.

The Plasma.—The liquid part of the blood is very complex. It is receiving water and digested food from the digestive system all the time, and various substances which the tissues are constantly producing. It is very evident that the blood must have dissolved in it all the substances which are required for the growth of the tissues, as they have no other source of supply.

Coagulation.—Soon after the blood is taken from the blood vessels it has the power to form into a mass which has the appearance of jelly, called *clot*. This process is called *coagulation*. This is accomplished by some substances which are always in solution in healthy blood. But the moment that the blood comes in contact with some other substance than the uninjured wall of the blood vessel, these substances form into very fine threads throughout the whole mass of the blood, holding the corpuscles entangled in their network.

The Use of Coagulation.—The power of clotting is a very important one. It is the method by which the blood can firmly plug up an opening made in the walls of the vessels. Without this, slight wounds would lead to bleeding to death. As it is, any but the larger arteries can stop their own bleeding. A clot will be formed even in one of the large ones also if it be held some time with a ligature.

Effect of Alcohol on the Heart.—(For discussion of effects of alcohol on the body, see pp. 185–191.) When any substance is taken into the body and it is seen that soon the activity of the heart is changed, it is impossible to say whether this effect on the heart is direct or reflex; *i. e.*, whether the substance gets into the blood and acts directly on the tissues of the heart, or whether it acts on other parts of the body and through the nervous system by reflex action affects the heart.

When all the proper precautions have been taken so that the results could be best understood, eminent physiologists have come to the conclusion that alcohol acts directly on the heart, weakening its action and decreasing its power of doing work. While the heart may beat faster through the presence of alcohol in the blood, the beats are not so strong, and the whole effect is to make the blood circulate less rapidly. Alcohol is thus regarded as having a paralyzing action on the heart.

When alcohol is given to a patient suffering from some disease or from an injury, the heart may be stimulated to greater action. In such a case the result, it is claimed, is not due to the direct action of the alcohol on the heart. But this whole question would require for its discussion much technical knowledge, and would be out of place in this book. It is here brought to notice simply to show that it is a more difficult subject than it seems to be considered by those who are ready to make so many definite assertions regarding it.

Whatever may be the immediate cause, however, it is well known that certain diseases of the heart are likely to follow the long-continued use of alcoholic drinks. The general vitality and tone of the heart are impaired, and it is thus rendered more liable to attack by disease. Its structure may become distinctly modified, fatty and connective tissue taking, to some extent, the place of muscular tissue, as seen in fatty degeneration of the heart. The smaller blood vessels in certain regions of the body may become in a measure paralyzed, and thus permanently distended. It is also claimed that alcohol has the power to take a part of the oxygen out of the red blood corpuscles, whose office, it will be remembered, is to carry oxygen.

Questions for Review.

1. Draw a diagram giving the course of the blood in circulation.

2. How many times must the blood pass through the heart in a complete circuit ?

3. Describe the action of the heart, giving that of each part in the order in which it occurs.

4. What is the cause of the pulse ?

5. What is the effect of the capillaries on the flow of the blood in the arteries ?

6. What causes the blood pressure in the arteries ?

7. What of the pressure in the veins ?

8. How does the stream move in the veins ? What of its velocity ?

9. What are the advantages of blood pressure ?

10. Show how each accomplishes these ends.

11. What does the blood carry to the tissues ? What away from them ?

12. How are these exchanges made between the tissues and the blood ?

13. What in the structure of the capillaries permits this ?

14. What may be considered as the aim of all the rest of the circulatory system except the capillaries ?

15. How may the rate of the heart's beating be changed ?

16. Illustrate this action.

17. How is an active part supplied with a greater amount of blood?

18. How is its supply lessened?

19. How are these actions regulated?

20. Describe the appearance of the blood.

21. Of what parts is it composed?

22. Describe the red corpuscles.

23. Describe the plasma.

24. What does it contain?

25. What is coagulation of the blood?

26. By what is it accomplished and when does **it** occur?

27. **What is the use of coagulation?**

CHAPTER VIII.

THE CHEMISTRY OF THE BODY.

Our Study of the Human Body thus far has shown us that it is really a very complicated machine, constantly active, at least in some of its parts. Further, it is always warm. We know that in some way the warmth and activity of the body are dependent on the food and oxygen. We shall now try to see what the dependence is. That will require a little knowledge of at least some very common substances, and how they act toward each other. This knowledge is usually put under the head of chemistry. The main facts are very easily observed in the action of an engine or of a common lamp.

What occurs in a Burning Lamp.—Let us make a brief study of this familiar lighting apparatus. The study of what occurs in a common lamp may be used to help in understanding some things which occur in the human body.

The Lamp Flame uses up the Oil.—As the lamp is burning, we may take note that it has oil in it, which, by means of a wick, is drawn up to a point where it is made to produce a flame, that gives out light and heat. After the lamp has been burning for some time, it is seen that the oil is disappearing, and if the flame is to be kept going we must keep adding the oil.

The lamp must have something else beside oil to keep it burning, and that is air. If we stop up the openings where the air enters the space about the flame, the lamp will soon go out.

The Flame uses Oxygen.—By many experiments, which each one can make for himself (and it is hoped he will do so), chemists have shown that air is composed of at least four gases mixed together. *Oxygen* and *nitrogen* are the main ones, but there is also some vapor of *water* and a very little *carbon dioxide*.

Of these gases in the air the lamp uses the oxygen. If the supply of this is cut off, the lamp will go out.

The lamp, then, while burning, is constantly losing weight by consuming the oil (and a very small amount of the wick), and in addition is using large quantities of oxygen from the air.

What becomes of these Substances.—Just to look at the lamp, it seems that they pass into nothing. But, of course, such can not be the case.

It is easy to show that there is a strong current of something from the top of the lamp chimney.

If we hold a cold piece of iron a short distance above the lamp, so that this current may strike it, the iron will soon become coated with *water*. If we hold an inverted wide-mouthed bottle over the chimney, so as to catch some of the gases, and afterward shake with the contents of the bottle a little clear lime-water (made by allowing a little lime to soak in some water), it will be found that the lime-water has become milky. Only one substance will affect lime-water in this way, and that is the gas *carbon dioxide*.

Evidently the water and carbon dioxide are coming out of the top of the lamp chimney. But as these are in the air all the time, it might be thought that nothing was proved by this. But if these experiments be repeated on the other air in the room, even from the heated currents from the top of the stove, they will not show the presence of these gases, because of the very small quantities in it.

The experiments succeeded with the air over the top of the lamp chimney because of the large quantities of water and carbon dioxide which came from the flame.

Relation of the Substances coming to and going away from the Flame.—The chemists have repeated this experiment more carefully, and find that if they weigh accurately every drop of oil and particle of wick consumed, and every bit of oxygen used, and then catch every bit of water and carbon dioxide coming from the lamp, and weigh them, the sum of the weights of the oil, wick, and oxygen is just the same as the sum of the weights of the carbon dioxide and water coming away.

We may then make this statement about the lamp flame. In its activity, oil and oxygen are united and changed into water and carbon dioxide. During these changes, light and heat are produced.

Now, what occurs in the lamp is exactly what takes place in the boiler of a large engine, with the difference that in the lamp we make use of the light and throw the heat away, while in the boiler we make use of the heat to expand the steam, which is made to do the work of the engine, and throw away the light.

Chemical Changes.—One other point may be noted. Oil is composed of carbon, oxygen, and hydrogen combined. Carbon dioxide is composed of carbon and oxygen, and water is composed of hydrogen and oxygen. The changes that take place in the flame are thus seen to be a rearranging of the parts of the substances which go to the flame to make the substances which come away from the flame. This kind of rearrangement of substances, in which new substances of a different nature are made from old ones, is called a *chemical change.*

Oxidation.—When the chemical change is made by oxygen uniting with something else, it is called *oxidation*, and the other substance is said to be *oxidized*.

Thus it may be said that the carbon of the lamp oil is oxidized, making carbon dioxide; the hydrogen is oxidized, forming water.

Many other examples of oxidation exist in familiar substances. Rusting of iron is the oxidation of the iron.

The Heat of Oxidations.—Whenever oxidation occurs heat is produced. If it occurs rapidly, as in the lamp, stove, or furnace, a very high temperature is produced, but if slowly, as in the rusting of iron, the heat is carried away before it accumulates in large enough amounts to make the iron warm to the touch. But even iron will burn rapidly and with a high heat and a bright light if the burning is once started in pure oxygen.

Comparison of the Body to the Lamp.—Now let us apply these ideas gained from the study of the chemistry of the flame to the chemistry of the body.

The body is losing weight at every moment, except when we are taking food or drink. It is just like the lamp in this respect.

If we hold a cold piece of iron in front of the mouth, or against the skin, it will become covered with moisture, showing that both by the lungs and the skin water is coming away from the body.

If we catch the air breathed out from the lungs and shake it up with lime-water, the lime-water will be milky, showing that the air from the lungs contains carbon dioxide.

The body, then, is like the burning lamp again in that it is throwing off carbon dioxide and water.

The body must have food and oxygen supplies, for if they be not furnished, the body soon ceases from its activity, just as the lamp goes out.

This food must be like the oil in containing carbon, oxygen, and hydrogen at least. Indeed, much of the common food is some kind of fat or oil.

Thus, the body in one more way is like the lamp: it is plain that somewhere in the body the carbon and hydrogen of the food combine with the oxygen that comes in at the lungs.

The body is like the burning lamp in one other particular: as the result of the oxidations, it is made warm. The oxidations are not so rapid as in the flame, and, consequently, do not produce so high a temperature and make no light, but they allow motions, and in this it could be compared to the heat

of the burning lamp if it were applied in such a way
as to run an engine.

The Agency of Heat.—If we examine the work
done in the world, it can mostly be traced to the
agency of heat.

Heat makes the currents of air which are the
winds that blow our ships and wind-mills, or form
the waves that beat against the shores of all lands to
break them down and grind them up.

Heat lifts up the water of the ocean by evaporating
it, which, carried by the winds, falls on the land,
to run back again, and in its course to carve out
mountains and hills and build up new land, and, as
a small matter aside from this great work, to carry
loads for us, or to run our machinery.

Heat from oxidations runs the many forms of engines now employed to do the vast amount of the
work which is accomplished by civilized nations.
The work done by the bodies of men and the lower
animals comes under this rule.   It is performed
through the result of oxidations, and one great object of food and air is with them to have the means
to carry on these oxidations.

**Necessities for the Process of Growth and Re-
pair.**—In one very important way the body is not
like either the lamp or the engine.   It not only
keeps warm and does work, but it *grows* and *repairs
its own parts*.

If a lamp or engine could grow or repair its broken
and worn-out parts, it is evident that we should have
to supply it with more than oil and coal.   Its supply
would have to contain the elements of glass, brass,

iron, and of the various materials of which each is made. Further, it would have to contain other chemical substances that are necessary in making the changes in the formation of these parts.

Composition of the Body.—Every tissue of the body contains compounds of *carbon, hydrogen, oxygen*, and *nitrogen*. These compounds, with *water*, make up by far the greatest part of the body. Besides these chief substances, there exist in many of the tissues some other substances which serve particular purposes. The most conspicuous example is that of osseous tissue, which contains, as we have seen in the study of the bones, compounds of lime. In the tissues small amounts of compounds containing sulphur, phosphorus, iron, sodium, potassium, chlorine, and some other substances may be found.

All these substances must be in the food and drink, the study of which will be taken up in the next chapter. It may then be said that one other object of the food is to supply these materials for the growth and repair of the tissues.

Wastes.—This is a term which applies to the compounds which result mainly from the oxidations of the body during its work and growth. They are mainly *carbon dioxide, water*, and a nitrogenous substance (which is formed and excreted by the kidneys) called *urea*. They are called wastes because they can no longer be of use to the body and must be thrown away.

Questions for Review.

1. What is a machine, and how may the body be compared to one?

2. How does a burning lamp lose in its weight?

3. What else does the flame use besides oil?

4. How can this be proved?

5. What are the gases in the air?

6. What becomes of the oil and oxygen used by the lamp?

7. How can this be proved?

8. What relation exists between the oil and the oxygen on one side, and the water and carbon dioxide on the other?

9. How has this been shown?

10. What is the case with engines?

11. How do they differ from lamps in this respect?

12. What are chemical changes? Illustrate.

13. What is oxidation?

14. Give as many examples as you can.

15. What of the heat from oxidations?

16. Does rusting of iron produce heat?

17. In what ways is the body constantly losing weight?

18. Show this to be the case.

19. How does the body compare with the lamp in the supplies demanded?

20. How does it compare with it in the matter of heat?

21. What are the sources of heat and power of doing work in the body?

22. What are some of the things which heat accomplishes in the world?

23. What is one of the principal objects of taking food and air?

24. In what very important particular do the bodies of animals differ from the lamp and from engines?

25. What are the main elements in the body?

26. Name others that occur.

27. What is one other object of food?

28. What is meant by the term wastes?

29. What are the chief wastes of the body?

CHAPTER IX.

FOODS.

The Forms of Food, as we see them brought to the table, are mixtures of certain substances, some of which occur in many different foods. For example, sugar is naturally in the fruits, and is often added to other foods in their preparation. Again, starch is present in the bread, in the potatoes, in the pudding, and in the pie. Fat or oil may occur in several foods, either naturally, as in the meats, or by its use in cooking.

Kinds of Food Substances.—For convenience in study these foods are put into groups which may be called *the food groups*. The food substances—that is, the substances which make up the foods that are placed on the table—are of two general classes, *organic* and the *inorganic*.

The Organic Food Substances are those which are derived from plants and animals, and make up most of the food we take. Among these substances those most alike in their composition are put together into groups.

The Starch and Sugar Group.—Chemists have found that the different kinds of starches and sugars are all composed of the same elements, and are alike in many other ways. Indeed, starch can be changed into sugar. Gums, such as gum arabic, belong to the same group. These substances are all composed of carbon, hydrogen, and oxygen.

The starches are derived from plants, and are especially abundant in all grains and seeds used for food. They occur also in the leaves, stems, and roots of plants, as in cabbage, lettuce, potatoes, and sweet potatoes. Sugars are usually obtained from plants, but one kind is found in milk. They are found in ripe fruits, and, indeed, may be in any part of the plant.

In the plant the starch is often changed to sugar, as is seen in the change from a green to a ripe apple. Man has learned how to accomplish this change, and every year large quantities of starch are made into sugar for the market. Gums form but an unimportant part of the food.

The Group of Fats.—This group includes the various fats and oils found in milk, in the flesh of animals, and in plants. The words fats and oils are simply relative terms, fats being applied to those of the group which are solid at an ordinary temperature, of which tallow is an example, while oil is a liquid at the same temperature, such as olive oil.

These substances, like the starch and sugar group, are composed of carbon, hydrogen, and oxygen. Although composed of the same substances, they differ from the starch and sugars very much.

The Group of Proteids.—A third group of organic food substances consists of a number of substances very common in the different forms of food, but since they are not commonly separated from them, as are starch, sugar, and fat, they are not familiar substances. The most familiar example of this group is the white of an egg. This is mainly *egg-albumen*, with a large amount of water.

Most of the other members of the group of proteids, if they could be separated from the substances which contain them, would look and act very much like the albumen of the white of an egg. For example, they would coagulate when heated, and act in other ways which lead chemists to recognize them as similar.

One such substance is in milk, and makes the main part of cheese. It is *casein*. One is found in the muscle substance, and is known as *myosin;* one in the blood, *serum albumen;* one in such seeds as peas and beans, called *legumen;* one is found in many grains, called *gluten*. It forms the sticky part of wet flour.

There are many other proteids, but those just given will serve as examples, and are, indeed, the main ones that occur in our foods. The proteids all contain carbon, hydrogen, oxygen, and nitrogen.

It may be observed that the last group given contains one element not in either of the other groups —that is, nitrogen. From this fact the proteids are sometimes called *nitrogenous foods*, and the fats, starches, and sugars are called the *non-nitrogenous foods*. Some plants can manufacture all the different kinds of food substances from the soil, water, and air. Animals can not do this, but must have the proteids, fats, sugars, and starches already made for them. Consequently, they must take for food either such substances as a plant has produced, or the tissues of some animal which has eaten the plant.

All animals live by the death of other organisms, man being no exception. There are many plants like animals in this respect. They are those which do not possess the green color found in leaves, which is called *chlorophyll*, and, consequently, they can not live on inorganic foods. The mushrooms, molds, mildews, and many forms of parasitic plants—that is, plants that live on the substance of other plants—are examples. All the plants without chlorophyll must have for their food some organic substance.

Table of the Food Substances.—The following table shows these classes of foods at one view :

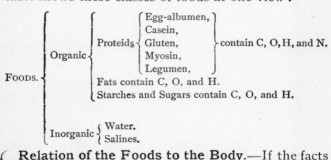

FOODS. Organic — Proteids { Egg-albumen, Casein, Gluten, Myosin, Legumen, } contain C, O, H, and N.
Fats contain C, O, and H.
Starches and Sugars contain C, O, and H.
Inorganic { Water. Salines. }

✓ **Relation of the Foods to the Body.**—If the facts of the preceding chapter in regard to the chemistry of the body be recalled, we may see from the above table that the fats, starches, and sugars are composed of the same elements as the oil in the lamp.

They can be oxidized with just the same results as occurred in oxidizing the oil—that is, the production of water and carbon dioxide, together with the formation of heat.

This is no less true of the proteids, with the exception that in burning them, in addition to water and carbon dioxide, some substance containing nitrogen is given off.

We could burn meat, bread, eggs, peas, beans, and the various grains in the furnace of a boiler and get sufficient heat to run the engine. We have already seen that they are oxidized in the body with the same results.

It may be noticed further that only one group of foods, the proteids, contains nitrogen. As nitrogen forms a part of every tissue in the body, it is very evident that some foods of the nitrogenous group must be taken. If only foods containing substances belonging to the other groups were used, starvation would result.

It will be seen that all the food groups contain elements which enter into the tissues, and, no doubt, they all help to form them.

The Inorganic Foods.—This division includes water and various mineral substances, of which the greatest amount taken is common salt. The others are taken in very small amounts mixed with the other foods. These substances, called salines, are the same as those mentioned as being in the tissues of the body. They are compounds of lime, magnesium, sodium, and potassium. They are absorbed by the plants from the soil, and from this source we obtain them, either directly from the plants, or indirectly through the flesh of animals which have fed on them.

The Use of Inorganic Foods.—Plants which

have the green substance in them which gives them their well-known color are the only ones of the living organisms which can live and grow on purely mineral food substances. Still, the body makes some use of them. From the inorganic group of foods the tissues obtain their supplies of the mineral substances used in their structure, but none of these can be oxidized, and hence can not be the source of heat or motion.

Water, the principal one of the inorganic foods, is also one of the most important. Its use is to form solutions so that the liquid blood and lymph may be possible, and that the tissues may make the exchanges by its means with the blood. All the processes of the body depend on the presence of water. The tissues might be said to live on substances dissolved in water. A slight reduction of this water causes a severe thirst, which drives us to make good the loss.

The Proportion of the Different Foods needed in the Body.—To accomplish the three main purposes of foods—viz.: to keep the body warm, to furnish it means to perform its work, and to furnish it with material for growth—it is evident that there might be a combination of food substances that would have the best proportions.

What these proportions are has been the subject of much investigation. It has been shown that if too much nitrogenous foods be taken, the labor of the body is greatly increased in getting rid of the extra amount. If this is continued for a considerable length of time, serious diseases are sure to follow.

The right proportion of the non-nitrogenous foods to the nitrogenous is said to be about four parts of the first to one of the second. These proportions are about those in milk, or in wheat flour when in the form of "Graham flour."

Meats, peas, and beans, when taken alone, have more than the needed nitrogen, while rice and potatoes do not have enough. As our food is served to us, we have various groups which are likely to give us enough of each kind.

One's appetite, if he is in good health, will guide him in the matter by making a demand for the kind of food wanting, and giving a distaste for that of which too much has been taken.

This is the body's method of regulating this extremely important matter, and it should never be abused by eating when one feels that he does not need food. This guide may be relied upon as a safe one to those who have not disturbed its healthy action by eating things simply to please the taste. The healthy action of this guide must be preserved.

Alcohol as a Food.—It has often been questioned whether alcohol can act as a food; that is to say, whether it can be oxidized in the body, and may thus furnish physical energy, or serve some other useful purpose. The question is one to which no positive answer can be given, since, as yet, it has not been definitely decided. But even if it were demonstrated that alcohol could serve as nourishment, the injurious effects it has on the body would outbalance any value it might have as a food. Furthermore, alcoholic drinks are made at great expense of good food substances, so that their manufacture destroys far more food than they can ever supply.

Questions for Review.

1. What is said of the composition of common foods?

2. Illustrate how one substance may be found in many forms of foods.

3. What are the two general divisions of food substances?

4. What are organic food substances?

5. What is said of starches and sugars?

6. Of what elements are they composed?

7. Where are they found?

8. What relation has starch to sugar in the plant?

9. What is said of the gums?

10. What constitutes the group of fats?

11. From what are they derived?

12. Give several foods that would furnish some of them.

13. What is their composition?

14. What are proteids?

15. Give some familiar example.

16. In what are they alike?

17. What are the chief proteids of the foods?

18. Name the source of each given.

19. What is the composition of proteids?

20. Which are the nitrogenous foods, and which the non-nitrogenous?

21. What are the inorganic foods?

22. What is their source?

23. Name some of the principal ones.

24. What plants furnish animals all the organic substances?

25. What kinds of food do they live on ?

26. What kinds of food must animals have ?

27. What plants are like animals in this respect ?

28. Write out the table of food substances.

29. What foods can be oxidized ?

30. What results would follow the oxidation of each ?

31. How could this be shown ?

32. What is said of the necessity of the nitrogenous group ?

33. What is the use of the inorganic foods ?

34. What is the use of water ?

35. Why would one group of foods not answer the needs of the body ?

36. What is the best way to mix them ?

37. What proportion is given as the best ?

38. What foods answer the requirement ?

39. What is the objection to a meat diet alone ? To a diet of rice alone ?

40. What is the body's manner of selecting the proper kinds and amounts ?

41. When may this be taken as a safe guide ?

CHAPTER X.

ANATOMY OF THE DIGESTIVE SYSTEM.

Digestion.—It has already been pointed out that the tissues live on the blood, and that the serum of the blood is kept up in quantity by food and drink.

But every one knows that blood and food are two very different things. Much of the food is of solid material and will not dissolve in water. To get into the blood vessels it must pass through the lining of the stomach or intestines. This process is called *absorption.*

After the food is dissolved and brought by the current of blood to the capillaries in the tissues, it must again pass through a membrane, the coat of the capillaries.

All this is only possible when the food is in a liquid form. Beans, meat, bread, potatoes, whatever the form of the food, that part which is to be food for the tissues must be dissolved. It is the object of digestion to *reduce food to a liquid form.*

Foods that require Digestion.—The sugar is readily soluble in water and is usually already dissolved in the food or drink that we take, and, consequently, needs no further action that it may be absorbed into the body. But of starch and the proteids, none of those taken as foods can dissolve in water sufficiently for this purpose, most of them not at all.

The oils, it is true, are in a liquid form, and the fats will be melted to a liquid form by the heat of the body, but still they will not soak through the membranes in their ordinary form. They must also be specially prepared before this can take place.

The water remains unchanged, being absorbed as water, passing anywhere in the body, and being thrown out of the body as water.

The mineral substances taken in the food are in minute quantities already dissolved, and, of course, need no digestive action.

It may be said, then, that of the foods, the proteids, the fats and oils, and the starches and the gums, must be digested.

How is Digestion Accomplished ?—The foods are digested by being taken into the alimentary canal, where at various portions they have mixed with them certain liquids which will change the food substances so that they become liquids ; then the food substances in liquid form are absorbed and brought into the blood.

The Alimentary Canal.—The alimentary canal is a tube about thirty feet in length, passing through the body, into which the food is placed to be subjected to the liquids which make these changes in the foods. It is variously modified along its course into different parts which perform different actions.

All these parts, together with the organs connected with them which form the digestive liquids, are called the *digestive system*. The digestive system consists of the *mouth* and the *salivary glands*, the *pharynx*, the *œsophagus*, the *stomach*, the *small intestine*, with the *liver* and the *pancreas*, and the *large intestine*.

Glands.—The essential part of digestion is accomplished by liquids poured upon the foods. These liquids are formed by organs called glands. Glands are also used in other parts of the body to form liquids, as, for example, to form sweat and tears.

Very simple forms of glands are very minute tubes or sacs, which are surrounded by a network of capillaries. The lining of a gland forms the liquid peculiar to it, which is called its secretion. This flows out of the mouth of the tube. The gland tissue gets from the blood near it the material from which it forms its secretion.

In large glands, the tubes are divided into very many branches, so that the gland comes to be in form like a tree with its branches, except that the branches are crowded and folded together in a somewhat solid form.

The divisions of the parts of the tubes greatly increase the secreting surface of the gland. In all the branching a network of capillaries follows each minute branch. A simple tube or sac is a *simple gland*, while a gland consisting of branched parts is a *compound gland*.

The Mouth.—This part of the system can be so well studied from a view of the object itself that such a view and not a printed description should be relied upon for a knowledge of its parts, except it be to learn the names of the parts.

The mouth forms a cavity, which, when closed, is

well filled by the tongue and the teeth projecting into it. It has very movable walls at the front and sides in the lips and cheeks, whose middle layers contain many muscles which produce their great number of motions.

The tongue projecting from the floor of the mouth is extremely movable. The roof, the *palate*, is hard forwards, and soft at the back, ending in a curtain which hangs down to make the posterior wall of the mouth. The two curved rows of teeth just strike each other.

Besides the motions of the lips, cheeks, and tongue, the whole lower part of the mouth can be moved up and down, from side to side, and from front to back, by the muscles that move the lower jaw.

Determine from your own mouth what these motions are and where the muscles are placed that produce them.

Placed in the surface of the tongue are the little organs of taste. In the walls of the mouth everywhere are little glands which secrete mucus, the liquid which, mixed with the secretion of the salivary glands, is the one which we know as constantly in the mouth. The salivary glands empty their secretion into the mouth.

The Teeth.—The position and characteristic forms of the teeth can be plainly made out in one's own mouth by the use of a mirror. Fig. 28 of the teeth in the lower jaw shows how they are set in the bone. The teeth appear in two sets. They are ten in each jaw of the first set, which appears in childhood, and sixteen in each jaw of the adult. The four front teeth in each jaw are called *incisors;* the next one on each side is a *canine;* the next two, the *premolars;* and the last three are the *molars*. The same teeth occur in many animals and in the same order, but not always of the same number. They are in them much varied in form to adapt them to the many uses that their owners make of

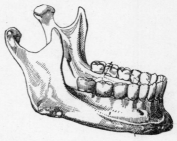

Fig. 28.

LOWER JAW-BONE WITH THE TEETH.

them. Very many of them use their teeth for other purposes besides that of chewing.

Structure of a Tooth.—Fig. 29 shows the internal view of a tooth cut through from the top or crown to the tips of the roots. It shows it to consist of three substances : A layer of *enamel* (1) over the crown ; a layer of *cement*, which is of the same structure as bone, around the roots ; these lie on the main substance of the tooth, the *dentine*, or ivory (2).

These are very hard substances, the enamel being the hardest. In the center of the tooth the hollow space is filled with blood vessels, nerves, and connective tissue. They come in at the points of the roots. These together are called the pulp.

Mastication.—The mouth has other uses besides its action on the foods, the chief one of which is that of speaking. Its work with the foods is to crush and divide them that they may be swallowed first, and afterward may be moved along the remainder of the alimentary canal to be acted upon by the digestive liquids. The process is known as *mastication.*

If one will take a portion of food into his mouth

and proceed to masticate it, and at the same time note the action of the tongue, lips, cheeks, lower jaw, and teeth, he will learn how deftly the food is handled by them, being first taken to one part of the mouth, then to another. All the hard portions are brought between the teeth, where they are crushed. In the meantime it is mixed with

Fig. 29.

STRUCTURE OF A TOOTH.

1, enamel; 2, dentine; 3, pulp cavity.

saliva until it is formed into a ball, when it is, by a quick motion of the tongue against the roof of the mouth, shot into the next division of the alimentary canal, the pharynx.

The Saliva.—The saliva has very important uses. In the first place, it allows dry food to be swallowed. It dissolves the food so that it may be tasted. It and the mucus moisten the lining of the mouth and the larynx, and thus make the motions of speech possible.

It has also the power to digest the starch. It does this by changing it into sugar. The food is in the mouth so short a time that this action of the saliva does not seem to be a very important one. The starch is mainly digested in another place, as we shall see.

The Salivary Glands.— The salivary glands are

arranged in three pairs : one pair in the sides of the face, just in front of the ears, the *parotid glands;* one pair by the angles of the lower jaw, the *submaxillary*, and one near the tongue, the *sublingual*.

Hygiene of the Mouth.—The mouth should be kept as clean as possible. The arrangement of the teeth is such that particles of the food are sure to become lodged around them. These kept at the warm temperature of the mouth will decay, and in the process form substances which corrode the substance of the teeth, leading to their decay and final loss, often with great suffering. In very many such cases these troubles might be avoided by constant cleanliness.

The mouth should be especially well cleansed after the evening meal, so that particles of food should not be left undisturbed on the teeth for so long a time. Whenever a tooth shows signs of decay, it should be promptly attended to by a dentist, as in such a case the great majority of ailing teeth may be saved.

A decayed tooth may be the source of greater danger than its pain and final loss. It and any other form of sore or wound in the mouth may become the points of introduction for germs of disease.

Questions for Review.

1. In what does digestion consist ?
2. What is the reason that digestion must take place ?
3. What foods do not require digestion ?
4. What foods require digestion ?
5. What of the fats and oils ?

6. How is it with the water? With the mineral substances?

7. What in general terms is the process of digestion?

8. What is the alimentary canal?

9. What constitutes the digestive system?

10. What are glands?

11. What are simple forms of glands?

12. What is a secretion?

13. How is the increase in the secreting surface in the gland brought about?

14. What is such a gland called?

15. What is said of the manner of studying the mouth?

16. Describe the mouth.

17. What motions are possible in the mouth?

18. What secretions come into the mouth?

19. Describe the teeth, giving the names, forms, and positions of each.

20. What of the teeth of the lower animals?

21. Describe with a diagram the structure of a tooth.

22. What is mastication?

23. Describe its processes.

24. What are its uses?

25. How is the food passed to the pharynx?

26. What are the uses of the saliva?

27. Which, as you regard it, is the most important, and what reasons can you give for the view?

28. Where does the saliva come from?

29 Give the location and names of the glands.

30. What is said of the care of the mouth and teeth?

CHAPTER XI.

DIGESTION.

The Pharynx.—Just beyond the mouth the alimentary tube becomes the *pharynx.* There are several openings into this portion — one from the mouth, one from each nostril, one from each middle ear, one into the larynx, the organ where the voice is produced; and the opening into the next division of the alimentary canal, the *œsophagus.*

The Œsophagus. — This is the portion of the alimentary canal which extends from the pharynx to the stomach. It is eight or nine inches in length. It and the pharynx are lined internally with

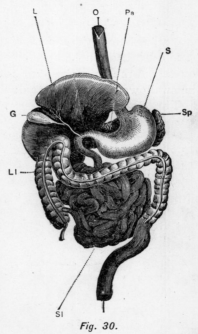

Fig. 30.

GENERAL VIEW OF THE ALIMENTARY CANAL.

O, œsophagus ; *S*, stomach ; *SI*, small intestine ; *LI*, large intestine ; *Sp*, spleen ; *L*, liver (raised up) ; *G*, gall bladder : *Pa*, pancreas.

(107)

a mucou: membrane. Outside of this are the muscular walls.

Swallowing.—The food is sent forcibly from the mouth into the pharynx. The pharynx acts something like a funnel over the top of the œsophagus. When the food is in the pharynx, its muscular walls close around it and quickly push it into the œsophagus, where portions of the circular bands of muscles relax before the food, and others contract behind it to push it on into the stomach. Water is served exactly in the same way, and both water and food can be swallowed up as well as down.

The Stomach.—This organ is a part of the alimentary canal m o r e dilated than the other portions, a n d so arranged as to retain the food in it a certain length of time. (Fig. 31.)

It is in the upper part of the abdominal cavity s o m e-what to the left

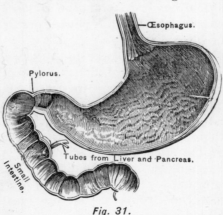

Fig. 31.

SECTION OF THE STOMACH.

side. The opening at the point where the œsophagus joins it is called the *cardiac* opening; the one at the opposite end, where the small intestine joins it is called the *pylorus.*

In this latter place the muscular walls form a ring, which remains contracted some time after a meal is taken, opening and closing from time to time to allow liquids to pass, thus retaining the more solid portions for the digestion which takes place in the stomach. It finally relaxes and allows all the contents to pass on to the small intestine.

The walls of the stomach have four layers: the outer the *peritoneum;* the next, a *muscular* layer; the next, a *connective-tissue* coat; and the inner, the *mucous coat.*

Digestion in the Stomach.—The mucous coat of the stomach is filled with small glands which secrete a liquid known as *gastric juice.* During the presence of food in the stomach, this liquid is poured out on it in considerable quantities.

Gastric juice affects only one of the food groups, the proteids. When these food substances are kept with gastric juice a certain length of time, they are changed into soluble forms of proteids called *peptones.* This change takes place slowly. To cause the gastric juice to become thoroughly mixed with the food, the muscular walls of the stomach, by contracting in many different directions, push it around, backward, and forward many times.

Absorption from the Stomach.—A very great number of capillary blood vessels forms a close network in the mucous coat immediately next to its surface. This arrangement brings the blood so near the liquid in the stomach that nothing but a very thin wall of membrane lies between them. This allows the liquid contents of the stomach and what may be dissolved in it to soak through to the blood.

Besides these blood vessels, there are also the lymphatics, arranged in the same position, so that they may also receive liquids from the stomach.

The process by which a liquid may pass into either of these vessels is called *absorption.* The rapidity with which it occurs is shown by the quick effect which some medicines have on the body when taken into the stomach.

The Small Intestine.—The small intestine is a

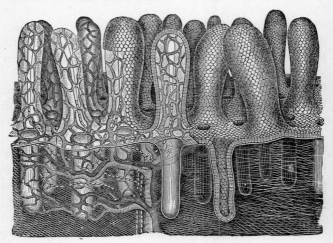

Fig. 32.

SECTION OF THE MUCOUS COAT OF THE SMALL INTESTINE. DIAGRAMMATIC.

Some of the villi have their covering layer removed to show the structure. The tubes are intestinal glands.

much narrower tube than the stomach. It is about twenty feet in length. It is suspended from the margin of a membrane called the *mesentery*, the inner edge of which is gathered together in one place and fastened to the back of the abdominal cavity.

The coats of the small intestine are exactly the same in name and arrangement as those of the stomach. But the mucous coat differs from the same coat of the stomach in being densely covered with minute projections.

These are shown very much enlarged in Fig. 32. They are the *villi*. They are special arrangements for absorption. Each one has in it, as shown in the figure, a network of capillary blood vessels, and another kind of small vessels called the *lacteals*, but they are really lymphatics, and, with many of the lymphatics, they empty into the thoracic duct. Over each villus is a very thin layer of tissue, which allows digested food substances to pass through either to the blood vessels or the lacteals, from which it soon enters the general circulation.

Secretions coming into the Small Intestine.— The mucous coat has in it besides the villi a few compound glands in the upper portion, and a very great number of simple glands in the lower (seen also in the figure), which secrete *the intestinal juice.*

The *pancreas* is a large gland lying just behind the stomach, which forms the *pancreatic juice*, and pours it into the small intestine by its duct, which empties into the small intestine a short distance below the pylorus.

The Liver.— The liver is a very large gland, placed just under the diaphragm, mainly on the right side. It empties its secretion, the bile, into the small intestine at a point very near the opening of the pancreatic duct. The pancreatic juice and bile are immediately mixed with each other and with the food.

Digestion in the Small Intestine.—The digestion which goes on in the small intestine may be considered as the most important of all, since the pancreatic juice acts with energy on proteids to change them into the soluble peptones; on the starches to change them into sugar, and on the fats to change them into a state in which their particles are extremely minute, small enough to find their way through the thin layer over the villi. Some of the fats are also changed into substances which will dissolve.

The Bile.—This liquid comes in very large amounts into the intestine during digestion.

It has been shown to have very slight direct digestive action on any of the foods, but it is known to aid the process of digestion in various ways. Among them may be mentioned that the bile makes the contents of the intestine *alkaline*, which is necessary

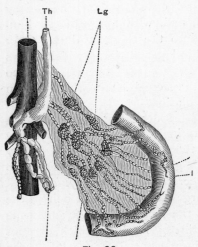

Fig. 33.

LACTEALS.

Showing the connection of the small intestine to the thoracic duct by the lacteals lying in the mesentery. Th. thoracic duct.

to the action of the pancreatic juice, and that it in some way aids in the absorption of the fats.

It has probably many other uses, as it is a very complex liquid. Our ordinary foods contain a considerable amount of substances which are not acted on by any of these fluids, termed indigestible parts.

These are, by the constant motions of the small intestine, sent along to accumulate in the large intestine. They move more and more slowly as they pass along, that the last amount of digested food may be absorbed before these substances are removed from the body.

Absorption.—As already mentioned, absorption may take place from the stomach and from the small and large intestines. It is mainly from the small intestine. The food, after being absorbed, may reach the heart, and from it the general circulation, by two different courses:

1st. That which is taken up by the blood vessels goes by the portal vein to the liver, through the capillaries of the liver to the hepatic vein in the liver, into the inferior vena cava, and thence to the heart.

2d. That which is taken up by the lacteals passes on to the thoracic duct, Fig. 33, from which it empties into the left subclavian vein, and from this it soon reaches the superior vena cava.

These two courses will be made clear by consulting the diagram of the circulation of the blood, given in the chapter on Circulation.

Conclusion.—In a former section it was said that the food of the tissues is the blood. We have now seen one source from which the food is constantly added to the blood. It is placed in parts of a vessel, the alimentary canal, and at different places the liquids change different members of the food groups into solutions. These are given in the following table:

1. *Saliva* acts slightly on the Starches.
2. *Gastric Juice* acts on the Proteids.
3. *Pancreatic Juice* acts on the $\begin{cases} \text{Starches.} \\ \text{Fats.} \\ \text{Proteids.} \end{cases}$

These made soluble and the sugar already dissolved include all the principal foods.

———

Questions for Review.

1. Give the position and description of the pharynx.

2. With what is it connected?

3. Describe the œsophagus.

4. How is swallowing accomplished?

5. What is the stomach?

6. Where is it placed?

7. Describe it.

8. What is the action of the pylorus?

9. What are the coats of the stomach, and what is their arrangement?

10. What liquid is secreted in the mucous coat of the stomach?

11. What food substances does it dissolve?

12. What are the motions of the stomach?

13. What is absorption?

14. How is it accomplished at the stomach?

15. What of the rapidity of the process?

16. Describe the small intestine.

17. What of its coats?

18. Describe a villus, giving its internal structure.

19. What is its use?

20. What secretion is furnished by the mucous coat of the small intestine?

21. What other secretions come into the small intestine, and at what point?

22. Give the position of the pancreas.

23. Describe the position of the liver.

24. Upon what food substances does the pancreatic juice act?

25. What of its importance?

26. What are some of the uses of the bile?

27. What are the chief places at which the foods are absorbed?

28. What are the two ways by which it is absorbed?

29. What is the exact course of the food to the heart when taken up by each of these?

30. Give the general conclusions in regard to the digestive process.

CHAPTER XII.

RESPIRATION.

What Respiration Accomplishes.—It has been shown in a former lesson that not only does the blood bring food and drink to the tissues, but it also brings air to them ; or, more correctly, that part of the air which they need, the *oxygen*. It was also shown that the blood removes from the tissues certain substances which were formed in them through their activity. They are the so-called "*wastes*." One mentioned was carbon dioxide.

These, in the air, are free gases; in the blood they are dissolved. As the parts of the alimentary canal are the places of introduction of food and drink into the blood, so the lungs are the place at which oxygen is introduced into the blood, and carbon dioxide is removed from it.

Respiration has for its purpose the bringing of the air to the blood, so that these changes may take place between the two. To speak accurately, the tissues carry on respiration between themselves and the blood when they take oxygen from the blood and give up carbon dioxide to it. This has been called *internal respiration*, while that at the lungs is the *external respiration*.

These are good terms, as they express the facts, but

for convenience we will use the term respiration in its common meaning, which is to represent external respiration.

The Respiratory Apparatus.—The essential part

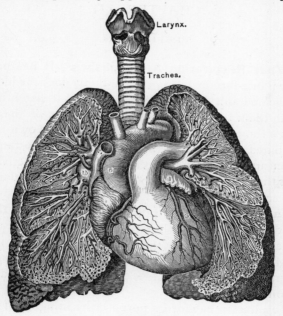

Fig. 34.

THE HEART AND LUNGS.

of the breathing apparatus is a thin membrane, so arranged that the oxygen can come on one side and the blood on the other. In such a case the oxygen can pass into the blood and the carbon dioxide out.

In the lower animals, the breathing apparatus is found in many different forms. The gills of a fish are familiar to all. In all these forms, as different as they may be in other regards, they all have the essential arrangement spoken of above. The oxygen is always either in the air, mixed with the other gases before given, or it is dissolved in the water which has obtained it from the air.

In the gills of the fish the delicate fringes are so many projections of very thin skin, through the core of which the blood circulates, but on the outside the water with the dissolved oxygen is made to pass. In the lungs of a man there are immense numbers of little thin-walled sacs, into the centers of which the air comes, and around the surface of which the blood circulates. The rest of the apparatus is to pump the air in and out of the passages which are connected with these little air sacs, so that there may be a constant change of the air.

The Respiratory Organs.—The part of the apparatus which accomplishes this constant removal of the air consists of the thorax and the lungs, which hang as two sacs in its cavity, and the tubes in the lungs, and the large ones which connect them with the outer air.

If we name the air passages in order from without, they are the *nostrils* and the *mouth*, the *pharynx*, the *larynx*, the *trachea*, its two large branches, the *bronchi*, and their numerous branches, the *bronchial tubes*, which become so small in their subdivisions as to require the microscope to see them. These end in groups of minute *air sacs*, mentioned above. They are microscopic.

A group of these air sacs, or vesicles, is shown in

Figure 35. Among these are close networks of pulmonary capillaries.

Structure of Air Tubes.—The trachea, bronchi and bronchial tubes have a framework of cartilaginous rings, which hold them open on all sides. The rings have connective tissue between them and around them. The lining of the passage is mucous membrane, in which is a large number of mucous glands, whose secretion is constantly forming.

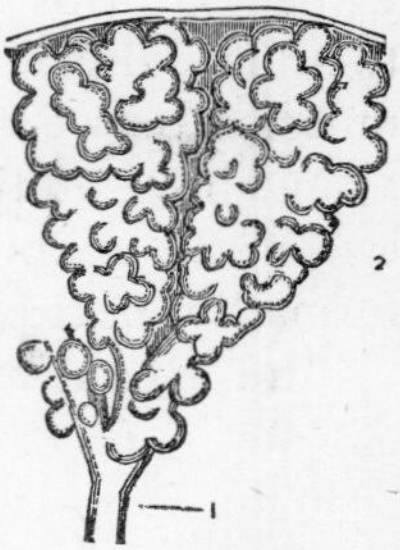

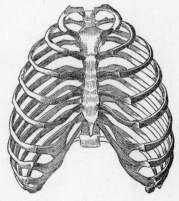

Fig. 35.

AIR VESICLES.

1, last division of bronchial tube ; 2, air vesicles, magnified.

The mucus is made to flow toward the throat by means of very minute projections, seen only with higher powers of the microscope, which are on the surface of the mucous membrane. These are the *cilia.* They keep up a constant waving motion, which carries the mucus along, together with dust which settles on it from the air.

The Thorax.—The lungs are suspended in the cavity of the thorax. The bony support of the thorax is shown in Fig. 36, and consists of the dorsal verte

Fig. 36

BONY WALLS OF THE THORAX.

bræ, the ribs, and the sternum. In this framework, while the ribs are attached at their extremities, their middle portion can be moved up and down by muscles between them and those attached to them from above and below. The muscular partition between the abdomen and the thorax, the *diaphragm*, forms the bottom of the thorax.

The Respiratory Acts.—Respiration consists of two acts: *inspiration*, by which an amount of air is brought into the lungs, and *expiration*, by which about the same amount is expelled. The lungs hang in the thorax as elastic sacs in air-tight cavities. The pressure of the air, which is fifteen pounds to the square inch, nothing but a little liquid being between their outer walls and the walls of the thorax, swells the lungs out against these walls.

If now the walls of the thorax are pulled away a little more, the pressure of the air on the inside of the lungs makes them follow the retreating walls of the thorax. On the other hand, by the walls of the thorax pressing upon the lungs they are emptied to the same extent.

Inspiration.—In inspiration the cavity is enlarged. This is accomplished in two ways: First, the diaphragm being curved upward pulls itself down by contraction. Second, by the contraction of one set of the muscles between the ribs (the external inter-costals) the ribs are raised, which motion, from the way they are attached (see Figs. 37 and 38), throws them out.

Expiration.—This act consists in making the cavity of the thorax smaller. This is done in two ways:

First, by the muscles of the walls of the abdomen, contracting and pressing upon the contents of the abdomen, and thus forcing the diaphragm up again.

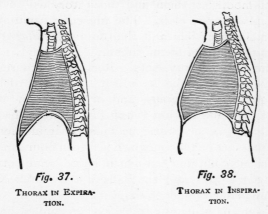

Fig. 37.

THORAX IN EXPIRA-
TION.

Fig. 38.

THORAX IN INSPIRA-
TION.

Second, by the other set of intercostals (the internal) contracting to pull the ribs down. In both acts many other muscles may take part which can not be discussed here.

Nervous Control.—These motions are regulated by nerves, so that one follows the other in the proper succession, frequency, and strength, each of which varies much with the varying activity of the body. For, the more work done the greater must be the supply of oxygen, and the greater the amount of carbon dioxide to be got rid of.

These actions are involuntary, yet the will may modify them, as it does in the act of speaking. Ordinary respirations average about seventeen a minute. One will be profited if he will study in himself ot another how this rate will vary, as well as the character of the act, by various kinds and degrees of exercise. Sighing, crying, laughing, coughing, sneezing—all are modifications of the respiratory actions, the character of each of which let the pupil study from the actions themselves.

Changes in the Respiration.—In the study of the chapter on the chemistry of the body, the experiment showed that when air came from the lungs it had in it an increased amount of water and carbon dioxide. It also has less oxygen and is warmer. Besides these changes, air from the lungs contains certain organic substances, which are very small in amount and can not be obtained in sufficient quantity to be weighed.

They are easily detected by the sense of smell when one passes from the open air into a poorly ventilated room in which there is a number of people.

From these causes, air once breathed is not fit to breathe again. There is not enough oxygen in it, and these organic substances seem to be real poisons.

Amount of Air breathed.—The lungs of an adult contain about one gallon of air. In an ordinary expiration only about one pint of air is thrown out. This can be shown by breathing through a tube passing under the mouth of a bottle filled with water, and inverted over water in such a way as to catch the air breathed out.

The amount of air breathed into the lungs is about the same. It can easily be seen that a pint of air would only fill the trachea and the upper air passages.

How the Oxygen is brought to the Air Cells.— Gases have the power to freely pass into each other. This property is called diffusion. If a pint each of a dozen gases were put in different parts of a close room, in a short time they would be equally distributed throughout the room.

By this property, the oxygen that is in the upper part of the lungs diffuses through the rest of the air to the air vesicles, and the carbon dioxide diffuses out to the upper part, where the acts of breathing remove the old air and bring in the new.

Changes in the Blood.—Once in the air vesicles, the oxygen passes through the very thin membrane of their walls and the walls of the capillaries into the serum, where it is taken up by the red corpuscles, which, by the current of the blood, are carried to the tissues, where the corpuscles give up the oxygen, and it passes to the tissues.

The carbon dioxide, on the other hand, passes from the tissues to the blood, which sweeps it around to the lungs, where it escapes. The water is also continually escaping at the lungs.

Thus, the organs of respiration and of circulation are made the mediums of exchange between the outside air and the tissues far removed from them.

Ventilation.—The tissues demand a constant supply of oxygen. If this supply is cut off for a very few minutes, death will follow. If in any way restricted or interfered with, more or less serious results will follow. It can not be too strongly emphasized that the body must be surrounded with an abundant supply of good air.

When one is engaged in in-door employment, it has been estimated on carefully obtained facts that each one should have at least three thousand cubic feet of space to himself, with a constant supply and removal of air. This space would be about the amount in a room fifteen feet long by fifteen wide, with the ceiling twelve feet high.

If less space is used, special care should be taken to secure perfect ventilation. It should also be remembered that every lamp or gas flame in the room is using up large quantities of oxygen, and pouring into the room large quantities of carbon dioxide.

In respired air it is found that the most injurious part is the small amount of organic substances that is given off. Besides being ventilated, living and sleeping apartments must also be kept clean.

Other Dangers in the Air.—Besides the things from the lungs themselves, other substances may occur in the air, which, reaching the lungs, may find through them an entrance into the body and become the causes of disease; or these foreign substances may even be direct poisons, as in the case of some gases.

Such substances are known to arise from sewers or unclean cellars, streets, or yards. All such places should be watched, that filthy accumulations may not be the sources of these evils. It has been clearly demonstrated that unclean houses and streets are dangerous.

It seems possible to live in such surroundings for a while in health, but in them one is in constant danger, and those in such localities suffer most from epidemic diseases. One should not dress in a manner to interfere with the respiration or circulation.

The Voice.—Vocal sounds are produced in the larynx by the air passing between the parallel edges of two folds of the lining membrane of that organ. These folds are the vocal cords, and are tightly stretched and close together at the time of the sound, but are relaxed and fall apart at other times.

The Larynx.—The larynx, Fig. 39, placed on the

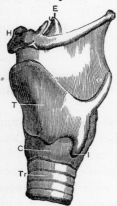

Fig. 39.

LARYNX—SIDE VIEW.

T, thyroid cartilage; *C*, cricoid cartilage; *Tr*, trachea; *H*, hyoid bone; *E*, epiglottis; *I*, joint of thyroid cartilage.

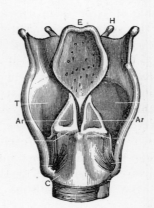

Fig. 40.

LARYNX, BACK VIEW.

Ar, arytenoid cartilages. The other letters the same as in the preceding figure.

top of the trachea, consists of a box formed of a frame of cartilaginous plates, some of which can be moved on the others by a number of muscles.

The largest of these cartilages, the *thyroid* (see the figure), forms the projection in the neck known as "Adam's Apple." It rests on a ring-like base, the *cricoid cartilage.*

The vocal cords are attached to small cartilages at the back called the *arytenoid,* and to the thyroid in front. By the movements of these cartilages the membranes of the vocal cords are stretched and brought together, or separated.

The sound is produced by the air passing these in a stretched condition and with their edges close together. Fig. 41 shows the ligaments and the cords with the covering membrane removed. The sounds of the letters are made to differ from each other by giving different shapes to the mouth, pharynx, and larynx.

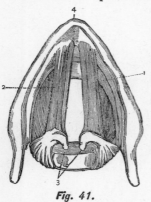

Fig. 41.

LIGAMENTS OF THE VOCAL CORDS.

(1 and 2), the ligatures; 3, arytenoid cartilages; 4, thyroid cartilage.

The *epiglottis* is a lid which is made to close over the larynx during swallowing, for the evident purpose of keeping food out of the larynx. It will also close promptly on breathing poisonous gases. The larynx, trachea, and lungs of some animal should be studied. Also the movements and forms of the mouth in forming the letters.

No other muscles in the body can be moved with the rapidity and precision of those used in speaking. They are greatly under the control of the will, and **can be** trained to wonderful feats of singing and speaking, and ought to be in every one at least trained to reading and talking well.

————

Questions for Review.

1. What does the blood bring to the tissues?
2. What does it carry away?
3. Which of these come to the blood and which leave it by the lungs?
4. What is the object of respiration?
5. How do the tissues carry on respiration?
6. What is this respiration?
7. What is external respiration?
8. What is the essential part of the breathing apparatus?
9. In what places is the oxygen always found?
10. In what form is the oxygen which is in the water used by fishes?
11. What is the arrangement of the essential parts in the gills of the fish?
12. What in the lungs of a man?
13. Name the respiratory passages in their order.
14. How is the blood brought to these, and to what part does it come?
15. Describe the thorax.
16. Describe the structure of the trachea and air tubes.
17. What are the cilia and their use?
18. Of what does the act of respiration consist?
19. What is the relation of the lungs to the cavity of the thorax?
20. What keeps the lungs expanded?

21. How is inspiration accomplished?

22. Give the action of the muscles employed.

23. How is expiration accomplished?

24. How is the diaphragm pressed up? What is the action of the intercostals?

25. How are the motions of respiration regulated?

26. How do they vary?

27. What of the control of the will?

28. Which respiratory act is each of the following: sighing? crying? laughing? sneezing? coughing?

29. How does the air coming from the lungs differ from that going to the lungs?

30. What of organic substances in expired air?

31. How much air do the lungs contain?

32. How much is thrown out at one expiration?

33. What is the diffusion of gases? Illustrate.

34. How is oxygen brought to the air vesicles?

35. How is carbon dioxide brought out?

36. How does the oxygen get to the tissues?

37. Trace the carbon dioxide from the tissues to the air.

38. What is the use of the red blood corpuscles?

39. What of the necessity of ventilation?

40. How much space should each one have in a working room?

41. How does this apply to your school room? To your sleeping room?

42. If there is not a space to each one, what must be done to counterbalance its lack?

43. What are some of the dangers in the air?

44. How may some of these be avoided?

45. Describe the larynx.
46. How are the vocal sounds produced?
47. What is the epiglottis and what is its use?
48. What are the motions in the larynx?
49. How are the different sounds of the letters produced?

CHAPTER XIII.

THE SKIN AND THE KIDNEYS.

The covering of the body is one of the most important, and at the same time one of the most interesting, organs to study. It has, as we shall see presently, several important uses. The one which is easiest seen is that of protecting the parts below it from mechanical injuries. In this way it acts as a strong suit of clothing—flexible and yielding, yet not easily broken or torn.

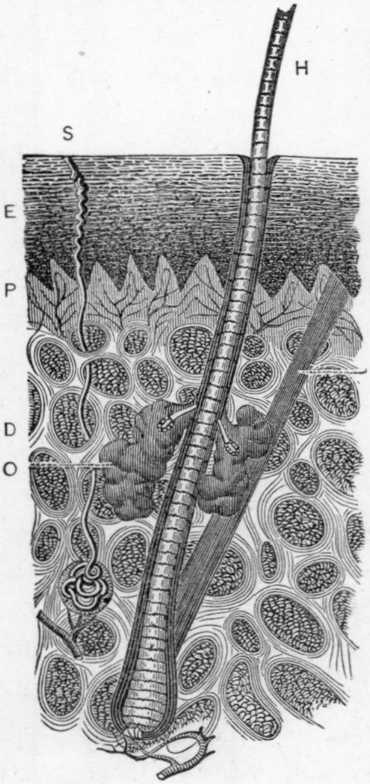

Fig. 42.

SECTION OF THE SKIN. MAGNIFIED.

H, hair; *E*, epidermis; *D*, dermis; *P*, papillæ; *S*, mouth of a sweat gland; *O*, oil gland.

General View.—The skin is of a very complex structure. It consists of two layers, which are so arranged as to support very many different organs. Fig. 42 shows a representation of a section made vertically through the skin, considerably magnified. The whole skin is about one tenth of an inch thick, less in many parts,

(130)

being thickest on the palms of the hands and soles of the feet. It is thinnest at the joints and wherever rapid motions are required, as over the eyelids.

Structure of the Skin.—The skin is composed of two layers, as shown in the figure. The outer layer is called the *epidermis*. It forms a thin covering over the dermis. The epidermis has no blood vessels in it, and as to nerves, it has only the smallest nerve fibrils in its lowest parts. It forms a layer that will not let water pass through it either into the body or out from the body. It prevents poisonous substances from passing into the body, and furnishes proper covering for the ends of the nerves of touch and of temperature.

Growth of the Epidermis.—The epidermis grows in its lower layer of cells, which crowd on those that lie above and push them out. The outer layers are constantly wearing away. Thus one's skin is always a comparatively fresh one.

The Dermis.—The lower layer of the skin is the *dermis*. It is composed of a closely woven sheet of connective tissue. In it are placed great numbers of blood vessels, a network of nerves, a network of lymphatic vessels, immense numbers of sweat glands, the sheaths of the roots of hairs, and the oil glands.

When the skin of an animal is made into leather it is mainly the connective tissue of the dermis that is tanned.

The dermis is tied fast to the rest of the body by a layer of connective tissue. It is so fastened that it may be loose enough to be pushed about a little over each point, and at the same time be pretty firmly held in place over the whole body. The skin is really stronger and tougher than one might suppose from its appearance.

Papillæ.—The upper surface of the dermis is

Fig. 43.

PAPILLÆ FROM THE PALM OF HAND, WITH THE EPIDERMIS REMOVED. MAGNIFIED.

raised into an immense number of small projections called *papillæ*. Fig. 43 shows some from the palm of the hand from which the epidermis has been removed. These are found everywhere in the skin, but are most numerous on the palms of the hands and the soles of the feet.

The epidermis fits closely over these and so nearly levels up the space between them that their existence would not be known if viewed from this surface.

But on the palms of the hands and soles of the feet the epidermis can be seen to be in fine parallel ridges. These ridges are over rows of papillæ, just beneath in the dermis. The papillæ are shown in both Fig. 42 and Fig. 43. In each papilla is a capillary blood vessel and a network of nerves, and in very many a minute, curiously formed body in which a nerve ends, which may be a nerve of touch or one of temperature.

Fat in the Skin.—In the lower layer of the dermis, in the meshes of the connective tissue, are many little globules of fat. Sometimes the fat may increase to such an extent as to make a thick layer between the skin and the muscles and other parts beneath. When this is the case the body is more rounded in outline.

This layer of fat serves to lessen the effects of blows on the body and helps to keep it warm.

In some of the lower animals, such as seals and whales, this layer is enormously developed, and is known as the blubber of the whale. The large amount of fat found in these animals causes them to be hunted for their oil. This arrangement allows these animals to live in extremely cold climates, and in the case of seals and walruses, to bear the rough contact with rocks and ice which the manner of life of a seal or walrus requires.

The Sweat Glands.—A sweat gland (Fig. 42) is formed of a knot of a coiled tube placed in the lower layer of the dermis. It is connected with the outer surface of the skin by a continuation of its tube through the two layers of the skin.

The coiled part secretes the sweat or perspiration, which, carried to the surface, is poured out, to evaporate completely if it comes out slowly, or to gather into drops if it flows out rapidly.

The secretion of the sweat is regulated by nerve fibers which come to the coiled part. The material of the perspiration, which is mostly water, is furnished by the blood flowing through a network of capillaries inclosing the coiled tube.

Perspiration and the Temperature of the Body.—Each one knows well that rapid running or exercise of any kind, or even very little exercise on a very hot day, will cause the sweat to form in large quantities over the surface of the body.

Now, as this always occurs under these same circumstances, it might be supposed that there is some reason for the connection of the two occurrences. And such is the case.

Source of Heat in the Body.—Let it be recalled that the increase of motion of the body can occur only by increase of the oxidations. This increase we found always to be accompanied by the production of heat. Increase of activity of any tissue increases the amount of heat in the body. When the digestion is most active it is found that the blood coming away from the digestive organs is warmer than that going to them. Besides the heat produced in connection with the usual activities of the tissues, the body has the power to produce oxidations in some of the tissues for the sole purpose of increasing the heat.

The body is so constructed that it works best at a temperature of 98° Fahr. If it rises above that limit only one or two degrees, it is very much out of its proper condition, and if one or two degrees still higher, life is in great danger. If it fall below 98° it is also in danger.

Regulation of the Temperature of the Body.— Now, special activity in the muscles in vigorous exercise produces heat which would raise the temperature higher than 98° if there were not a way to reduce it by some cooling process. This process is by evaporation of the water of the sweat.

Evaporation is a very effective means of cooling. It requires a large amount of heat to evaporate a small amount of water.

This is shown by placing a moist cloth on the bulb of a thermometer. As the cloth dries, the mercury shows, by falling several degrees, that *it is cooled.* If some substance like gasoline or ether, which evaporates more quickly, is used, a very low temperature can be produced, although the experiment is carried on in a warm atmosphere.

The sweat glands are all the time sending out water, which generally evaporates as soon as it reaches the surface. When an increase of heat in the body that might bring the temperature of the body above 98° Fahr. occurs, the nerves stimulate the glands to work, and thus to pour out a greater amount of sweat. The amount sent out will be according to what may be needed at that particular time to cool the body sufficiently to overcome the increase in the heat.

This arrangement must act very promptly and very perfectly, as the body will keep the same degree of temperature on going from a cold room to a warm one, or from a cold day to a warm one, or from one season to another.

We may say, then, that one of the most important uses of the sweat glands is to regulate the temperature of the body.

Perspiration as a Secretion.—The sweat is mostly water, but as it passes out it carries a very small amount of salines and a small amount of organic substances. These are regarded as excretions to be cast out of the body.

The Skin as an Organ of Touch and Temperature.—In the skin, as was mentioned, the nerves of sensation end in special organs, which are affected, the one by pressure, the other by change in temperature.

By means of these bodies, the skin becomes an organ with the most important duty of giving the knowledge obtained from these senses. It thus becomes both a constant guard to warn us of all danger, and to give us the information needed at every moment of our existence.

The Hair.—The hairs are really epidermis grown out into long threads. Each one forms on the top of a special papilla. This papilla is very much like any other papilla, except that it is at the bottom of a little pit.

The cap of epidermis (which is formed over it) remains, new portions being formed beneath it, and so on until it becomes a very slender, but in some cases an enormously elongated rod of epidermis.

Minute hairs are scattered all over the body. A little experiment with some of them, say those on the back of the hand, will show that they greatly aid in touch. Each one has a nerve at the bottom of its papilla.

The Nails.—The nails are thick plates of epidermis growing out from a number of papillæ. They grow continually, and thus provide for a comparatively new nail all the time. One may determine the rate of growth by making a line on one and observing the number of days it takes to move a certain distance. The use of the nails is made very plain in attempting to take hold of very small objects.

Uses of the Skin.—We may sum up the most important uses of the skin as follows :

1. It makes a strong suit of clothing to protect the body against mechanical injuries.

2. It prevents the absorption of injurious substances from without.

3. It prevents evaporation, except under control.

4. It helps regulate the temperature of the body.

5. It gives us, through the organs of sense in it,
very important and really necessary knowledge.

Hygiene of the Skin.—To accomplish these very
important functions to the best advantage, it should
be kept clean. When clean it is in the best condition and in the least danger.

Bathing.—Bathing the body often enough to keep
it clean is essential to the best health, and is a fun-
damental requirement of good breeding.

No special directions are necessary to regulate
bathing if it be done for the purpose of keeping
clean. Each one can decide such matters for himself. The time, place, and amount of water may
safely be left to his judgment. The temperature of
the water is best at that degree which is comfortable
to the bather.

Common sense will teach every one the precautions
against taking cold in the act of bathing. The only
rule necessary to be emphasized is that the bath
come often enough to keep the body clean.

From what has been said of the structure, uses,
and needs of the skin, it need hardly be added that
the smearing of the skin with any kind of dirt, no
matter of what color or price it is, is not to be done
in safety to the skin so treated. Fortunately this
fashion is no longer practiced by the most refined
people.

The Kidneys.—It may be repeated here that from the changes that take place in the body the three principal wastes are :

1st. *Carbon dioxide*, which is got rid of mainly at the lungs ;

2d. *Water*, which is principally thrown off at the skin ; and

3d. The waste containing nitrogen, a substance something like ammonia, called *urea*, which is thrown off by the kidneys.

The kidneys are placed one on each side of the spinal column in the abdominal cavity, near the last dorsal and the two or three upper lumbar vertebræ. They are large glands, through which a great amount of blood passes. They separate from the blood that goes through them certain substances dissolved in water. The principal one is *urea*.

These substances are removed from the body. Thus the blood in its circuit passes the lungs, where it loses carbon dioxide; the kidneys, where it loses urea, and the skin, where it loses water. If any one of these excretions be stopped, the result will be fatal.

————

Questions for Review.

1. What use of the skin is the most easily seen ?
2. Of what layers is the skin composed ?
3. What of its thickness ?
4. What are the uses of the epidermis ?
5. How does the epidermis accomplish this ?
6. Of what is the dermis composed ?

7. What organs does it contain?

8. How is it attached to the body?

9. What are the papillæ?

10. Where are they and what of their number?

11. Why do they not show on the surface of the skin?

12. Explain the parallel ridges on the palms of the hands.

13. What does each papilla contain?

14. How is the fat of the skin arranged?

15. What use may the fat serve in this place?

16. What of its development in seals and whales?

17. Describe a sweat gland.

18. What of its action?

19. How is its action regulated?

20. Under what conditions is the secretion of perspiration increased?

21. What is the temperature of the body?

22. What are the sources of heat to the body?

23. What is the effect on the temperature of special activity of the muscles?

24. How is this effect counterbalanced?

25. Show how evaporation is a cooling process.

26. How is this process in the body governed?

27. What of the sweat glands as organs of secretion?

28. How is the skin an organ of special sensation?

29. What is a hair?

30. How is it formed?

31. What are the uses of hairs?

32. What are the nails, and their mode of growth?

33. What are their uses?

34. Give a summary of the uses of the skin.

35. What is the most important point to be considered in the hygiene of the skin?

36. What is said of bathing?

37. Give the position of the kidneys.

38. What are their functions?

39. What are the three important wastes of the body, and where is each thrown out of the body?

40. What of interference with either of these processes?

CHAPTER XIV.

THE NERVOUS SYSTEM.

The Nervous System as a Means of Coördinating the Organs of the Body.—In our first lesson it was noted that in any movement of the body the parts worked together in some sort of harmony. The boy in climbing a tree sees a limb and reaches out his hand for it. In this action the eye and the arm must have some connection. In the whole action the feet, legs, hands, arms, eye, ear, the heart, the lungs, and very many other parts of the body work with each other, and not against each other, in accomplishing this act.

Now, when the muscles of the legs are in greater activity, the heart must beat more vigorously. This could not occur if there were not some means of communication between them. So it is with the hundreds of other examples that might be given. The means of communication in all these cases is the Nervous System. We shall try to see as clearly as possible how this is the case.

Nerves in the Arm.—In studying the motions of the fingers it was observed that nerves pass to each muscle, and that every muscle was made to contract by a nervous stimulus sent into it. What this stimulus is like it would be hard to say.

If the nerves of the arm could be exposed as shown in the figure, and a single nerve be cut, then the will would lose all power to cause the muscles to which the nerve is distributed to contract, and at the same time a touch on the hand could not be felt. Now, if the end of the part of the nerve connected with the muscle should be pinched, the muscle would contract promptly. If the end connected with the brain were pinched, pain would be felt.

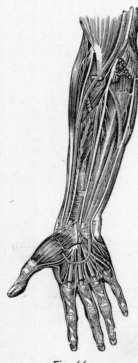

Fig. 44.

NERVES OF FORE-ARM.

Nervous Impulses.—This shows that the nerves conduct some kind of energy which, coming into the muscle, makes it contract, but coming into the brain causes a feeling of pain, touch, or other sensation.

What these nervous impulses are like we can not answer. In electricity we have an example of an impulse which metal wires will conduct a long distance. By its means an instrument in one city may be set in motion by a movement in a distant city.

Nervous impulses act in somewhat the same way, yet we think they are not electrical currents. But we do not understand what electrical currents really are.

The Structure of Nerves.—The larger nerves appear as white cords. These, as they go to be distributed to the various parts of organs, divide and subdivide until they are so small that they can not be seen with the naked eye. The larger cords and all their branches are called nerves.

A Nerve Fiber.—The microscope shows the nerves to be made up of very definite parts. Each one is a bundle of very minute tubes, through the center of which runs a fine core of substance, which is really the conducting part of the nerve. One of these tubes with its central core, which is the *axis cylinder*, is called a *nerve fiber*.

The parts of a nerve fiber are arranged very much as those of an insulated wire of an electrical apparatus. The axis cylinder corresponds to the metal wire, and the parts around this to the wrapping around the wire.

A nerve is like a bundle of these insulated wires made up into a cable, such as is used when a number of wires are to be laid under ground or in the water, or gathered together to occupy less room, as in the telephone cables.

How the Nerve Fibers are Connected.—Each nerve fiber in the nerve runs independently of the rest in the nerve. As the nerves reach the parts of the organs, their fibers separate into smaller and smaller bundles, until finally one single fiber ends in a single part of the tissue to which it goes.

These outward ends are in muscles, glands, the

skin, and, indeed, in all parts of the body. **Because** of the color of nerve fibers they are said to be composed of "white matter." But it is necessary to remember that the white matter is always composed of these nerve fibers.

The fibers traced toward the axis of the body are found to run to the spinal cord. Some end here, and some pass on through the spinal cord. But when the final ending is reached each fiber is found to end in a substance in the spinal cord and in the brain called the "gray matter."

Structure of the Gray Matter.—It requires the

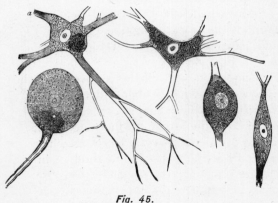

Fig. 45.

NERVE CELLS.

a, axis cylinder of a nerve.

microscope to see the structure of the gray matter. It shows it to be made up of very great numbers of little bodies of an irregular shape, called *nerve cells.* A nerve cell, Fig. 45, may have many projections from its surface, but one of these projections continued a long distance makes the axis cylinder— that is, the nerve core of the nerve fiber.

To make this a little clearer, let us imagine that we could take hold of one of the nerve cells in the spinal cord or brain and lift it out without breaking the delicate fiber connected with it, and that we could also unravel it from the nerve until we reach the outer organ to which it goes, which in this case, let us suppose, is a muscle.

Now, let us take out the microscopic bit of muscle to which the fiber is attached. If this could be done and the parts magnified, we should have the arrangement represented in Fig. 46.

This figure shows well the connection between the nerve fiber and the nerve cell on one side, and the muscle substance on the other. The tube-covering of the axis cylinder is removed part of the way. In one thing the figure is wrong; the length of the fiber is very much greater in most cases than is represented in the figure.

Fig. 46.

DIAGRAM TO SHOW THE RELATION OF NERVE CELL (*NC*) TO MUSCLE (*M*) THROUGH ITS NERVE FIBER.

What is the Action of the Nerve Cell?—It is from the nerve cell that the impulse starts which makes the particle of muscle contract. If in this figure (46) we substitute for the muscle some part that is sensitive to touch, light, sound, or some other things which affect us, the slender nerve fiber would conduct the impulse from this part of the organ to the central nerve cell. Then the nerve cell is stimulated or shocked, we may say. Some nerve cells in the brain or spinal cord receive these shocks by means of their fibers, and others send them out to muscles and glands.

The sensations which we receive are made by the impulses which come to the nerve cells in the brain, and the motions and other forms of activity are caused by the impulses which go from the nerve cells of the brain and spinal cord. It may be said that the functions, in part, of the cells are to *receive impulses, change them,* and *send out other impulses.*

Distribution of the Nerve Fibers and Nerve Cells.—The nerves are composed of fibers. The white matter of the brain and spinal cord is also of nerve fibers. The gray matter is composed of nerve cells, with some fibers. It is placed mainly in the core of the spinal cord and over the surface of the brain, and in certain bodies at the base of the brain.

The Divisions of the Nervous System.—The whole nervous system is divided into two great divisions—the *cerebro-spinal* system and the *sympathetic* system.

The Cerebro-spinal System.—A general view of this is shown in Fig. 47. This system consists of the brain and the spinal cord, and the nerves that branch from these—twelve pairs from the brain, and thirty-one pairs from the spinal cord.

The Brain.—The brain is the large portion of the nervous system enclosed in the cranium. The weight

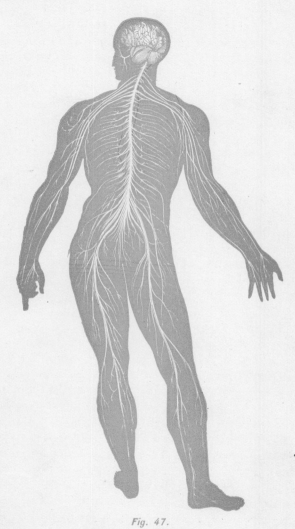

Fig. 47.

GENERAL VIEW OF THE CEREBRO-SPINAL SYSTEM.

is about three and one fourth pounds. Fig. 48 shows it seen from above; Fig. 49 the same seen from below; and Fig. 50 shows a side view with certain parts cut through vertically.

Of the parts shown in these views the *cerebrum* is the largest and is also the upper-most. It is di-vided into the right and left hemispheres by a deep ditch, called the longi-tudinal fissure. Its surface is broken up into many curving ridges, which are called the con-volutions. They are shown in Figs. 48, 49, and 50. The part which is like a stem to the cere-brum is the *me-dulla oblongata, MD* in Fig. 50, and 9 in Fig. 49.

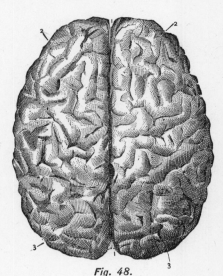

Fig. 48.

BRAIN SEEN FROM ABOVE.

1, longitudinal fissure separating the hemi-spheres; 2, frontal lobes of the cerebrum; 3, pos-terior lobes.

The medulla continues down into the spinal column as the spinal cord. In Fig. 50 that portion marked *Sp N*, to which the roots of two nerves are attached, is a part of the spinal cord.

Attached to the back part of the medulla close up

to the cerebrum is the *cerebellum*. This is shown as cut through in Fig. 50, *Cbl*, and at 4 in Fig. 49.

At the base of the cerebrum, near where the medulla joins it, are several parts not shown in the figures, which are sometimes referred to as the ganglia at the base of the brain.

In Fig. 50 are shown the twelve pairs of cranial nerves, which are often known by the terms first cranial nerve, second, third, etc.

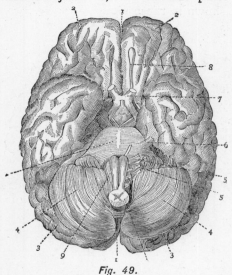

Fig. 49.

BRAIN SEEN FROM BELOW.

1, longitudinal fissure ; 2 and 3, front and posterior lobes of the cerebrum ; 4, cerebellum ; 7, optic nerve ; 8, olfactory nerve ; 9, medulla.

The Spinal Cord.—The spinal cord continues from the medulla, at the opening in the occipital bone, to about the second lumbar vertebra. It is about eighteen inches in length.

The Spinal Nerves.—From the spinal cord thirty-one pairs of nerves pass out to be distributed to the organs of the body. Each of these nerves starts from two roots, an anterior and a posterior root, which soon join together to make one nerve; but the nerve soon separates into a great number of smaller and

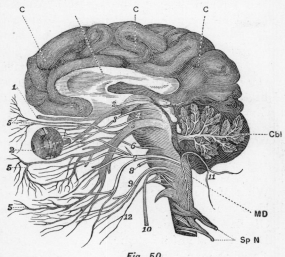

Fig. 50.

BRAIN AND CRANIAL NERVES SEEN PARTLY IN SECTION AND PARTLY IN SIDE VIEW.

C, convolutions of the cerebrum ; *Cbl*, cerebellum in section ; *MD*, medulla oblongata : *Sp N*, spinal nerves. The numbers indicate the twelve pairs of cranial nerves in their order.

still smaller branches, until, as was seen in a former section, they reach all the smallest parts of each organ.

The Sympathetic System.—This term is applied to that part of the general nervous system which consists of a row of ganglia on each side of the spinal column, and the network of nerves with which it is connected, that run all through the body. The ganglia are connected with each other, and, through

the spinal and cranial nerves, with the spinal cord
and the brain. It is really not a separate system, bu
a part of the general nervous system.

———

Questions for Review.

1. How is it shown that the nervous system connects distant parts of the body?

2. Give examples of parts of the body working together in harmony.

3. What effects would appear in each case if the cut ends of a nerve of the arm were pinched?

4. What would this prove?

5. What of the nature of the nervous impulses?

6. How are nerves distributed?

7. Of what is a nerve composed?

8. Describe one of its elements.

9. To what may a nerve fiber be compared, and to what a nerve?

10. What is the relation of the nerve fiber to its nerve and to its fellow nerve fibers?

11. How do the fibers end outwardly?

12. What is the white matter?

13. What is the gray matter?

14. How does each fiber end in the central axis of the nervous system?

15. Draw a diagram showing how the nerve fiber is connected outwardly and centrally.

16. What is the function of the nerve fiber?

17. Where is the impulse received?

18. From where is it sent out?

19. In what part of the nervous system are the fibers found?

20. Where are the nerve cells principally located?

21. What are the divisions of the nervous system?

22. Give an outline of the cerebro-spinal system.

23. Where is the brain and what is its size?

24. What are its principal parts?

25. Locate each and give its connections.

26. Describe the cerebrum.

27. Describe the medulla.

28. Describe the cerebellum.

29. What are the ganglia at the base of the brain?

30. What of the cranial nerves?

31. Describe the spinal cord.

32. How many spinal nerves are there?

33. How are they connected with the cord and how distributed?

34. What is the sympathetic system?

35. What are its relations to the cerebro-spinal system?

CHAPTER XV.

THE NERVOUS SYSTEM—(Continued).

Structure of the Spinal Cord.—The spinal cord is about as large around as the little finger. It is really a double cord, the two halves being joined by a narrow portion, but the outside sheath of connective tissue gives it the appearance of being single.

Its central portion is occupied by gray matter—that is, the nerve cells. Outside of these are nerve fibers, making up its white matter. The roots of the spinal nerves are nerve fibers, most of which are connected with the cells in the spinal cord. Many fibers run on up to the brain just outside of the core of nerve cells. The spinal cord is like a large nerve, except that it has gray matter in its central portion, while the nerves do not have nerve cells.

Structure of the Brain.—The *medulla* is really a continuation of the spinal cord, and is very much like it. But toward the upper end the gray matter containing the cells, instead of being simply in the center, becomes broken up into several portions, and the nerve fibers are scattered among them.

In the cerebellum the gray part with the nerve cells is mainly on the surface, which is greatly increased by being much folded. The white fibers in it run from the medulla, in the center of these folds,

(152)

to reach the cells of the surface. When the cerebellum is cut through, the arrangement of the gray
and white portions has the appearance
shown in Fig. 50.

In the cerebrum the surface of the convolutions is covered with a layer of gray
matter (nerve cells). These convolutions
greatly increase the amount of surface.
At the bottom of the cerebrum are several
masses of gray matter called the ganglia at
the base of the brain. Some nerve fibers
from the medulla pass to the nerve cells
of these ganglia; others pass to the nerve
cells of the convolutions.

Nerve fibers in the cerebrum also run
in many other directions—some to connect cells of one hemisphere with those of
another, or one part of one hemisphere
with those of another part of the same
hemisphere. All these fibers constitute
the white matter of the brain.

A General View.—When one studies a
large city, one thing that impresses him is
the immense number of wires that run in
every direction. They seem to be in utter
confusion through their great numbers and
the many courses they take. If the wires
are traced they will all be found to issue
from several points in large groups; these
are the telephone stations and telegraph
offices.

Some of the wires connect these stations with each

Fig. 51.
Spinal Cord.

other; others go to rooms in separate houses all over the city and surrounding country.

Messages are continually arriving at the central stations, and are continually going out from them again, and by this means an immense amount of business is carried on, including movements of railroad trains, so that they will not collide, the meeting at a special time and place of thousands of people engaged in thousands of transactions which require the most perfect working together of the people at a considerable distance from each other, moved by a knowledge of facts still more scattered and from more distant sources.

To such a system of communication in the city and its surrounding country could the nervous system in the body be compared. If in the city there were no other means of communication except through the wires and the central offices, and if to accomplish this a wire went to every room in the whole city and country, the comparison would be a closer one.

Nerve fibers pass by means of nerves to the spinal cord from every small portion of each tissue of the body, except from the upper parts of the thin epidermis, but even there the nerves lie so closely under it as to be affected by pressure on it.

In the spinal cord some of the fibers are connected with the nerve cells in the center, which form a series of central offices connected with each other by many fibers. Other fibers pass up the cord to the brain, where they make a most intricate maze, some connected with cells of one nerve mass, or nerve center, as it is called; some to another.   These centers correspond also to central offices.

In the body some of the fibers are connected with parts from which messages can be sent in but by which they can not be received.   They are the sensory fibers.   Others are so connected that messages are only sent out; they are the motor fibers.   The nerve cells in the centers both receive these messages and send them out.

Messages are constantly pouring into the central offices, and constantly others are being sent out over the hundreds of thousands of fibers.   The result is seen in the various forms of activity of the body, which occur in just the right way to correspond to the necessities of the body at every minute.

Thus the nervous system, by impulses received, changed, and sent out, like that of the system of telegraph and telephone, is enabled to make very many separate parts to work in harmony, some at great distances from the others.   This process is called coördination; and it may be said that one great function of the nervous system is that of coördination.

Action of the Nerve Centers.—We may now consider how the nerve centers act and how it is that just the right nerve centers will act at the right time and place, and with the proper strength.   All the motions of the muscles and the secretions of the glands are caused by stimuli sent to them from the nerve centers through the nerves.

We have seen in the study of the muscles that motions may be voluntary or involuntary, as they are called into action by the will or without its influence.

A very large number of motions are involuntary, and any muscle, whether voluntary or not, may be made to move without the action of the will.

When a nerve center sends out impulses which produce what we term voluntary motions, it has been stirred to action in some way by the will. When it sends out impulses which produce involuntary motions, it must have some other source from which it receives its stimuli.

Voluntary Nerve Centers.—By studying the effects of injuries to certain parts of the brain and spinal cord, which have occurred either by accident or disease in man, or which have been made on lower animals for the purpose of experiment, it has been decided that all voluntary motions proceed first from some part of the cerebrum. In the cerebrum, in all probability, the primary sources are in some part of the convolutions. We have seen that the gray matter in the convolutions is connected by fibers with each of the centers below, in the medulla, the cerebellum, and in the spinal cord.

In a voluntary movement of the hand we may picture to ourselves the events that occur, as follows :

The will, in a way which we do not at all understand, causes certain nerve centers in the surface of the cerebrum to discharge their impulses ; these impulses go to certain groups of nerve cells in the base of the brain ; these, from the action of these stimuli, discharge impulses along their fibers into the group of cells in the spinal cord which control the muscles that move the hand.

The method may be compared to that used in an army. If the general commanding the whole army desires certain movements in the army, he issues his orders to the group of subordinate officers next to him; they in turn give commands to other groups of officers subordinate to them, who at last give the orders to the men, who execute them in performing the movements desired by the general.

Functions of the Cerebrum.—It has just been shown that one of the functions of the cerebrum is that of causing the voluntary movements. It has also been proved that it is only when the nervous impulses reach the cerebrum that any kind of sensation is produced, such as seeing, hearing, and feeling of any kind. It is only when the cerebrum is in a healthy, uninjured condition that the memory, judgment, or emotions, such as love, fear, hope, and the like, are possible. The cerebrum seems to be necessary in producing consciousness and is the source of every form of mental activity.

Reflex Actions.—The spinal cord is able to produce motions when entirely independent of the brain. Every one has seen a chicken jumping about and flapping its wings violently after its head has been taken off. In the headless body it is the spinal cord that is sending out the impulses that cause the violent motions seen. By very careful study of the action of the spinal cord in animals whose brains have been removed, and in man when by accident the spinal cord has been severed from its connection with the brain, it has been found that the spinal cord never acts except on impulses coming to it from outside sources.

In the case of the jumping of the headless chicken, every motion is caused first by a touch on the outside of the body, which starts impulses that reach the nerve cells in the spinal cord. These stimuli cause the nerve cells to send out stimuli which cause motions. It acts just as it is acted upon. This sort of action is called *reflex action*, and such a nerve center is termed a *reflex center*.

Functions of the Spinal Cord and the Medulla.—The gray matter of the spinal cord and the medulla, which may be considered as two parts of the same thing, is mainly made up of reflex centers. The cord and the medulla may be said to have chiefly two functions: that of the conduction of the nervous impulses between the brain and the rest of the body, and that of reflex action.

Examples of Reflex Actions.—If the finger is touched with a hot object it is suddenly jerked away. This will occur even when the owner of the finger is asleep, or so busily engaged in thinking of something else that he does not at first notice what is happening. The motion is accomplished by the spinal cord stirred to action by the impulses from the heated nerve ending in the skin.

The question might be asked, *How is it that just the right muscles act to pull the hand away?* The answer is that, as the whole arrangement is for the purpose of taking care of the hand in such cases, the nerves of the skin of the hand are made to connect directly with the nerve center which con-trols the muscles of the hand, and not those which control other parts.

All along the spinal cord are reflex nerve centers, which act for other parts as this center does for the hand. Very many of the motions in walking, in running, in the movements of the arm and hand, and in the movements of the trunk, are really reflex actions of the spinal cord.

In the medulla are the centers which produce the motions of a cough, when impulses come from some-thing irritating the lining of the throat; a sneeze, when the nasal passages are stimulated; a deep breath, when water is dashed on the body; the involuntary act of swallowing, when the food has reached the œsophagus; and very many other nec-essary actions.

Reflex Action of other Centers.—While the reflex actions of the medulla and the spinal cord are very numerous, and include the great majority of motions, either in being their sole cause or in influ-encing them to a greater or less extent, yet at times all the other nerve centers serve as reflex centers.

Many movements which are at first caused by an effort of the will accompanied by the closest atten-tion may, on sufficient repetition, come to be accom-plished by reflex action. For example, if one should have to begin again to learn to walk, every move-ment of the feet and legs, and every movement of the arms and body in balancing the body over the legs, would have to receive attention and effort for their production.

But with one who has learned to walk well these motions are guided by the sensations which come to the nerve centers from sensations of sight of the path, from feeling it with the feet, and from many sources, so that walking may be accomplished when one's mind is wholly occupied with other matters. Indeed, it is sometimes accomplished during sleep, when there seems to be complete unconsciousness.

Uses of Reflex Action.—If the pupil will now put his body under close observation for a single day, and make a list of actions which are purely reflex actions, or partly so, he can better see how much a day's life of action is accomplished by reflex centers, and how important they are. It would be impossible for one to carry on the necessary motions of the body for even a very short time by voluntary action.

If only the comparatively few processes that have been mentioned in this little book be recalled, such as those that regulate the beating of the heart, the movements of respiration, the secretions of the many glands, the movements in digestion, besides those just mentioned in walking, in controlling the hand, in speaking, and if to these be added a thousand others, then the force of the truth stated above of the importance of reflex action may be seen.

Functions of the Cerebellum.—The cerebellum, no doubt, possesses functions which have not yet been discovered. Its size would lead us to suppose that it is of considerable importance, while, up to the present time, not a great amount is definitely known of its functions.

It appears to be connected with the power of making voluntary motions work together and in harmony; for example, in such a motion as making the thumb strike any one of the fingers, or, in walking, the keeping one foot back while the other is brought forward. This function is described as that of *coördinating voluntary movements.*

Blood Supply to Nervous System.—The nervous system is well supplied with blood, the largest part, the brain, having large arteries going to it. Its tissues are very sensitive to any changes in the character or amount of the supply of the blood. A lack of oxygen in the blood quickly shows itself in its effects on the brain. If the lack be great, fainting and loss of consciousness is the immediate result, and if continued but a short time, death will be sure to follow.

Poisons in the blood affect the brain very quickly. One of the most noted of these is the poison *alcohol.* In a few minutes it deranges the action of the nerve centers in a powerful manner, with often the most terrible results. Its continued use never fails to impair all the functions of the nervous system, involving as well the mental and moral nature of the individual.

The nervous system requires the rest found in sleep. Loss of sleep, if carried to an extreme, is a very dangerous experiment. Of all the parts of the body, none make so strong a demand for good air, good food, free from poisonous substances, and sufficient rest, as do the highly organized tissues of the nervous system.

The Effect of Alcohol on the Nervous System.—
(For a fuller discussion of effects of alcohol, see pp.
185–192.)

There is no part of the body on which alcohol has
so marked an effect as on the nervous system. When
taken into the stomach it is soon absorbed and circu-
lated through the body, and its effect on the central
nervous system (brain and spinal cord) is immediate.
Even a small amount of alcohol disturbs the action
of the brain. This is seen in the false judgments
directly following its use. The person may feel
warmer when it can be shown that he really is no
warmer. He says the drink has produced an exhil-
arating effect on him. This simply shows that the
alcohol has so affected his brain that he cannot judge
correctly even about his own bodily state.

In the next stage he gets very happy or angry
about almost nothing, or he becomes silly where, in
his normal state, he would be much in earnest. All
these feelings are the result of a disordered condition
of his nervous system. He is deceived, and he cannot
adapt himself to his conditions. If he should be in
such a state a considerable time, he could not escape
making great mistakes in his conduct. A man thus
deliberately makes himself a less intelligent being.
He disturbs those functions which we regard as the
highest, and which we are accustomed to look upon
with pride as the chief characteristics by which we
are distinguished from the lower animals.

If greater amounts of alcohol are used, all these
symptoms are intensified until there may be a complete overthrow of the reason and a loss of voluntary

control over the body. The sense impressions may be wholly misinterpreted. Such excessive use of alcohol, if long continued, will so profoundly disturb the action of the brain, that the patient may be attacked with such diseases as *delirium tremens* or *insanity*, whose final outcome, after much misery, is death.

The moderate but long-continued use of alcohol has not the same effect on all people. In some it may cause little apparent injury, while in others it will in time produce changes in the structure of the brain. These changes are similar in character to those which occur in the kidneys, the liver, and the heart; that is, there is a greater development of the connective tissues at the expense of the nervous elements of the brain. The effect, however, is more injurious on the body, as a whole, when the central nervous system becomes deranged, for through it all the other organs are more seriously affected.

Questions for Review.

1. Describe the structure of the spinal cord.
2. How is it like a nerve, and how is it different?
3. How are the nerve cells and nerve fibers arranged in the medulla?
4. What is the arrangement of the cerebellum?
5. How are the nerve cells of the cerebrum distributed?
6. How are the nerve fibers of the same arranged?
7. In what ways may the nervous system be likened to a telegraph or a telephone system in a city?

8. What things are accomplished by the telephone system?

9. What things are accomplished by the nervous system?

10. What is meant by coördination?

11. Give examples illustrating its use in the body.

12. Explain how one of the functions of the nervous system may be considered to be that of coördination.

13. What is the cause of every action of either a muscle or gland?

14. What are voluntary and involuntary actions?

15. At what place do the voluntary impulses originate?

16. What is the evidence that such is the case?

17. Describe the course of these impulses from their origin to the muscles that move the hand.

18. How may the action of the nerve centers be compared to the methods in the movement of an army?

19. What are the functions of the cerebrum?

20. What of motions produced by the spinal cord when not connected with the brain?

21. Give examples of such cases.

22. What is found to be necessary to cause the spinal cord to thus act?

23. What is reflex action?

24. What are the functions of the medulla and spinal cord?

25. Give as many examples as you can of reflex action, and state in each case what causes the stimulus to go to the nerve center, and the part moved.

26. How is it that just the right motion is produced in each case by the outer stimulus?

27. What other centers may act as reflex centers?

28. Give examples of such actions.

29. How may an act which is voluntary become reflex?

30. What proportion of the actions of the body are reflex?

31. Of what advantages are the reflex centers?

32. Give many examples of such advantages.

33. What of the functions of the cerebellum?

34. Illustrate how it is supposed to act.

35. What of the blood supply to the nervous system?

36. What is the effect of a lack of oxygen?

37. What of the presence of poisons in the blood?

38. What of the use of alcohol?

39. What of sleep?

CHAPTER XVI.

SENSATIONS.

Definition.—By the term sensations is meant the impressions or feelings which are made upon our minds by the things outside of our bodies, or by changes within our bodies. For example, a bright light gives us one kind of an impression, a vibrating tuning-fork another, an odor still another. Or, we may have sensations from changes within the body, as a feeling of thirst or of fatigue.

It is through parts of the body which give us these impressions or feelings that we gain our knowledge of things outside of us, or of the state of our own bodies.

Special and General Sensations.—If one considers the various sensations he has, and will compare them with each other, he will see that they differ very much in the definiteness with which they can be located in the body. When one feels tired, it is hard to say just where the feeling is located. Even after one has become tired from continued action of the arms, the feeling of fatigue can not be located in any particular part of the arms, nor does it seem to be confined to the arms alone.

It is very different when we receive a sensation from an object touching the finger. In this case it can be determined just where the point is that is touched, and the idea gained by the sensation is more definite and distinct.

The last sort of a sensation is called a special sensation, while those like that of fatigue are known as general sensations.

Sense Organs.—The special sensations are those of *sight, hearing, smell, taste, touch,* and *temperature.* Each of these has a special kind of apparatus with which the sensation is produced. In each case it consists of, *first,* an outer part which is so formed that it can be affected by some peculiar kind of energy, the perception of which energy, as something different from any thing else, leads us to call the organ a special-sense organ. Besides this outer part there is, *second,* the sensory nerve ; and a *third* part, the nerve center in the brain.

General Sensations.—In the production of general sensations there are also the inner parts, the nerve centers, and the sensory nerves, and there may be special outer nerve endings. But how they appear and where they are located is not known. The general sensations are numerous, and many of them hard even to describe. Among them are *pain, hunger, thirst, nausea,* and *fatigue.*

Pain.—Any one of the sensory nerves, whether of the special or general sensations, seems to be able to give rise to the sensation of pain if stimulated with too great energy. Thus, light, sound, things that touch the skin, or that affect nerves connected with any part of the body—in fact, which either give rise to a pleasurable sensation or to no feeling at all, and thus are only known by the reflex actions which

they produce—may cause intense pain if the stimulus be increased beyond a certain degree.

The Use of Pain.—A means of producing *pain* is
of the greatest importance to the body. It is simply
the way in which the nervous system calls attention
in the most emphatic manner to the fact that something is wrong.

Pain even does more than call attention to the
wrong. It drives us to right the wrong, to get rid of
the pain. We are sometimes rather slow to do what
is right, even when our attention is called to it. We
must have a stronger stimulus to action. Pain furnishes us that stimulus. Pain is graded all the way
from simply being an unpleasant feeling up to the
most intense suffering. To avoid the latter it is certainly well to pay attention to the former.

Hunger and *thirst* are forms of sensations which
arise from a diminished supply of food and water to
the tissues. They are produced through parts of the
nervous system not definitely known. These, together with the feeling of having had enough when
sufficient food and drink have been taken, are of the
utmost importance in regulating the supply of both.

Above all, we should attempt to preserve the
healthy action of these sensations, since, when they
are not abused or abnormally developed, they furnish us with the very best guides in the extremely
important process of taking food and drink. With
these disturbed, the preservation of the general
health is almost impossible.

The Sense of Touch.—This sensation is produced by pressure on the epidermis, also on the mu-

cous lining of the mouth and in the beginning of the nasal passages. The special organs of touch are microscopic bodies of a peculiar form placed in the papillæ, or just underneath the epidermis. The nerves of touch end in these bodies, and when pressure is brought to bear on the epidermis it starts impulses in the nerves which, coming to the brain, give the sensation of touch.

These organs are unequally distributed in different parts of the skin, being much greater in number in the palms of the hands, the lips, and tongue, and in the soles of the feet, than in other parts of the body. The little hairs scattered over the body, which have at their roots branches of sensory nerves, greatly aid in determining the pressure of any thing against the skin.

Different parts of the skin differ very much in the accuracy with which they report about the things touched. It is only by the palms of the hands, bottoms of the feet and toes, tips of the fingers, and by the lips and tongue that the shapes of things can be made out when touch alone is used.

Other parts of the body, such as the skin on the forehead, can determine the presence of a lesser pressure than can the fingers and the palms of the hands. It would be profitable for the pupil to experiment in these particulars with different parts of the surface of the body.

The Sense of Temperature.—This is the sense by which we determine the differences of the temperature of objects. Its outer organs are in the skin, in the lining of the mouth, pharynx, and œsophagus. These outer parts of the sense organ of temperature

are mingled in many places with those of touch, but
the two have been clearly proved to be distinct sensations and must have different nerves.

One may, by employing a warm or a cold rod, ex-
plore the surface of the skin and determine what parts
are most and what are least sensitive to heat and cold.

The uses of the senses of touch and temperature
are very obvious. We may say for them that they
are not the least important of the senses. The sense
of touch seems to be possessed to a greater or less
degree of definiteness by all animals.

The Sense of Taste.—The nerves of taste end
in little bodies in the mucous covering of the tongue,
and in the soft palate. This sense determines certain properties of liquids. The forms of the sensation of taste have been stated to be included in the
four following : *bitter*, *sweet*, *saline*, and *sour*.

The little bodies in which the nerves of taste end
are placed in some of the papillæ in the parts named,
and are only affected when the substances are dissolved. In this the saliva is of great aid.

We are accustomed to think that we taste many
things which we know only by the sense of smell.
This is the case with flavors, like that of vanilla, of
onion, of garlic, and with the flavors of different kinds
of meats.

Our opinion in this regard is only an example of
how we often make use of things a long time without stopping to determine accurately any thing about
them. By carefully keeping the odors of such substances that have flavors out of the nostrils their so-
called flavors can not be tasted.

The Sense of Smell.—The fibers of the nerve of smell end in little cells imbedded in the mucous membrane of the higher parts of the nasal passages. These cells come to the very surface, where their extremities are kept moist by mucus. They are affected by vapors and gases.

A very great number of odors can be distinguished by the organ of smell. Its sensitiveness is remarkable when it is considered what small quantities of substances can fill a large room with odors which can be detected by the sense of smell, although but a very small part of the air containing the odor can reach the olfactory surface of the nose.

The Uses of Taste and Smell.—The chief uses of these senses are plainly to examine both the food taken and the air breathed, and both organs are located admirably for these purposes.

———

Questions for Review.

1. What are sensations?
2. Illustrate this by examples.
3. What of the difference in the definiteness of the sensations received?
4. Illustrate this by examples.
5. Define a special sensation.
6. What is a general sensation?
7. What are the special senses?
8. What are the parts of the sense organ?
9. In what do the organs for general sensations differ from those for special sensations?
10. Name some of the general sensations.

11. How is pain produced?

12. What are the uses of pain?

13. Give examples.

14. How are hunger and thirst caused?

15. What are their uses?

16. What produces the sense of touch?

17. Where are the endings of the nerves of touch?

18. How are the touch organs distributed?

19. What function have the small hairs scattered over the body?

20. Where can points touched be most definitely located? Where can shapes of objects be best made out?

21. What parts of the skin are most sensitive to pressure only?

22. What is the sense of temperature?

23. Where are the outer parts of the organ distributed?

24. How may the sensitiveness of different parts of the skin to touch and temperature be determined?

25. What are the uses of each of these senses?

26. How do the nerve fibers of taste end?

27. What are the properties that the sense of taste determines?

28. How does the saliva aid the sense of taste?

29. What are flavors?

30. Where are the endings of the nerve fiber of smell?

31. What of the sensitiveness of the sense of smell?

32. What is the use of the sense of taste?

33. What are the uses of the sense of smell?

CHAPTER XVII.

SIGHT AND HEARING.

The Organ of Sight.—In the organ of sight, just as in the other sense organs, there is a part that is sensitive to a particular stimulus, which is connected by nerve fibers with a nerve center in the brain.

In the eye the part that is affected by the light, the *retina*, is in the back of the eyeball, its exact position to be made out presently. The nerve is the optic or second cranial nerve. The remaining parts of the eye are all helps in bringing the light on the portions sensitive to it.

External Parts of the Eye.—We may begin our study of the eye by observing what is exposed to view in our own or in our companion's eye. First we have the curtain, the *eyelids*, fringed by the eyelashes. Just back of the eyelids is the front part of the ball of the eye.

This looks like glass. Its shining appearance is due to its being very smooth and continually washed over by the secretion of tears. This secretion is rubbed over the eye by the act of winking, which is kept up incessantly.

As the tears pass over the eye they flow away and are gathered up by two tiny openings in the inner corner of the eye. These openings lead to the *tear ducts* (*lachrymal ducts*). The ducts, after passing through the lachrymal bones, empty upon the inner surface of the nostrils.

The very front of the eyeball is transparent, and when viewed from one side is seen to protrude slightly from the rest of the surface. This is the *cornea.* Beyond the edges of the cornea comes the white of the eye.

Looking through the cornea we see the colored part called the *iris.* It has a round black spot in the center known as the *pupil.*

The pupil is only a round hole in the iris. It is black, as is a hole in any closed box, because there is very little light inside to come out.

Fitting closely over the visible front part of the eyeball is a very thin layer of skin called the *conjunctiva.* It runs from the eyeball to the under side of the lids, at whose edges it becomes continuous with the skin of the outer surface of the lid.

The conjunctiva is well supplied with nerves, which give a sensation of great pain on the presence of any foreign body on the surface of the eye or under the lid.

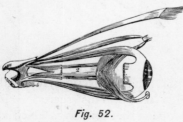

Fig. 52.

THE EYEBALL WITH ITS MUSCLES.

The Eyeball.— The ball of the eye is a globe of about one inch in diameter. It rests in a bony socket, in which it can be turned in every direction by its muscles. Between the eyeball and the walls of the socket is a padding, principally of fat and connective tissue. The eye is held in place very firmly, as one will find when he attempts to remove the eyeball from the head of some animal for study.

Fig. 52 shows the eyeball with its muscles attached. The upper muscle not attached to the ball belongs to the upper eyelid. The muscle in front is cut away

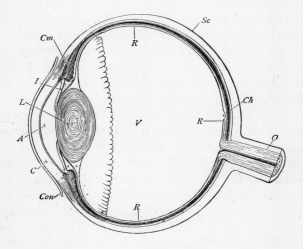

Fig. 53.

SECTION OF THE EYEBALL.

Con, conjunctiva ; *C*, cornea ; *A*, aqueous humor ; *I*, iris ; *L*, crystalline lens ; *V*, vitreous humor ; *Sc*, sclerotic coat ; *Ch*, choroid coat ; *R*, retina ; *O*, optic nerve ; *Cm*, ciliary muscle.

to show the optic nerve just back of it. The ball and optic nerve are also shown in Fig. 52 at 2.

The Walls of the Eye.—The eye may be considered as a globular box. The outer walls consist of three layers or coats. Fig. 53 is a section of an eye which well shows these parts. The front part consists of the transparent cornea, continuing as the white of the eye, which is called the *sclerotic coat* (*Sc*). This at the back extends over the optic nerve as its sheath.

This covering is of very tough connective tissue, and is the main part of the wall of the box, supporting the other parts and furnishing places for the attachment of muscles, as seen in Fig. 52.

Just inside of this coat lies the *choroid coat* (*Ch* in Fig. 53). It is dark in color and closely filled with blood vessels. Toward the front part of the eye it contains the muscular fibers (*Cm*) of the ciliary muscle. Farther forward it is continued into the *iris*, marked (*I*). Just inside the choroid is the very thin transparent *retina* (*R*). It is continuous with the optic nerve (*O*).

The walls are held out firmly in their spherical shape by the contents of the globe, which are the *vitreous humor* (*V*), the *crystalline lens* (*L*), and the *aqueous humor* (*A*). The vitreous humor looks like a very transparent jelly; the lens is firmer, and when fresh has the appearance of a clear convex lens of glass, while the aqueous humor consists of but a few drops of a liquid that is mostly water. The lens is held in place by a sheath of a kind of connective tissue.

Seeing.—As was stated above, it is a part of the retina that is affected by light. It is that part which lies against the choroid coat. The retina, although exceedingly thin, is a very complex structure. While the description of its microscopic parts may be omitted, it may be stated that the fibers of the optic nerve pass to the front of the retina, where they spread over the whole retina. The end of each fiber, however, turns toward the choroid coat, and, through different parts of the retina, becomes connected with each one of the vast numbers of minute bodies in the retina known as the *rods* and *cones*, whose ends point toward the choroid coat.

The light affects these rods and cones, and they start the stimulus, which, traveling along the optic nerve to the nerve center in the brain, produces the sensation.

Distinct Vision.—Perception of the exact outlines of an object can only occur when a definite image of the object is formed on the rod and cone layer of the retina. Every one knows that an image of a lamp flame or of the window can be formed on a sheet of white paper by the use of a convex lens.

The photographer uses a convex lens also to form an image in the camera. In the eye, the cornea and the crystalline lens are the convex lenses which form the image on the rods and cones.

The iris, by narrowing or enlarging the pupil, which actions it accomplishes by circular and longitudinal muscular fibers in its substance, regulates the amount of light, and thus helps to make the image more distinct.

Accommodation of the Eye to Different Distances.—If, while you keep your eyes fixed on the words of this page, you give attention to some object beyond the book, the farther object will be found to be indistinct. If now you look at the object beyond, the words of the book are indistinct. The reason for this is that a lens can not make on a screen definite images of objects at different distances at the same time. If the lenses and the retina of the eye were to remain just exactly the same in shape and distance from each other, we could never see any thing in definite outline except at one certain definite distance.

The eye is enabled to accommodate itself to objects at different distances by changing the amount of curvature of the crystalline lens. This is done by the action of the ciliary muscle, *Cm*, in conjunction with other parts. The lens becomes more curved for a near object, and less so for distant objects—that is, objects more than twenty feet away.

Short-sightedness.—A normal eye can accommodate itself, as has just been shown, to both near and distant objects. In a near-sighted eye, generally on account of the too great length of the eyeball, the lens can not make the image of distant objects fall on the rods and cones, and even near objects must be brought close to the eye to be seen clearly. Concave glasses will correct this defect.

In Long-sightedness the eyeball is commonly too short, and thus prevents images of near objects from being formed at the proper place. Convex glasses are used to correct this defect.

There are many other defects which eyes may possess, which can not be explained here. As most of them are such in nature that they grow worse in time and may prove serious, it is always best, when any are suspected, to have the eye examined by one skillful in such matters.

Sensation of Hearing.—An object producing a sound, such as a violin string, does so by vibrating very rapidly—that is, it swings backward and forward with great rapidity. These vibrations give their motions to the wood of the body of the violin, and this in turn sets the air to vibrating. Every little particle of air is swinging to and fro with the same rate as the vibrating body.

The sensations of hearing are produced by these vibrations being transmitted by parts of the hearing apparatus to the little bodies in the innermost part of the ear in which the auditory nerve fibers end.

The Auditory Apparatus is very complicated, and our description will include but a brief outline. The apparatus is generally considered in three divisions: the *external* ear, the *middle* ear, and the *internal* ear.

The *external ear* includes the visible projection called the *pinna*, and the tube that leads from it, known as the *external auditory canal*, which, at its inner end, is closed by a membrane called the *membrana tympani*, which separates it from the middle ear.

The *middle ear* is a small cavity in the temporal bone, lined by a thin

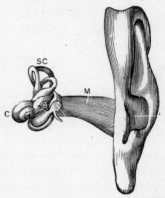

Fig. 54.

THE AUDITORY APPARATUS WITH THE SURROUNDING BONE REMOVED.

M, external auditory canal; *SC*, semicircular canals; *C*, cochlea.

mucous membrane. It opens into the pharynx by the *Eustachian tube.* It is separated from the external canal by the membrana tympani. A series of three small bones, the *malleus*, the *incus*, and the *stapes*, fastened together and attached to the sides of the cavity, connects the membrana tympani with a membrane between the middle and the internal ear. The middle ear contains air, which comes into it through the Eustachian tube.

The *internal ear* consists of very small tubes of

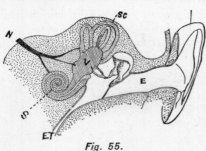

Fig. 55.

A Diagram of a Section of the Auditory Apparatus.

E, external canal ; *M*, in the middle ear, where is the chain of bones ; *V*, vestibule; *SC*, semi-circular canals; *N*, auditory nerve; *S*, cochlea; *ET*, Eustachian tube.

membrane, which lie in corresponding tubes of bony channels in the temporal b o n e. Both inside and outside of these tubes of m e m brane is a liquid which is mainly water. The three divisions of the internal ear are

the *semi-circular canals*, the *vestibule*, and the *cochlea.* The auditory nerve fibers end in cells on certain parts of the internal lining of these membranous tubes.

The functions of some of these parts are not definitely known, but it is believed that the sensation of sound is produced by the stimuli to the nerve endings in the internal parts of the cochlea. The cochlea consists of three tubes wound around in the shape of a snail shell. The nerve fibers end in the walls of the middle tube.

General View of the Action of the Auditory Apparatus.—The motions of the vibrating body set the air into vibrations; the vibrating air causes the membrana tympani to swing to and fro with the same rate; these swings are communicated by the series of bones to the membrane to which the stapes is attached. The motions of this membrane set the liquid of the internal ear in motion, and this acts on parts that set in motion the bodies in which the auditory fibers end. The motions start this stimulus, which causes the sensation of hearing.

Questions for Review.

1. What are the parts of the eye immediately concerned in seeing?

2. How are the remaining parts of the eye to be regarded?

3. Describe the eyelids, and give their use.

4. What is the use of the tears?

5. Describe the cornea.

6. Describe the iris.

7. What is the pupil?

8. What is the conjunctiva, and what is its use?

9. Describe the eyeball.

10. How is it held in place, and how moved?

11. Describe the arrangement of the coats of the eye.

12. What are the humors of the eye, and what are their functions?

13. Describe the crystalline lens.

14. How is vision produced?

15. Where are the rods and cones, and what is their use?

16. What is necessary for perception of exact outlines?

17. How is this provided for in the eye?

18. What are the actions of the iris, and for what purpose?

19. How is the eye accommodated to objects at different distances?

20. What is a long-sighted and what a short-sighted eye?

21. How is each of these defects provided for?

22. What is the cause of these defects?

23. How are sounds produced?

24. How is the sensation of hearing produced?

25. What are the general divisions of the ear?

26. Describe the external ear.

27. Describe the middle ear, giving also the arrangement of the bones and their connection.

28. Describe the internal ear.

29. Where do the auditory nerve fibers end?

30. Give a general statement of the action of the auditory apparatus.

CHAPTER XVIII.

ALCOHOL, TEA, COFFEE, TOBACCO, OPIUM.

IN certain chapters throughout this book we have called attention to the effects of alcohol on the special organs there described. It seems desirable now to speak of the effects, on the body as a whole, of alcohol, as well as of tea, coffee, tobacco, and opium. It is on the body as a whole that the most injurious work of these agents is to be seen. These substances are so widely used, and the consequences of their excessive use are so serious, that a special chapter may well be devoted to a discussion of their effects in the hope that many may be deterred from the formation of these dangerous habits.

Description of Alcohol.—Alcohol in a pure state is a transparent liquid. It is somewhat lighter than water. It is so nearly a true liquid that it forms no lasting bubbles when shaken up in a bottle. It burns with a pale blue flame, without smoke, thus producing a great amount of heat. Pure alcohol is known as "absolute alcohol." Alcohol mixes readily with water in all proportions. The alcohol usually sold, known as "commercial alcohol," generally contains five per cent or more of water.

Source of Alcohol.—Alcohol is formed by the growth of the yeast plant in solutions containing sugar. When yeast is placed in a solution containing sugar of the right proportions, and it is kept in a warm place, the yeast grows rapidly, and in its growth converts the sugar into alcohol and carbonic acid. The carbonic acid, being a gas, generally bubbles up through the solution and escapes; but the alcohol, being a liquid, remains dissolved in the solution.

In making bread, however, the carbonic acid resulting from the growing yeast is held by the sticky dough, which it lifts up and makes "light." In the process of baking, both the carbonic acid and the alcohol are driven off.

The juices of ripe fruits contain sugar. If these juices are left exposed so that the minute yeast plants in the air can get into them, they undergo a process called "fermentation." This process of fermentation is the growth of the yeast plants, and, as just explained, it produces carbonic acid, which mainly escapes from the juice and leaves the alcohol remaining in the liquid. Thus the juice of grapes is changed into wine, the juice of apples into cider. If the juices, after the formation of alcohol in them, are allowed to stand exposed to the air, other minute organisms grow in them, which will change the alcohol to acetic acid. Wine and cider are thus changed to vinegar. Many other solutions of sugar are used to allow the formation of alcohol, and thus many forms of alcoholic drinks are produced.

Beer, ale, and porter belong to the group of malt liquors. In making these, barley is kept moist and warm till it begins to sprout. In the act of sprouting, the starch of the grain is changed to sugar. The sprouted grain is dried and ground up, and water is added, which dissolves the sugar and other substances of the grain. To this solution yeast is then added, which converts the sugar into alcohol and carbonic acid. The resulting clear liquid containing the alcohol separated from the undissolved parts constitutes beer, ale, or porter, the distinctions between these being due to certain differences of treatment in the manufacture of the liquids.

Another class of alcoholic drinks is produced by first allowing alcoholic fermentation by yeast to take place, and then separating the liquor by distillation from the other matters in the mixture. Examples of such drinks are whisky, brandy, rum, and gin. These contain a far greater amount of alcohol than the wines or beer.

The quantity of alcohol in the different drinks varies greatly. In some kinds of beer the amount is as low as two per cent, while in some forms of brandy it reaches fifty-five per cent. In all alcoholic drinks, however much they differ in flavor, the alcohol is of the same nature, and has the same origin. The different flavors by which the various alcoholic drinks are distinguished are due mainly to substances extracted from the materials used in their manufacture. The most characteristic effects resulting from the use of alcoholic drinks are due to the alcohol contained in them.

Physiological Action of Alcohol.—In considering the physiological effects of alcohol, there are certain facts which must be kept in mind.

First, there is the great difficulty of determining the *exact* effect, on any special organ, of any substance taken as food, medicine, or poison. We can usually say that a certain food is good or bad because, when it is used constantly, the general health of the body is improved or impaired. But it would in most cases be impossible to tell the special effect of that food on the various tissues. Of course, in all such cases there are people ready to advance theories to explain the exact action of the various foods on each of the tissues. But explanations which have not been experimentally proved are of no value. There are many medicines whose general tendencies are pretty clearly known, but whose special effects on the cells of any tissue are wholly unknown. Quinine is a good example. It is well known that if given in a proper way it will, in a great number of cases, cure certain diseases; but it is impossible to say definitely how the cure is effected, and it certainly is not possible to show with microscopic sections any changes in the tissues produced by such small quantities of quinine.

Some of the most active poisons, while they show, by causing death, their sure and speedy effect on the body as a whole, give no indication, under the most careful examination, of their special action on the various tissues of the body.

There is no doubt that when any substance, as a food, a medicine, or a poison, produces an effect on the body, it does so by causing certain changes in the cells of some or all of the tissues. But what these changes are, it is usually impossible to determine.

A second fact that should be kept in mind in considering this subject is that individuals vary greatly in the way they are affected by different kinds of foods and drugs. Often it is found that a food which seems beneficial or harmless to most people may produce in certain individuals unpleasant or distressing symptoms. A drug which may powerfully affect a majority of people may be used by a few without marked injurious results. Even the effects that generally follow the use of any drug vary greatly in character and degree in different persons. Hence we must not draw any definite conclusions from a single experience or from a few observations on a few individuals.

A third fact important to remember is this: The effects of substances may vary under different conditions; as, in various degrees of health; in connection with different kinds of diet; in activity or rest of the body; in different climates; and in different ages. In view of these facts, the following statements of the physiological effects of alcohol must of necessity be of a general character, and they cannot be made applicable to each individual case.

If a small amount of alcohol is taken, it may produce no perceptible effect except a slight increase of the pulse rate.

The effects of large amounts of alcohol are well summed up by Dr. Emerson, as follows:

" If large doses be given a healthy person, the usual course is, first, a flushing of the face, with a greater flow of words and ideas, and tendency of muscular activity; then imperfect articulation, loss of judgment, unsteady gait, dulled moral sense, irregular eyesight, loss of sensation, then of consciousness, and, finally, even impaired (vegetative functions) breathing and circulation—all of these phenomena being successive paralyses of nervous centers of the brain, medulla, and spinal cord.

" If large doses be often repeated, the alcohol carried through the various organs modifies their nutrition and the growth of the mere connecting tissues (framework) at the expense of their more important special tissues. Thus the stomach and liver, kidneys, and, finally, even the voluntary muscles, and the all-important involuntary muscle called the heart, degenerate. These processes are slow and only result from the decided abuse of alcohol, especially spirits."

The student is referred to the chapters on circulation (p. 77), foods (p. 96), and the nervous system (p. 162), for a description of the special effects on these organs of the use of alcohol. But to understand the full action of alcohol on the body as a whole, we must remember that the results described for these various organs occur all together. These organs, as we have learned, have very important functions. When the action of one is interfered with, its effect is felt on the whole body, and thus the direct injury occasioned by alcohol is heightened. If the functions of these important organs are being interfered with, the general health of the body is sure to be undermined. The capability of the body for accomplishing physical or mental work is greatly lessened. Its power of resisting the attacks of disease is decreased. Its power of recovery when disease has invaded the system becomes much weakened. This condition of the body is sometimes described as " an undermined constitution " or " a lowered vitality." While it is hard to describe accurately what has occurred to the body, the condition is none the less real. It can be easily recognized, and is indeed a serious matter.

If the body sustains accidental injury, or for some cause a surgical operation is to be performed, the surgeon realizes that recovery is likely to be less speedy, or less sure, if the patient has been accustomed to the use of alcoholic drinks.

Under training for any athletic contest, experience has shown that the greatest success cannot be secured when alcoholic drinks are indulged in ; consequently their use is forbidden. In cases where long-continued, severe bodily exertion is necessary, or an unusual amount of exposure to fatigue, cold, or heat, experience has also shown that the drinking of alcohol is detrimental. In these cases the objection to the use of alcohol is clear. Still the effects are the same whether we are engaged in a severe contest or not. We are all the time in some sort of contest, and certainly each one wishes to be at his best. Experience shows clearly that we are not at our best after using alcohol. The same may be said of the use of tea, coffee, and opium and its compounds.

Alcohol as a Medicine.—The discussion of the question in regard to whether alcohol may be beneficial in the treatment of disease is out of place here. When we are sick we should be put under the care of a well-trained physician. Then we must trust to his learning and skill, and follow his directions. The forms, conditions, degrees, and courses of diseases are so varied, and so obscure, that it would generally be dangerous to trust ourselves to any one not trained or skilled in the practice of medicine. There are many poisons and other injurious substances that may be used with great benefit in certain conditions or phases of disease. Physicians differ in opinion as to whether alcohol is one of them. But, in any case, the problem must be solved by the physicians, and, however settled, it will not affect the question of the effect of alcohol on the healthy body.

Other Substances in Alcoholic Drinks. — Thus far we have spoken only of the alcohol in alcoholic drinks, but they contain a number of other substances. Some of these occur naturally, and others are added either to change the flavor or as adulterations. Some of these are known to be injurious and others to be harmless. The number of these substances is so great that a special treatment of each is impossible here.

Intoxication. — Thus far we have mainly dwelt on the effects of long-continued use of alcohol on the general health of the body. There is, however, one result which is so evident that neither physiologist nor physician is needed to detect it or to point out its evils; that is, the intoxicating effect of alcohol taken in large doses. This is known in common language as getting drunk. The evils of drunkenness are so great and so well known that we need not dwell on them here. Fortunately, a large number of those who use alcoholic drinks do not become habitual drunkards. However, it is of the greatest importance that the fact be emphasized that the moderate use may become immoderate. It is only from the ranks of the moderate users that the great army of drunkards is recruited. It is impossible for a man to foretell, when forming the habit of drinking, whether or not he will be able to control himself from running into excess. Hence when a man cultivates this habit he runs this risk.

It would seem as if no person who has contemplated the terrible things which have been done under intoxication would voluntarily assume a habit which involved even the bare possibility of such an end. Indeed, all such arguments against the use of alcohol as those contained in the facts of its effect on the heart, the kidneys, or the liver, or on the general health, pale before the undisputed evidence that by means of alcohol an intelligent man may act without reason; that a kind-hearted man may become brutal to his most loved friends; that an honorable man may become dishonorable; that a man with a noble nature may acquire the most depraved tastes; that its use has over and over again been the cause of bitter disappointments, of intense sufferings, and of crime.

Effects of Alcoholic Drinking on the Community.—It has been shown beyond any doubt, by repeated study of statistics gathered from prisons, insane asylums, and almshouses, that the use of alcoholic drinks is the most frequent cause of crime, insanity, and poverty. These facts are so well known, and have been before us so long, that they do not impress the general community in proportion to their enormity. If some new form of drug or food, or some new political or social movement, were introduced which, in a year after its introduction, would bring about in the civilized world physical and moral results as great as those produced by alcohol, the fact would stir every class up to arms. There would be a universal, energetic, and immediate movement towards its suppression.

Most other poisons so affect their victims that they alone suffer the consequences of their use. But alcohol renders its slaves active agents in bringing suffering and degradation on others in the community. Other vices are the usual associates of drunkenness.

The evil influences of most drinking places and of many drinking customs are well known and undisputed. Thus alcohol comes to affect not individuals alone, but the moral tone of the community as a whole. In these facts, again, we are forcibly shown that arguments against the use of alcohol based on moral grounds far outweigh all those drawn from physiological considerations.

Tea and Coffee.—Tea consists of the dried leaves of a plant extensively cultivated in China, Japan, Ceylon, and India. The leaves contain a number of vegetable substances common to all leaves, but in addition they contain an alkaloid known as *theine* which is characteristic of tea leaves. There is also a large amount of *tannin*.

Coffee consists of the seeds or so-called "berries" of a plant which is cultivated for drinking purposes.

The berries are roasted, and by this means an *aromatic substance* is developed which gives coffee its peculiar flavor. Besides this aromatic substance there are, of course, many other ingredients in the berries, prominent among which are *tannin*, certain *vegetable acids*, and *caffeine*.

Theine and Caffeine.—It is to these substances that the characteristic physiological effects of tea and coffee are due. Theine and caffeine are exactly alike in their chemical composition, and the same physiological effects have been assigned to both. In tea there is a greater amount of tannin. This has an injurious action on the digestive processes.

After speaking of the beneficial effects of a moderate use of tea for some persons, Dr. Yeo says:

" On the other hand, it is quite certain that tea taken in excess, and in some constitutions, may become very injurious. It will not infrequently excite and maintain most troublesome gastric catarrh, the only remedy for which is an entire abstinence from tea for a considerable period. It is often also the cause of troublesome cardiac palpitations, together with muscular tremors and general nervous agitation. We have noticed that tea will often commence somewhat suddenly to disagree with a person, and excite dyspeptic symptoms, coincidently with the occurrence of nervous worry, and that after the cause of the nervous worry has passed away tea may again be taken, in moderation, with impunity. In irritable states of the stomach tea is also apt to disagree, especially if the coarser teas containing much tannin are taken ; these when taken in large quantities during, or too soon after, a meal, will disturb and often seriously hinder the digestive processes.''

The beneficial effects which are thought to belong to the moderate use of tea and coffee are no doubt often more apparent than real; they produce an agreeable feeling, which makes the user believe that he is benefited when perhaps only a harmful change has taken place.

If no other harm came from the use of these substances than the constant deception as to the true state of the body, even that would be considerable damage. For, if the proper appetite is interfered with, it is quite certain that at times too much or too little food will be taken. Tea and coffee have also the power of relieving the sense of fatigue, and while they may thus be valuable aids as a temporary relief from suffering, they become very harmful if they lead us to overlook and disregard the cause of the weariness. Fatigue itself has its uses, and we would sooner or later suffer if deprived of its warning voice. In other words, the delicate balance of coördination between the processes of nutrition and necessities of the various organs would be lost. Such a state continued could not result otherwise than injuriously, the extent of injury depending on the degree to which the organism was affected. The claim that tea or coffee will enable the body to do more work on a smaller amount of food is absurd. Energy cannot come from nothing. As the source of energy in the body is oxidation of oxidizable substances (foods), it is impossible for a substance to cause work to be done by doing away with its source of energy.

Whatever makes us " feel better " when we really are not better, forces our nervous system to tell lies to us. This " feeling better " is also followed by " feeling worse," which is also a lie. These waves of feeling caused by stimulants destroy the unity and effectiveness of life. The greater the wave of exaltation, the lower is the depression which follows. This depression finds its extreme in discouragement, pessimism, and delirium tremens. The user of stimulants leads in a sense a double life, and no form of " double life " can be an effective one.

It is unwise to use even in so-called moderation these stimuli which thus distort the natural action of the nervous mechanisms regulating the nutritive processes. But it is worse than folly to indulge in them to an excess which brings on one the most serious results. Between moderation and excess the gradation is very gradual. Moderation in the great majority of cases becomes a greater or less degree of excess. It is certainly the part of wisdom to forego the passing pleasure that these beverages may give, and avoid the risk of the more lasting suffering or disability which their use may entail.

Tobacco.—Tobacco, as is well known, consists of the leaves of a plant which is raised in many warm countries. It is used in the form of snuff, or is chewed, or smoked as cigars, cigarettes, or in a pipe. It was introduced into Europe at the time of Queen Elizabeth by Sir Walter Raleigh, who learned its qualities from the Indians of North America. From this time its use gradually spread throughout the civilized world.

Among the many substances in the leaves of the tobacco plant the most characteristic is *nicotine*. This is oily and aromatic. It is distilled from the leaves by the heat of the burning tobacco. The vapor of this oil is partly condensed in the cigar or cigarette, or in the bottom of the bowl or along the stem of a pipe; but part of it passes on to the throat and lungs of the smoker.

From these regions it gets into the body. Nicotine is an active poison, even in small quantities. The amount that usually gets into the body by the user of tobacco is very small, otherwise the results would be fatal. As it is, many persons use tobacco for many years, apparently without bad effects. The body, which at first is greatly shocked at the introduction of the poison, seems later to adapt itself to its presence. Still to a great number of persons it is always a poison, more or less undermining the health, or even breaking it down entirely; used in excess— and there is constantly this danger—the results are most serious. The physiological effects of tobacco are as follows:

It affects the heart, and excessive use may produce palpitation and weakening of that organ; it interferes with the digestion and causes a loss of appetite. A long series of carefully conducted experiments shows that immediately after smoking there is a marked loss of the power of doing work with the voluntary muscles. Tobacco is also said to interfere with the development of the red blood corpuscles, whose great importance has been shown in another place.

Of the other substances besides the nicotine which are vaporized by the heat of the burning tobacco, and pass with the smoke into the mouth, throat, and lungs, some produce irritation of the mucous lining and may bring about a diseased state of those organs, such as a chronic sore throat, and other affections. It is thought that many cases of cancer of the mouth can be traced to the habit of smoking. It is agreed on all sides that the use of tobacco is very injurious to the young, and should be avoided by them in every form. There have been many cases recorded of death of young boys through nicotine poisoning from excess in smoking.

The evil effects of tobacco come on in such an insidious way, that very often the sufferer has no hint of the true cause of his troubles; this renders it all the more a dangerous enemy.

The tobacco habit grows on a person till it becomes, in the great majority of cases, a somewhat tyrannical master, demanding great sacrifices of time, health, and money to satisfy its desires. This itself is a form of disease. There is another point of view we should consider. How will it affect our associates? Both smoking and chewing are offensive to most people who do not use tobacco. We should indeed hesitate before forming a habit which will render our close presence disagreeable to many, if not to most of our friends.

Opium.—The use of opium or some of its compounds may become a habit impossible to control. When this is the case the result is usually a most disastrous one. Opium occurs in various forms.

Morphine is a substance made from it. Some compound of opium is found in many medicines, such as paregoric and laudanum. Many of the so-called "cough mixtures" and "soothing syrups" contain some form of it. It is a very dangerous drug. A small amount of it will produce death. In the hands of the doctor it becomes, in disease, one of the most important medicines; but, on account of the danger in its use, it should only be given under direction of a physician. The frequent use of medicines containing opium or its compounds may lead to the formation of the opium habit.

General Considerations in Regard to Stimulants. —The body, as we have seen, is a combination of delicately balanced mechanisms. Through the nervous system many of them are self-regulating. These work most correctly when the stimuli which direct their action come from the actual condition of the body. Thus the movements of respiration are controlled by the amount of carbonic acid in the blood. The beat of the heart is regulated by nervous impulses arising from actual conditions of various parts of the body. We have shown that the actions of the glands, and of other organs, are regulated in a similar manner. Now, if any artificial stimulus acts on these mechanisms, they no longer work in just the manner they should, to be in harmony with the remainder of the system. The body is then not in its best condition.

By means of the nervous system we have sensations which tell us of the outside world through the special senses, and of the state of our own body through such sensations as those of hunger, thirst, fatigue, pain, etc. Furthermore, we have the power of coming to conclusions in regard to our actions on receiving impressions through these sensations. The whole is a very complex means by which we adapt our actions to conditions in which we are placed.

For the greatest success, for the clearest seeing, for the most efficient action, it is of the utmost importance that correct reports come in for the judgment to act upon. In other words, we wish to know the world as it really is, and we wish to know the actual conditions of the body. This is impossible when the sensations are modified by stimulants. They make us feel warm, cool, hungry, thirsty, well, or ill, when we are not really in such condition. We have reporters about us which tell false reports; hence when we act on those reports our conduct cannot be right.

In the close competition we are sure to meet with in any pursuit in life, the degree of success will depend upon our equipment. How great, then, is the importance of keeping in good condition the delicate mechanisms upon the true working of which depend our chances of success and our capability for happiness! How unwise is the person who voluntarily does anything that may prove a hindrance to the best action of his mind or body!

INDEX.

The explanation of all the words in the index may be found by reference to them in the text.

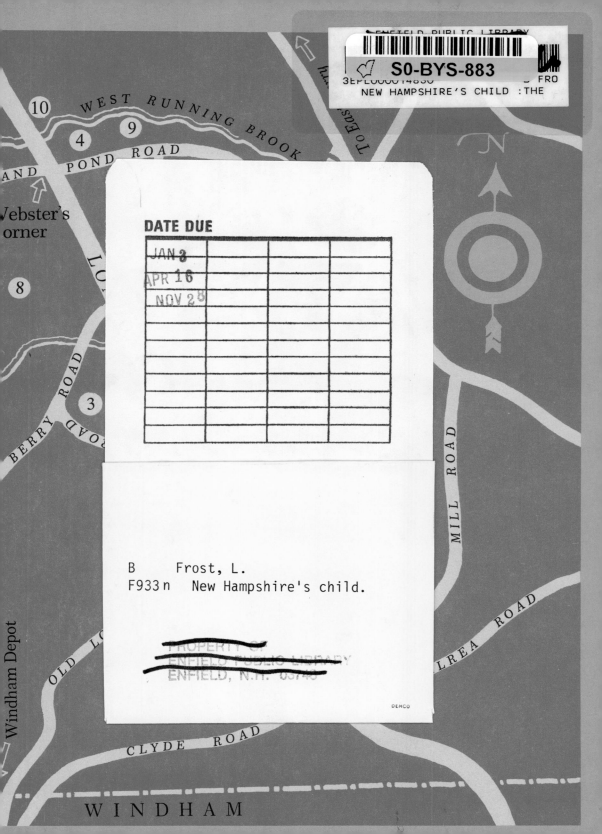

NEW
HAMPSHIRE'S
CHILD

NEW

HAMPSHIRE'S

CHILD

THE DERRY JOURNALS OF

LESLEY FROST

WITH NOTES AND INDEX BY

LAWRANCE THOMPSON AND ARNOLD GRADE

———

STATE UNIVERSITY OF NEW YORK PRESS

ALBANY, NEW YORK

1969

Published by State University of New York Press,
Thurlow Terrace, Albany, New York 12201
© 1963, 1969 by The Research Foundation of
State University of New York. All rights reserved

Grateful acknowledgment is made for permission
to quote the full texts of seven poems by Robert Frost
from *Complete Poems of Robert Frost*. Copyright 1916, 1928, 1934, 1939,
© 1967 by Holt, Rinehart and Winston, Inc.
Copyright 1944, © 1956, 1962 by Robert Frost. Reprinted
by permission of Holt, Rinehart and Winston, Inc.
The poem "The Blue Bird to Lesley" which appears in the Notes
is © 1969 by the Estate of Robert Frost
and is used with permission of
the executor of the Estate.

Standard Book Number 87395-043-7
Library of Congress Catalog Card Number 69-12099
Manufactured in the United States of America
Printed by The Riverside Press, Inc. and The Meriden Gravure Co.
Designed by P. J. Conkwright

To
"the children"

CONTENTS

Introduction

ILLUSTRATIONS

INTRODUCTION

IN presenting these "journals" which I began to write when I was
five years old, I cannot resist quoting one brief essay I wrote when I
was nine. It was entitled "Journeys on the Farm" and it sets the
right tone for all the other entries, regardless of misspellings:

"Our farm has interesting places to travel to, just like the world,
though you do not have to journy so far as in the world. We go to
some places almost every day that it is good enough to go and that is
only when it is nice, but when it snows we sometimes dress up and
go tramping [no further than] out to the gate. When it shines we go
everywhere on our farm though we have been there a hundred
times.

"The alders is one of my favorit places to go, because it reminds
me of the brook that said 'I sparkle out among the fern to bicker
down the vally,' and the brook out there is just like it, though
there isn't any fern, but it sparkles out among the woods to bicker
down the vally. The next best journy I like is going over in the
grove. That doesn't remind me of anything, but it is best to play in.
You can make little houses and everything with the sticks and pine-
needles that are over there and we go there very often, but we only
go out in the alders once in three or four days.

"The big pasture is my next favorite place because there is a little
round grove out there of about six trees and they all touch together
at the top and make a lovely shade to sit under as soon as it is warm
enough, and it is very comefortable. After the big pasture the field

over across the road is next best. That is noted for its checkerberrys. We go there almost every day to get checker*berrys* or checkerberry *leaves* whatever we find there both just as good to us. All these places that I am speaking of we travel to about every day and play in each one half an hour and play that half an hour is half a year at some far off place in the world."

The farm I am writing about might well be called "The Gift Outright" to my father and mother. "The land was ours before we were the land's," but by the time I was writing my composition books it had become ours in a double sense. We had lived on it — these thirty acres of pasture, mowing field, woodland, with farmhouse sheds and barn (all one piece) — since the fall of 1900. The *Derry News* for October 5th, in that year, had announced, "R. Frost has moved upon the Magoon place, which he recently bought. He has a flock of nearly 300 Wyandotte fowls." He had not bought it: his grandfather had bought it for his use. I was then all of sixteen months old, having been born April 28, 1899. Therefore what I am now saying, as a child of New Hampshire upbringing, I shall be trying to say as though I had no knowledge (and for those years, of course, I had none) of my parents' previous lives: the tragedies and disappointments as well as the happiness and ecstasies, that were theirs before I came on the scene. For me, life on the Derry farm was to be a long and passionate borning. For them, it became "the sweetest dream that labor knows." Emerson had written, and my father was reading aloud to the family,

"Prayer is the contemplation of the facts of life from the highest point of view. It is the soliloquy of a beholding and jubilant soul. It is the spirit of God pronouncing his works good. . . . As soon as the man is at one with God, he will not beg. He will then see prayer in all action. The prayer of the farmer kneeling in the field, the prayer of the rower kneeling with the stroke of his oar, are true prayers heard throughout nature."

And so we had, and have, Robert Frost's "Prayer in Spring," written on the Derry farm, beginning,

INTRODUCTION

Oh, give us pleasure in the flowers today;
And give us not to think so far away
As the uncertain harvest; keep us here
All simply in the springing of the year.

I learned, when I was very young, that flower and star, bird and
fruit and running water, tree and doe and sunset, are wonderful
facts of life. The farm was enough of a world for learning, no
matter how short the "journeys." A child (who else but myself!)
could take the long, long path down to the lower pasture, eating the
seeds of the sweet fern as she went, to bring the cow home at
almost dark; could ride beside the driver (who else but Papa) on
the high, narrow seat of the horse-drawn hayrake and be permitted
to press the pedal that released the hay at the windrows (the timing
was most important and took practice); could ride beside another
driver (who else but Mama) with reins wound tight about her hands,
doing her level best to control Eunice-the-horse as the little sleigh
(with bells) swept out of the Church stables in Derry Depot after
the Saturday night grocery shopping at the Grange store; or, as one
of "the children," could go on the all-day picnic (usually on Sunday)
across the orchard to the alders, where Papa was forever clearing
the underbrush with axe and clippers (two of his favorite "weapons"
together with the scythe and the hoe), and where Mama sat on a
board bench nailed between two young pines (old pines, now, heal-
ing over the board that is still there) mending stockings or reading
aloud to her children when they became weary of dam-building,
playing house with plantain leaves for dishes, or hunting May-
flowers (arbutus) under the mats of winter-blackened leaves.

We were allowed to take part in whatever our parents did, whether
it was haying, or going down to John Hall's farm for a setting of
White Leghorn eggs, naming the constellations at midnight, clearing the pasture spring, seeking the rare orchid and even rarer fern,
taking part in the conversation around the kitchen table at meal-
time, or talking and walking up the Berry Road in the early evening

as stars pricked out and birdsong hushed. For my father had his ideas about education then as always ("They would not find me changed from him they knew — / Only more sure of all I thought was true"). Being summed up, those ideas can perhaps best be expressed by the words, "the right exposure," which only gets us to the question, what *is* the right exposure? Southern for peach, northern for apple? Is it in the market place ("the trial by market everything must come to"), or in the contemplation of beauty, of peace and seeming harmony ("The woods are lovely, dark and deep"), or in promises kept? Leaving the question unanswered — and leaving it unanswered proves a serious trouble in later years — the *grounding* at least would seem to have been where it is best to have it, and safest: in the ground itself.

As children, we were exposed to a certain environment, strictly stationary in most respects, even isolated. Living was as uncomplicated, as simple, as it was humanly possible to have it. Yet it was filled to the brim ("and even above the brim") with a certain ardor, strong and rich. It was this ardor, keeping the heart's grief at bay while admitting the heart's hold ("We love the things we love for what they are"), that was my father's formula for always having miles to go before he slept. The farm was not just a place that eked out a tiny income, and did not even do that with any great efficiency. To us it was the cranberry bog through the woods. It was Klein's hill, with its chestnut burrs, like baby porcupines, to be gathered for the eating. It was the sound of cowbells on hazy sunny mornings. It was the needle-smooth paths through the pine grove, cool and clean, slippery and scented. It was the turns in the Berry Road where the slow wheel poured the sand, and where a child could be stationed, somewhat terrified, to head off the runaway horse. It was the cut-over woodlot in the summer solstice. It was the secret nooks where grew the hepatica, bloodroot, Indian pipe, coral root, trillium. It was the blueberry patch on the burnt-over lot:

> It must be on charcoal they fatten their fruit.
> I taste in them sometimes the flavor of soot.

It was the big pasture with its six pine trees touching together at the top and making a lovely shade to sit under or the little pasture where our one cow would stand chewing her cud with an expression of timeless patience in her amber eyes. There was a succession of cows, but each was called Bossy, though there was one I did name Cusha from the Jean Ingelow poem, "The High Tide on the Coast of Lincolnshire."

Those were the days, the slow days, as season melted into season, that were slow for Robert Frost's sake as well as for the grapes' sake along the wall. And if it is true, as Wordsworth said, that poetry "takes its origin from emotion recollected in tranquillity," those were the days when my father's poetry was ripening to the fall. They were the days when soil was *built*:

> *Build soil. Turn the farm in upon itself*
> *Until it can contain itself no more,*
> *But sweating-full, drips wine and oil a little.*
> *I will go to my run-out social mind*
> *And be as unsocial with it as I can.*
> *The thought I have, and my first impulse is*
> *To take to market — I will turn it under.*
> *The thought from that thought — I will turn it under*
> *And so on to the limit of my nature.*

There was turning over and turning under on the Derry farm, year after year to the limit of endurance. Memories were plowed under to crop up again and be plowed under until finally, as in "Blue-butterfly Day," "The Runaway," and "The Death of the Hired Man," they were to come up as poems. Through it all, across the orchard to the alders and Hyla Brook (its name later translated to West-running Brook in poetic license), along the woodland paths, in and out of the screen door of the woodbine porch, up and down the stone steps, to sit and sew under the apple trees her children were climbing, moved my mother, the presence within which all else moved. By the time I was writing my daily "story" at the age of five, I was calling her Mama, but my earliest name for her was Enna and then

Mama-Enna in my attempt to pronounce Elinor. As for my father, I kept calling him Rob — my mother's name for him — until I was six or so.

It was to Mama we all returned at evening, bringing "bokas" of flowers often crushed in hot and dirty hands but still worthy of being put in a glass of water on the kitchen table. It was to Mama we returned with full accounts of our adventures, adventures encountered on our own or out walking with Papa. The house was her castle, her province, and she *was* home. Going home from anywhere, at any time of day or night, meant returning to her. She would have answered my father's "Home is the place where, when you have to go there, / They have to take you in" with "I should have called it / Something you somehow haven't to deserve."

It may seem a paradox that, from all accounts (I never asked her), my mother was an atheist or at least an agnostic. Yet the power she exercised on all about her was a spiritual force, a *depth* of godliness (or goodness) that did not need God for backing — only love, human love. She refused to accept the cruelty of life and death, but neither did she cry out against it, or ask for mercy, or blame herself — or anyone else. In contrast, my father tended to self-pity. He was given to self-torture, even taking a certain pride in the idea that God had possibly *chosen* to give him a hard time. There was Job, wasn't there?

The difference between my parents lay in this sphere. It is a common difference between a man and a woman — particularly when one or the other has the creative genius. Creative man is given to wildness, and thence to wilderness, of soul — "desert places." This was true of Robert Frost. He gloried in wildness, in saying, "Poets get their knowledge cavalierly . . . They stick to nothing deliberately, but let what will stick to them like burrs where they walk in the fields. . . . No tears in the writer, no tears in the reader." While this could mean, and did, that life in his vicinity was both intellectually and emotionally exciting and rewarding, it also had its dangers for himself and others. It was by miraculous good fortune, or by the figure a poem makes ("it begins in delight and ends in wisdom — the figure is the same as for love") that he was saved through discovering the protection of "The Silken Tent." Pascal said, "We know the truth not only by the reason but by the heart. The heart has its reasons that reason knows not of."

But here I am, doing something I said I would not do: making *after*-images instead of staying *on* the farm, where time was divided into different kinds, each with its own distinction. There was chore time (something a non-country child sadly misses) when we brought in the chopped wood from the woodshed for the woodboxes behind the stoves; swept the kitchen with the better broom and swept the porch with the worn broom; brought in two pails of water from the yard pump, one for drinking, the other for washing dishes and hands and clothes; led the cow and horse to drink at the trough under the pump; fed the chickens and gathered the eggs. Then there was playtime (even "studying" was called Play School) and apple-picking time, and picnic time, and hay-raking time and blueberrying time. By the time we had divided up the time of day, even the time of year, there was very little time left over to worry about. The "remainder" was "evening time," when we went for very short walks after supper to see the sun go down and hear the birds go to sleep, and smell the soft mist rising from the meadow along Hyla Brook. After that, we settled down in the front room for the being read aloud to that came as certainly as night followed day.

Reading (by the age of four) and being read aloud *to* (until the age of fifteen!), I unconsciously heard the warp and the woof of literature being woven into an indestructible fabric, its meaning always heightened by the two beloved voices going on and on into the night as a book was passed from hand to hand. We children could linger to listen until we were sleepy, however late. There was the Bible, of which of course we grasped little at the beginning, but again it was the *sounds* of the voice reading that gave it sense: "The Lord gave him wisdom and understanding exceeding much, and largeness of heart as the sands that are on the sea shore." Our hearts were being stretched, as were our minds. There was *Pilgrim's Progress*. Christian and Hopeful and the dragon Appolyn were our friends; but perhaps we also felt, too young, the shadow that fell in the Valley of Death. For me it seemed to have to do with a grieving for a brother who died before I could know him, a terrible sadness that had entered the house.

There was poetry, poetry and more poetry. There was Keats ("season of mists and mellow fruitfulness" which related apple-picking time); Shelley's "wild west wind" that tossed the big maples along our roadway; Byron standing on the Persian's grave (very young we sided with Greece against Alexander); Tennyson's "The Brook" which could just as well have been Hyla. We became, as children, extremely partial to King Arthur and his knights, Richard Coeur de Lion and his Crusades, Robert Bruce and his spider, George Washington and his cherry tree, Leif Ericson and his Viking ships; Columbus and his Nina, Pinta and Santa Maria, Aeneas and his father, Sohrab and his, Magellan and his Straits, Nathan Hale and his life to give; Odysseus and his wine-dark sea, Barbara Frietchie and her flag, Balder dead. We even named two baby bunnies Marcus Aurelius and Uther Pendragon — Mark and Penny for short!

It was Marcus Aurelius whom we were hearing quoted: "Wretch, are you not content with what you see daily? Have you anything greater to see than the sun, the moon, the stars, the sea?" Or again Emerson: "There is no event but sprung somewhere from the soul of man and there is none but the soul of man can interpret. He is a divine pilgrim in nature and all things attend his steps. He *is* the world, and the epochs and heroes of chronology are pictorial images in which his thoughts are told." We heard Longfellow saying that lives of great men leave behind them footprints on the sands of time. Follow these prints, we were told. "For who is it that darkens counsel by words without knowledge. Canst thou bind the sweet influences of Pleiades, or loose the bands of Orion? Canst thou bring forth Mazzoroth in his season? Or canst thou guide Arcturus

with his sons?" At least I knew the Pleiades, Orion and Arcturus
well, if not Mazzoroth, and felt some kinship to what was being
read even from William James: "The greatest revolution of my
generation was the discovery that by changing the inner attitudes of
our minds we can change the outer aspects of our lives."

Clearly this brings me to speak of the kind of education we
children were getting. In our own way, we were doing a lot of
plowing-under, on our own. Our gardens were cut to size, but well-
planted. Too far from town to learn baseball (we learned it, though!),
or even to attend school, we were getting a book education by night
and a do-it-yourself education by day. Reading on the one hand, and
acquiring a "seeing eye" on the other, we were unconsciously
acquiring a literary yardstick. In our writing, just as unconsciously
at first, we were learning to put the thing seen, heard, or felt on
paper in words that made our parents sit up and take notice. If we
brought Papa something born of half a look, a glance, he sent us
back for a whole look. And to look meant to compare, to bring on
metaphor, which is at least the cloth of poetry. Let *him* "wait for
form"! I was content, deeply satisfied, if he commented on "a swal-
low, like a bow that has gone off with its arrow," or "woodbine,
looking through ice like candlewicks," or "needles of morning mist
standing upright on the silver pond like ghosts of grass on a ghost
of desert." This last may have been inspired by *his* "ghost of sleigh-
bells in a ghost of snow" — or vice versa. And nothing could have
pleased me more than to hear the delighted laughter as Mama
read aloud my description of "Carol Grumpy at Apples." Here was
the character differentiation, done with "tones of voice," a principle
that was to become a key to my father's originality. I was getting
early advantage because, though we didn't know he was a "poet,"
or even one in the making, we thought he was pretty good at this
metaphor game, at this "imagination thing." We respected him for
it! And over and above the brown paperbound composition books
we filled with a sort of daily theme, we later and secretly (at least,
we were allowed to believe, secretly) compiled omnibus volumes of

essays, poems, and short stories for Christmas gifts "to Mama and Papa." So it cannot have been that we were wearied with the *task* of writing. This again was how the ardor was preserved.

As for the *reading,* what was set before us we had no reason to doubt was all that was worth the reading — even worth reading twice or three times. There were no comparisons around. There was not even the seduction of a public library, the nearest being some miles away in East Derry. Our own library was actually quite small (the idea being that a book worth reading twice was worth owning, and we *were* poor). But it was large in relation to our other possessions, and our use of it was enormous in relation to our other activities. I was so *possessed* that, of the two nightmares which haunted my childhood, the most terrifying was the loss of our books by fire. With the flames crackling around me, I would take an over-large armful from the bookcase, only to have them buckle and crash at my feet — as I woke up crying.

The "academic" work was also progressing, and without protest, or so it would seem. There was the Play School I have mentioned: "Almost every day about ten o'clock mama calls us in the front room and we have to sit up on the sofa [horsehair, and prickly!] and tell storys and then we have to count 1 2 3 4 5 and then sing a song and then read and then we do a b c d and when anyone says a word right he gets the word and then we sing anouther song and then we do our exersizes and then we march around the room once or twis and then march out into the kitchen to show papa how we can do it."

My written work was sometimes turned in to Mama. I stood beside her, against her, while she read it through once and then turned back again to the beginning. With a paper and pencil on the table before her, she copied out the mistakes in spelling (she never marked up the original or made corrections as my father often did). Misspelled words were the grist to her mill for next day's spelling lesson. As for grammar, errors were merely pointed out. Then finally came the critical acclaim — or lack of it. Most devastating to the author's soul was the silent treatment, when the manuscript was returned without comment. But more often than not, my father was summoned to corroborate the praise that came for the right (true) adjective in the right place, for the amusing twist of character analysis, for the exact phrase that would help bear out Keats' "Beauty is truth, truth beauty . . ."

My father and mother, having both been teachers before raising a family, must have somehow persuaded the educational authorities (known as truant officers in those days) that they were quite capable of instructing their children at home, and that living so far from school (and no buses!) would work a hardship, as it indeed would have. For this we were advantaged. Today it would be called *dis*advantaged. So now, though we still have the three R's, it's remedial reading, remedial writing and remedial 'rithmetic, and one cannot enter first grade before he is six.

As for me, I was typing (very bad spelling, 'though phonetic) at three, reading by four, composing essays at five, writing literary criticism at eight. At ten I entered seventh grade in a two-room schoolhouse (still there), in Derry Village, with a fine teacher, Miss Whipple, whom the community honored as did we children. And at home I was soon struggling with Caesar's *Commentaries* (minus grammar) and Cicero's *Orations*. Years later, when I took my one full year of high school in Amherst, Massachusetts, I had read and memorized whole passages of the *Iliad*.

Memorized! — a word to conjure with. We conjured with it. We memorized as a means to an end; memorized as an educating process; memorized as a short cut to understanding the human spirit through first-hand knowledge of its greatness; memorized in order to know *by heart*. My father said then, as later, "Say something to us we can learn / By heart and when alone repeat." We memorized short poems, long poems — poems that taught courage, honor, generosity, pity, discipline, beauty, love, and hatred of evil. "A liberal education, a culture," as Ortega y Gasset has said, "is the system of vital ideas by which the age lives. It is our conviction as to the hierarchy of the value of things." We learned Emerson's

"Concord Hymn," Wordsworth's "Lucy Gray" and "Daffodils," Keats' odes — "On a Grecian Urn" and "On Melancholy;" Henley's "Invictus," Longfellow's "My Lost Youth" (from which Robert Frost was to get the title of his first book, *A Boy's Will*), Emily Dickinson's "There is no frigate . . . ," Whittier's "Snowbound," Scott's "Lady of the Lake," Kipling's "Ballad of East and West," Coleridge's "Ancient Mariner," and so on and on, indefinitely.

We also learned much through making a lot of celebrations — even Hallowe'en, April Fool's Day, and May Day (non-revolutionary!). We made a lot of Christmas and New Year's Day and the Fourth of July, Washington and Lincoln's birthday, and our own. There has been some discussion as to how religious a man Robert Frost was, all considered. But that he *was* a religious man one can be sure if his way of bringing up his children can be said to witness. With Blake and Christina Rosetti and Eugene Field, Emerson and Longfellow, the Psalms and the hymns, we were inoculated with the certainty of a Supreme Being, an over-all Authority. And Christmas was a birthday. It was not difficult to make of it a special *kind* of birthday, and to enlarge upon it. Particularly since, on a farm, we were blessed in having certain aspects of the Nativity a part of every day. Our barn was a more important place because we had read Martin Luther's hymns. We *knew* what a manger was. Our cow was not only capable of jumping over the moon; she had a distinct relationship to the cows that gazed wonderingly at a newborn baby misplaced in their hay. There was somehow a connection between the Three Wise Men who brought gifts to Jesus and Santa Claus who brought gifts to us. The gradual translation of Santa Claus into Mama and Papa came about naturally — no trauma there! And how could a man not *believe* who was to write,

> *I could give all to Time except — except*
> *What I myself have held. But why declare*
> *The things forbidden that while the Customs slept*
> *I have crossed to Safety with? For I am There,*
> *And what I would not part with I have kept.*

INTRODUCTION

But here I am again, ahead of myself, if only momentarily. And it would be all wrong to leave the farm without first telling something of the "lives," other than our own, that crowded our fields and woods and skies: the animals, wild and domestic; the birds, wild and all-but-tame; the flowers, wild and garden; and the stars above us all. These were our intimacies: the deer "crossing" the meadow below the house, going from wood to wood before and after drinking at the brook and trailing their fawns behind them. (They also fancied the vegetable garden behind the house!) There were the foxes, seldom seen, but welcoming the dusk with their soft-sharp barks at the edges of field and wood; woodchucks daring to sit forth "where two rocks almost meet. / And still more secure and snug, / A two-door burrow . . .[they] dug." And there was the bluebird who advised me, by way of a poem, to "look for skunk tracks / In the snow with an ax." My father should have written hatchet (he carried the axe), but it didn't rhyme with tracks! Hatchets were, for us children, the weapons in trade even more than hammers. We trailed Papa to the woods where he felled the tree, and we trimmed the branches and helped carry home the firewood.

Our birds were so close *out*side as to *seem* inside. Not only bluebirds, whom we seemed to favor and who favored us, but robins of course, and bluejays, scarlet tanagers, cedar waxwings (who fought us for the cherries), vireos, flickers, redheaded and downy woodpeckers, orioles, phoebes, barn swallows, chickadees, peewees, nuthatches, brown thrashers, hermit thrush, rosebreasted grosbeak, wrens, juncos, warblers, blackbirds. I could go on naming, and go on telling of the songs and manners that we came to know by *heart,* as we knew poems — intermingling.

Birds intermingled with flowers, too: steeplebush, goldenrod, meadowsweet, cowslips, anemone, violets (blue, yellow, white), innocence, dandelion, Queen Anne's lace, Indian pipes, rose pogonias, calopogon, arbutus, lady's slipper, trillium, lady's tresses, pipsissawa, butterfly weed, thistles. The trees in flower: plum (wild and tame), cherry (wild and cultivated), peach and apple (crab,

Baldwin, Northern Spy, Russet, Astrachan). Together with garden flowers: the quince hedge in its red glory surrounded our front yard; the morning glories, blue and white, that Mama spread over the porch "pillars"; the nasturtiums and sweet peas that were the *work* of "the children." (I was graduated to weeding the vegetable garden!)

Flowers and birds mixed well with stars, for astronomy was not neglected. Every constellation was *by heart,* also: Orion, the Pleiades, Leo, Scorpio, Capricorn, Cassiopeia, and the planets Mars, Venus, Saturn, Jupiter. We heard of Galileo, Copernicus, Kepler, Halley (indeed, I was awakened to see Halley's comet one midnight in 1910). Everything was the beginning of choosing "something like a star / To stay our minds on and be staid."

Not to forget the domestic animals! Our cows came in single file relay — as did the horses (Billy, Eunice, Roy). We loved them all. Going to the barn could mean squeezing into the stall against a warm flank and holding a handful of grain into the very jaws of danger — scary but thrilling. Hens were our *crop,* so to speak. We raised them for profit, hundreds of them. It seemed thousands. Many were the times when, going for eggs, I was all but lost and destroyed in the crushing thunder of feathered wings and screaming cackles! I believe we had quite a variety of hens for experiment in egg production — Buff Orpingtons, White Leghorns — but it was White Wyandottes we had in number. My greatest delight in the hen business was going to the lantern-lit henhouses in the evening with Papa, to candle the eggs, testing them for fertility with a little contraption of light which x-rayed the inside of the eggs. If an embryo within showed life, with vague movements (like the genie in Stevenson's Bottle), it was quickly returned to the warmth of the setting hen or the incubator. Then came the excitement of the "big hatch," with *what* a racket of peeping, louder than the spring peepers in the meadow, though these too could shake the air with their million cries.

So it was the Derry farm became a place to stand on, not only physically-in-fact but also spiritually-in-wisdom, if only as the blue herons stood in the lower meadow, one match-stick leg in the dew-crystaled grass, but with a balance as serene as if cast in bronze; in determining things so that heel and toe would always remember the ruts of the Berry Road, feel the polish of the hermit-brown needles on the floor of the pine grove, where the smoothness seemed more a matter of color than texture; feel the cool mud halfway to the knees in the cranberry bog; smell the hot granite outcroppings, mixed with the tang of juniper, on Klein's hill; a place where, in other words, earth and poetry were fused in a momentary stay against confusion.

In his "Preface" to *The Poems of Ernest Dowson*, Arthur Symons wrote,

"There is not a dream which may not come true, if we have the energy which makes, or *chooses,* our own fate. We can always, in this world, get what we wish if we will it intensely enough. Whether we get it sooner or later is the concern of fate, but we shall get it. ... So few people succeed greatly because so few people can conceive a great end, and work toward that end without tiring and without deviating. The man who works day and night for no matter what material power, gets that power. It is the same with the deeper, more spiritual, issues, which make for happiness and every intangible success. We get out of life, all of us, what we bring to it."

Finding the New Hampshire farm, finding *on* it what he came to seek, so that one day he would say, "the core of all my writing was probably those free years I had down on the farm a mile or two from Derry Village," is what happened to a man whose "passionate preferences" were love at sight for a certain person, a certain place, and certain poems. Robert Frost was a man who *chose* his future.

LESLEY FROST

New York City
May 1968

BOOK I

February 22, 1905 to June 1905

(Aet.: 5 years, 10 months to

6 years, 2 months)

FOREWORD TO BOOK I

I WISH I could remember how and when my parents began teaching me to read and write. My little "First Speller" notebook has survived, and yet I have completely forgotten how it was used. It bears the date, "March 1st, 1904" — almost two months before my fifth birthday. Clearly, I must have taken to reading and writing better than I took to spelling! But my letters and words in "Book One" are formed with enough care and self-discipline to show that I had been practicing for some time before my father started me writing "stories" in journal form.

I say that my father started me. The evidence in these notebooks points that way. In my own responses to that starting, there seems to have been some doubt whether I was going to be a painter or a writer. On page 4 of "Book One" I am insisting that I will get back to my painting just as soon as I can, "aftu i rit my story for papa."

Now that I have tried to help my own children and grandchildren read and write, I marvel that my father ever persuaded me to write so conversationally about whatever interested me when I was five years old. The sentences of my first "story" flow into each other with the naturalness of a child talking. Perhaps I was instructed to write the story just as I would say it if I were telling it out loud. If so, I may have been the first one to benefit from my father's theory about the relation between writing and "the sound of sense."

BOOK I

CONTENTS

NOTE: *Lesley did not write on pages 56–59 of Book I. These pages have not been reproduced.*

1.

carole new shose
one day we cood not find
carols shol and all the thime
we were hunting for it it was
im the ufun brning and the
ufun door was shut at last
we found it and it was all
ringkled and so he had to
one uf myn for a week or to
and then rob went ofu to
derry and got some for him
and thoe did not fit him
and the next time he went
ofer he got some beter ones
and thoe fitid him and he
cold them tuni day too
and at frst he did not
want you to look at them
too much.

2

go and get mama

one day mama went of
to sta all day and we went afta
her at nitht and on the wa
ufu we wood see hoo wood
find the stars frst rob
fond fenus frst and i fond
all the rest exsept
the dipu it was not
dack enuf far that
i found the dog star and
the stars in the giunt
and then we went and got
mama and we askt her if
she had a nice time and
she said she did and we
went home and ate our
super and went to bed.

playing cards
we hav some cards and
when we play with them
some times i deul and mama
and papa six in the middle
and six to us and this is
anuthu way put three out on
the table and tri to
thingk which one will win
and i like to play cards
mama papa and me and
some times i play cards
with my doll when
mama and papa donet
have time to play with
me and i thingk it is
nice.

febuary 29

4

about my pants
i lookt at one ma
gisen and their wer some pritty
picshus to pant and
i am going to pant
aftu i rit my story for
papa and i like to pant
piacshus if i can
find ani nice ones

i do not like
to rit a story when
i go out doors because
i want to pant ana
i sho mama and pa
pa them aftu i pant
them and i pant them
all over the skrt and wast
some times i pant the
skrt blu and the wast
red

5

about the woolf
rob was reding the
paper and my chaire
began to whirl a round
and rob stopt it and
just then came a
woolf and i grabd a
chair and hit him in
the noise and then i
let him go and rob
said to and i took
the uolf and chand
him and he strugul
d to get a uay
and mama found a
little paul and gave
it some bread and i ga
ve it three pauls of
water and some sweet

finished on page 8

6

my bow and arrow
this spring we thought
uf makeing a bow and
arrow we have got the bow
redy and the string redy
but not the arrow and
if i shoot it in the
snow i will loos it
this spring i will have
to go out without carol
becaus i mit hrunt him
and i will go ufu in
the grow and play shoot
woolfs and carol cood
not go with me and
snidu will come ufu
with me and bark up
trees.

at   how winter enddid
              it is six weeks befor
spring will came and
that is cweit a loug
time you no and there
will be some very nice days
and some very bad
some cold and rany
some cold and snowy
and i like it for a
whirle but not very
long and i go sliding
done the hills and a
ronua and i like
the nice days and i
wish it ewood ran to
day to take some of the
snow a way.

8 apples

apools and every night
i used to clen out
the stol and by and
by the baby ones came
and we had to have
six chans and this
is whut i tola my self
in the night.

abaut the blu and robins
in three weeks the snow will
fe about gone and they will
be no more sliding
and in a week we will see
blue brids and a week or
to we will see robins
and when we go out
doors we wont need so meny
clothes and the blue brids and
robins will sing to us and
we will like to hear them
sing and rob will put
up the hamuk and the blue
brids will sit up in the wo
od peker tree and in the
nut tree and sing to us
and i will play in the
yad and we will have a
nice time

about the flours
it will be nice when spring
comes there will be lots of
flours and carol can pick
the very first ones with me
and i and carol can
pick uve in the grove
and pik them and may
be irma can go and rob
will take me to the far a
way flours off in medos
anemenis vilits cow
slips dasis butrucup dandalion
goldunrod inusens
and carol and i will
like to get the very fust
flours and i will have
to tell carol how to
pick the long stems

11

and after we pick
them i will put
them in a base
and after thos fad i
can go and get more

12

about my doll
when i take my doll
out of the clasit i aluis
play with it and i took
it out to day and
carol and i playd with
it and it said whar
is the nose and he point
id whar it was and i
akst whar his was and
he pointid whar his
was and he walkt up
and done with it
and rokt it in my
littel chare and then i
tolkt about puting it to
bed and then we undrest
it and put it to bed
and swept up with

carol and then dres
st it and then went
done to the frook wit
h rob.

about the kite
some one was fling a kite
and it dird done so far
that i catht it and the
man that was fling it
froo a ston ufu to see if
it cood hit me but it
fel on the grond and i
ran and pikt it up and
lookt at it and then
throo it done i told this
to my self in bed.

14

about the cow
one day rob let the
cow out doors and she ran
a way from us and we
did not no whar she
had gone and we went
done the derry roed and
we sor her traks up the
wooddun roed and we
had to go in the deep
snow after her and i
went done to mr.
webstus bars and the
cow wooddunt come
done and rob cold me
up and she was
chand and we made
a path ufu the ston
wall and took her

ufu and took her home.

16

going to sll mrs wil
sun one day we went to
sll mrs. wilsun and we
took the dlm acrat
wagn and mama and
irma slt in the
barck slt and papa
carol and me set
in the front and it
was cind of cold but
we had a nice rild
and we went into
mrs wilsuns house and
carol and irma crid
and i stad in a
little while and then
i went out to play
with helen and she
gave me a rid on her
sled.

carol and irma
carol and irma
are susth misshufueis
that we dont no what
to do but we have
to stop them and
when tha dont stop
we have to spanc
them and tha criy
tha frak dishis and
cups and bend spoons
and get hold of
the sager bol and
take a spoon and
eat arry bit of the
sager that is in it
and tha are grat
misshofs.

18
/1

to day
in the mornig it
was clody but it did not
raen or snow but stad
clody for cuit a long
tim and then came
out and i haw not
bin out to play in
the sun and it is
nice out now but the
sun is going done and
pritty soon it will be tim
to put carol and irma
to bed and it is ufu
cwatll of one a clok
now.

snider and me
i took the chan
and chand snider with it
and statid up the bery
road and snider want
id to go home so mutsh
that i took him part
wa home and then we
turnd the coner by the
bars and went up fro
the little packer and
up to the big apple
tree and a little sqrale
live in the tree
and i hit my fists
to gether to see if i coo
make it come out but
it would not and so
i went to see if i cold
find too stons but i
codunt and so i got

20

ufu the stone wall
and done thru the
booshis and in the
house.

going to mr clacks
one day we hanist up unis
and went to see mr. clack
and ther war stons all
arond his house and one
of the stons was big and it
tipt the woglen ufu a
little way and we went
into the house.

Mr. Clark?

the dog and the
cow.
go a way dog come
here dog go and git
are cow. she has gone
into the woods.

cat and the dog
cat gos up the tree
till the dog gos away
and so she went up
the tree and the dog
bakt up the tree but
the cat did not come
done till the dog went
a way and by and
by the dog went a
way and the cat
came done and went
in the house

27

Maguy and mama.
mama made some new
close far a new baby becas
wethot we would have
a new baby and a long
long time after that
some body came with a
new baby ana i like
it very much and if
it hadn't come we would
have to give the close
to some body els.

3

carol i and irma
it is a very cold day
i and irma carol went done
by the nut tree to play
and then went out in
the big pasture and irma
would not come to
the hill but i and
carol went to it and
got a bauka of
violets and irma sat
on the ground and
plad ants and flowers
i and irma carol had
a nis time and then
we came home and we
brot some flowers for mama.

24
4

pares and cheres
the peares cheres
and apales pechis and they
are all in buds wont
they look pretty when
they are all in blossum
the cheres are the
earlyus to eat ther is
a stone in them don't
eat it will you.

colors and smells
of flowers
the colors of flowers are
very pretty some are white
some are yelow some are
red some are purple
some smell so sweet and come
dont and rob askt why
the calors and smells
came to it and i said it
was for us and mama
thot it was for the bees
to take polung off the pistils
onto stamens they saw
the color and flew to it.

26

the fire

we lit a fire done in the
medo and rob new it would
not go a cross the brook
and the wind bleo frome
the west to the est it
cavd haf of are feld
and went thruw the stone
wall and by are grape
vine and birnd some of
the brush but it did not
go on the other side and
we are glad and we
pourd to or three pals
of water on the smoky
plasis.

7

27

the vilits

you no that wire in the little
pasher with no stone wall
and there arelots of
vilits beside it and i pik
them and bring them home
and put them in water
and i papa mama like it.

2⁸

once on a rainy day
on a rainy day mama got
my things out of the
stove and tabul and i plad
with them a long time
and she got some things
done for carol and irma
and we plad a very
long time and then it
clerd of and we put are
things away and went out
dors the rest of the day
and then it came night
and we went to bed
and we were very tired
of are long play you
no yes.

7

the vilits

you no that wire in the little
pasher with no stone wall
and there arelots of
vilits beside it and i pik
them and bring them home
and put them in water
and i papa mama like it.

288

once on a rainy day
on a rainy day mama got
my things out of the
stove and tabul and i plad
with them a long time
and she got some things
done for carol and irma
and we plad a very
long time and then it
clerd of and we put are
things away and went out
dors the rest of the day
and then it came night
and we went to bed
and we were very tired
of are long play you
no yes.

my birthday
a little whyl a go i had
my six yer old birthday
and i had a nice
cake and some binnana
puding and we had
some canndy and carol
and irma mama and
papa came to it and
we had a very nice
time.

30

going and piking long
stemd vilits

one day carol i irma
papa went ua out in
clins woods and pikt a
lot of long stemd vilits
and we had a very
nice time and we trampd
a round in the deep woods
hunting for long stem
vilits and we went
evry whear and we had
a nice happy time and
carol and irma
pikt flowas to.

the fire in the medow
we had a fire in the
medow and we new it
would not go acrass the
brook and it set haf af
the feld an fire and
it went to the rod and
it birnd are grap vine
and rob thout it would
get across in the ather
feld that a spark mite
fly across but it did not
and and when the brush
had nlly gone out we trid
to put it out rob put it
it out with a bourd
and i put it out with
a pes of of pine stik
and i ran up and got
a pail and rub the smoky places.

32

i saw foer hming birds
one was in the curins
bushis and to around the
plum blosoms and becas
they calld them
huming birds becas
they cep ther wings going
all the time ther coler
is blak and whit and
they have a very long
bill they stik it way
into the flower and
get hunnyout and evin
when they stop they
cep ther wings a buzzing
it wos yestudy.

the lefes.
we came by the brnt up hous
we went out in berie
wood to take a wake
and we falod a brook
and then the brook trnd
and we did not see
it trn and we went
strat aheard to folo it
we thoeht it went
under ground but it
had trnd some where
els and we came out
to a brnt up houses
and then we went to
see if the lady slíprs
and callumvine were out
bt they wrnnt and then
we went home.

34

how i went out
the lagus rod.
i went out the lagus
rod and i saw a lot
of soing sparos and
piles of strar berry blosums
and alot of peach
blosums i wantid to pik
some but i thought i
better lef them to come
to peachis and the
strar berrys were very
pretley and i wantid
to pik them to but
i wantid strar berrys
so i left them and
then the little sang
sparos hopt around evry
were i saw one in the
grass

we got lost

ome day mama and
i and carol we were going
to tle pamers [Palmers] arouned
that way but we got
lost we went to windham
and we trnd the coner by
the store in windham. we
went past clids and done
where the gobling trky is he
went like like gobul gobul
and where the brch bark
tent was that is all.
torn done now and then
went to a lake and a house
we did not no befor so
we came back the same
way and told rob about
it.

36

   a bout the phoebe nest
one day i went down the stone
stepes and went under the
barn and ther ruster be
   a nest on a bord but that
is torn down now and
that is last yers and now
unuther is bilt ther and
this one is bilt quit a
while a go one day
we lookt into it
we fond five little
white egs in it and
some time after
that rob sead he hrd
little ones peeping in
it i was glad papa
was glad mama was
glad.

mama i and papa.

last night when the choldrun
had gone to bed mama i and papa
took a little wake out in the
feald we went to that little
sweet apall tree and pickt a
boka of apale blossoms and we
faind a pile of strar berry
blossoms and nob went down
to the coroner of the big cow
paschur to see how mach was
theer ther was qwit a little
and then mama saed we better
be geting home and as we
went home the sun was
gust gouing down and it
made a blasing light on
the front room windo and it
it was gust the same on the

38.

barn it looked like a pikcher
and then i went in and
at my supper and went
to bed.

papa and i took a lang
wake.
first part
one day papa and i took
a laning woke we went
to the gate and an the
way out we sow a red
tanugu he had to black sides
and all the rest was
red he was a tanugu shure
and then he flue a way
and then we went on
we trnd the corna by
the gate and went down
the path till we came to

the brook we crosst the
brook and i gut my foot
a little wet but we went
on we went clere up on
clinse hill and tend umitha
path and went went out in
a big upran feld and then
we went out in the deep
woods and then we came
to a gate and gut under
it and came out in the
est deery road and wapt
on a little way and then
went in the woods agen
and be gan finding flours
and i will tell you about
the flours to morow.
second part

40

and we found alot of
flours we found a one
cind of stare flour there
are alot of cinds of
stare flouer we found bell
wrt we found clintoneru we
found yello vilit and
lady sliper the clintoner was
gust a greenish coler the
yello vilit is yelo the
bell wrt i do not no gust
what coler that is the stare
flouer is whit the lady
sliper is pingk we brout them
home and put them in
water and mama liket them
very mich and all the time
we were eting irma wold
came and say boo to us all the
thime.

we went danduling.

yestedy papa and i went
dandelinig down in the feld
by the meadow we gut a
hole baskite fole i do thingk
i is a nuf for a dinner
we are goneg to cook them to
day becoese after dinner
igstedy and when we cook them
they cook down to a little
bituw off a boll and then
we do not have hadly a
bit of dinner but evry body
has to or three spoon fools
and it is fun geting them
dont you thingk so yes.

42

the froot trees.

on the froot trees the petels
are all cameing off the flowers
the ground is white whith
them it looks like snow
and so do the trees look
like snow and now the
little green cheeryis are
begining to gro they are
cwit big now but they
are stile greem and we cant
et them now they are
to gren we will hafto
be pritey caful of the
choldren betose they will
want to et them wen
evry thing is green
we will tell them go
away dont play with

this play with some
thing els wontwe.

    a little gril.
one nigt long time a
go a little gril came here
she was lost she was
gouing to dover but evin if
she was lost she wanted
to go right on to dover
but we thout she better go
home she lived upon the
hilands and if she was
gouing to dover i shoud
tlingk she woud go on
the tran and dover is
terebly far of from her
house and we had to take
to her qwit a long time

44

to sef we coud get her
home but she would
not and at loct we
went ufer where she lived
and told her papa abort
it and her papa came
ufer and took her honre.

my hoop.

i love to rol my
hoop i have toplasys to
rol it i do rol it
most all the time

it role better on the
hill by the barn it
role fathr ther and its
better then ever on the
big big hill i cood
hadly clp up with it
and i did not clp up
with it and the hoop
fet me down to the brook

and i cood not get past
it but i liket it very
much even if i did not
get past it.

46

we went to gonhols
a froow days aga w
took ar carol down to
gonhols and gonhol had some
ducs and we thaut carol
woldnt not no whut
they were and when we
gut ther we askt him wlats
that and he saed duculs
and we new what theat
mint it ment ducks
and carol likt to look at
them and so did i
but we likt the littl
chicins best and by and
by we went home but
carol did not wont
to go home we went
home a pretty way home

and we came out by
websters and i was glad
to be home and to see
mama.

my stoer in the grove
i do have a nice little
stoer in the grove i do have
a little conter i like to
play in it i do sell all
difrunt cinds of dirt to
carol and irma i like to
sell them thigs very much
i go ofer ther a long
time evry day to play
with them and carol and
irma like it.

48

the rany day

yestedy it was a verey
rany day and to day
it isint but its clouldy
and my little store over ther
in the grove got all rand
on and i did not like
it but i could not stope
it iff i hit it it
would not stop so there
is no us tring do we
thinck there is no way
i can stop it.
can we, no.

the cow got out
we took the cow and
tied her done by the nut
three to ete grass the
grass is long down ther
and so she gut loos and
rob and i trid to
cathe her but we could
not for cuit a while
papa went done the derry
road and i in the bery
road and she went
arould be hind the
the blak bery pach and
at last rob got her.

50

the leve.
the leve are out fool
on evry tree now
the little pasheur is
fool of frehys and evry
levf is out on them
and i can see them from
my little store in the
grove it must loock
pritty musnot it.

the robins.

tw robins desidid to bild a
nest in one of the mapal
trees here in the yored
and wen they got it
haf hilt they gave it
up and now they are
bilding over in the little
paschuer in a apale tree
and now ther got that
haf bilt and givn that
up and now there filding
a nest behind the houes
in the brch tree now
then they will give that
up dont you beleve
so ~~yes~~ no i do not
it looke so merly bilt.

52

bere footed
i like to go ber
footed

going bare footed
i like to go bere
footed when the grass
is wet i like to
put my shoe and
stokings on but when
it is woem wether
i like my shoe
and stokings off
and carol and inma
do not like to
go bare footed
exsept in the house
becase it hrts there
feet out doors and
it hrts my feet
a little but not much
i do not care.

54

  yeeteday in the cranberry
bog.

  yeetedy we took ore
wake we have a
day for the wakling
day the day is sundy
well this sundy we
went out to the
gate and went down
the hill and in to
the cran berryfag.
we took off our shoes
and stockings and
wadid in we we fond
a lot of flowes
we found snakmouth
and calerpoger and
we got a boka and
took them up to

*(bouquet)

the gate and then
went and got the
larel and came
home.

60

     going Out To The Big Pasture
yesterday it was quiet a nice
day. mama said if we went
out we would have to go to
walk and then come in, we
went out in the big pasture
out through the grove not out
through the lane. when we got out
to the end of the grove i
happened to look over the fence
into the little grove of poplers
and there was quite a big tree
of pussy willows. we were under
the fence in a minute but our
hats and caps got caught on the
wire so we had to turn
around and get them before we
got to picking. But in a minute
we were in the middle of the bush.

we all got franches and i got
a big part of the bush and took
it home to mama. after we
had picked all we wanted we
went down in the big pasture
and then came home.
march 24 1907
Written later than the others
by several years

BOOK II

October 8, 1905 to December 1905

(Aet.: 6 years, 5 months to

6 years, 8 months)

FOREWORD TO BOOK II

THIS is mostly an autumn journal. It starts with my regret over signs that even the crows are getting ready to go South. It continues with my joy over finding that the chestnuts are ripe for gathering. The leaves change colors and some trees begin to shed. Bags of leaves are brought into the barn so we can have a good supply of them for use as bedding in the henhouses during the approaching winter.

Signs of fall gradually merge with signs of winter, here. My father takes me to the first football game I can remember. A goblin who comes and stares in our window is named Jack-o'-Lantern. A special story has to be written about the first snow-storm which drives hard enough to make me pull my knitted cap down over my face. Even before there is enough snow on the ground for making a snow-man, I am already looking forward to making one. At the same time, I start counting the weeks to Christmas. My last story in this book is of how delighted we all were when we took our first sleigh ride of the year, with harness bells jingling all the way.

Each fall, I suppose, we Frost children began our "Play School" just when the other children were returning to public school. Although our school hours were irregular, we seem to have responded quickly whenever summoned. My entry dated October 15, 1905, tells of how I was on my way to the big pasture with a small cart to collect stones, "but just then papa called me to rite my story."

BOOK II

CONTENTS

our crows are geting redy
to go south they are haveing a
holerbellu they are geting in a
line to go papa said that he
thout that they had gust
chosun a king to led them
or tring to find won who will
be it. then i thout they
mite be saying good by to
all of us. then mama thout
ther mite be a hundrid. then
i thout there mite be hafe a
hundrid and they have been
working all night becos they
have only a few more to put
in the line.
Oct 8, 1905

2

we went to walk yesteay
papa and i licke to go to
walk. we went in gays
woods we fona to haf
pockits of chest nuts. we
gut them way out under the
big chest nut tree where we
gut so meny last year.
i licke chest nuts more than
i do wall nuts. but mama
lickes wall nuts best. then
when we gut all we cold
find we stated home and
on the way home i climbed
up a hi birch and came down
with it and i stopt in
the air about three feet and
papa cout me.
          oct 9, 1905

3

every time papa goe out
to get a pail of water
snider qumps of the
piazza if he is ther and
runs up the berry rod
evry tirae. and down
it other times i and
carol and irma run
after him and some times
he will run evry
way and we think it
is fun runing after
him. and some times he
likes to run up in nat
heads woods he has
sevrel squirrel holes up
ther he likes to bark down
them. but he cant

4

catch them becas they
can run faster then
he can. and when he
is a way up in nat
heads woods they can
run out and run to a
new plase. so then ther
isint much use barking then
becas he will never get it.
and i bet le will be
sorry dont you.

Oct. 10, 1905,

i like to climb trees very
much but mama doesnt
like me to becose i tare
my stocings so so i have
to stop i do not like
to but i have to at
frst i was scared to
swing with birchis but
now i am not so much
scared becose it wont
hurt me. and i am not
scared if it swings doun
with me if it gose klere
doun with me i dont
like it if it dosent i
climb uther threes but
they dount swing as
the birchis do so i doun

6

like them as well
i climb oak and mapel
but with me they swing
with me. i like tlat to
but not as well but
papa likes to swing
beter i climb apale trees
and thos dount swing
a toll do they.
oct 11, 1 90 5

fun
pretty
interesting

i like spring beter then
i do sommer becose there
are more flowes in spring
thats why i like it
more and there are
hadly eny flowes in
summer exsept blasing
stare and gechuns and
those as pretty as the
spring but there is won
nice thing about summer
that you can play out
and you can do that in
spring to but you cant
pike flowes in summer
and i feel cindov bad
about that but we get
lotes and lotes of flowes

8

in the spring but i down
care very muchs. i like
to play out a lot.
and gust now there has
bin about a week and
a haf of brutufol days
but now its rainy a
gen and we hav to sta
in.

Oct 12, 1905

we have a nut tree near
are house and day befor
yestedy we begegan to put
then them away for the
winter and yestedy i was
siting on a stone i saw
some holes in the trunk
of the tree that have bin
there a very loing time.
then i gut up and lookt
in them and do you
no whut i sow i sow
lotes and lotes of nuts
that the sqrels had put
there. and yestedy papa
took us up the lane to
sefe there wer eny up
there and we fond a very

10

nice tree a good deal better
then eny of the trees
very thin sheled and
and esy to get out and
we've gut hafe a bag fole.
Oct 14, 1 9 05

about all the trees are sheding
there now but they have
only have shed them haf
way done the trees. but
over in nat heads woods
there hadly trning a
tall ecsept chest nut
and wall nut. and
ork brachis but the chest
and wall nut they are
sheding there leavs but
they are trning there
callus and the uthus are
still green. and apple
trees havent trnd yet.
and the have trnd
mostly ecsept at the
tip ends in sum plasis

12

and the little oaks
have trnd but the big
oaks havent, and are
big maple tree has all
trnd. and the other
maples havent quit trnd
and the pins dont ever
trn and i am glad
becase i like to look at
green things.
oct 15, 1905

sunday we took are wack
all of us margery and i
and carol and irma papa
and mama we all went
out in the big grov margery
liket it very much she did
not have a bottle she did
not cry a toll and we
wer glad becase we do
not not like to hold
her very well she aches
your ams so she is a
goodel biger then she was
when she gust came
and she is more intrist
in things well when we
gut there we left her in
the cariag and i and

14

carol and irma went
down a little frther in
the woods and ate partig
berrys and i and took
some up to papa and
mama but thay dont
like them as well as
they do patrig berrys
but i like them gust
as well. and on the way
ofer we fond the ston
wall nokt down in
to plasys and carol fond
a shell that they emty
out after the little
bulits have gone out he
fond that and pickt
the shell and i wisht i
had won but i fond wor

on the way home and
it was like a rele won
becase i fond an acorn
and i put it in it and
pinsht it as fare as
i put it in. and it cam
out at the opun end
and went cwit a little
way. and margery la
very still and lookt up
in the tall pins but
at last she gut fusy and
mama had to hold her
then she tried to put her
down a minit or to and
mama and papa and
i playd puss in the
coner a frew minits
and carol irma dount

16

no how to play it
but margery crid we had
to stop then papa took
margery and we went
down to the other end
ob the grov. and i
was runing and i
fell down and hurt
my hand very badly
on a stick. and at
last irma and carol
got tird and we went
home.
Oct 16, 1905

yestedy papa went over
to derry and he took
me with him we went
to willsuns on the way
over but he wasunt there
so we went a long
over to derry and
stopt on the way
bak. when we gut
to derry i gut out
and mald the letter
then we went bak
a little frther and
i gut out and gut
papas shose that
he had left there
to get fikst. then
we went to the

18

willsuns a yen to
to get some meat he
wos there this
time we both gut out
then we gut the meat
and came home.
Oct 17 1905

day before yesteddy we
took are sundy wak
ogean we all took a
wake rksept irma and
margary we went
ritht after dinner
and thats the time
irma has her nap
evry day we went
when she was a
sleep papa took me
and mama took
carol mama and carol
didunt go but a
little way frum
the house they only
went over a cross
the road in the

20

little pasture to get
levs in bags to put
in the hen house
and papa and i
went way out in
noisise land we
fond to little ponds
and a watrig trof
and one of the
ponds was where
we trid to get some
cat tals last year
but we codent they
wer too fare in the
water and ritht beside
noisise house they
have a very pritty
grov they hav sets
in it and a fens

arond to ceep pepole
out then they hav
a cow path down
to the to ponds and
it is a very pritty
cow path there are
pins on the sids
and they are skartring
and it is very pritty
we fond a shell on one
side of the pond it
was very fresh it lookt
if it had bin shot gust
a little while a go.
then we went home
and when we gut
there i gave it to
carol becase he didunt
take as looing wak
as i did. oct. 24, 1905

22

i am going to holle
stones out of the big
pactuer with carols
hay cart and clen
it up and make grass
grow there carol
made me think i
he began to find
bugulis under stons
carol likes it very
much and so do i
but irma dusunt
she sits on the side
of the hill and plays
with little stiks and
watchis us some of
the time. i pik them
up on top of the

just

hill mostly but some
down below and i
gut one on top that
was ofule big i
cood not cary i had
to roll it but
most of them i
cood pik up and throw
down i am going to
bring them over here
make a pille of them
down by the bak
barn so i can make
little stone walls
when i want to
i hav got a little
pille of them out
there now i havent
got hadly all of them

24

inyet in the pille
that i hav pilld
up and pretty soon
we went home to
self dinner was redy
but it wasent so
we took the hay
cart a startid out
a gean but gust then
papa called me to rite
my story.
— Oct 15, 1905

we went to the
foot boll game
yestedy and gust as
we went around
shouts cornner the
foot boll begain
it was three a
clock they alewis
begain at three a
clock when they do
play it they do not
play it evry day
this time they playd
it on wendesday they
do not play it evry
wendesdy they play
it when they can
we coud here there
noisis and gust when

26

we trnd the cornner
to go in and see it
right behind us
an otermobell came
shuckin up behind
us and came in to
all the pepoll stand up
in the foot boll gaem
but dount very ofen in
bass boll gaem there
wer coincud boys there
and acadumy boys
there and the acadoumy
boys beet the coingcud
fellos the coingcud
fellos get doun on
there hands and feet
on one and the
acadoumy on the

other side then they
run a little was on
there hands and
feet and then gump
up and the acadaumy
nockt the coingcud
bak and got upon top off
them and they all shouted
and made an ofell
nois they had things
on there nosis to pertect
there nosis from geting
smasht and things on
there there heads and
ers and thoes are to
pertect there heads and
ers from geting hert.
Oct 16, 1905

28

we went to chester
yestidy to see mis
scroue it wos nine
milles to chester and
three milles when we
gut into shester and
when we gut there
i had a very good
time they had a very
pretty siting room
they have an opon
fire plase i shoud
be afraid to hav
it becase id be
afraid that the
cloldren might fall
into it after it
had gone out and
get brnd and

they had pictures
and all sots of
shiney things little
shiney boksis they
had sadys home
grnils with pictures
in them they liket
me very much
we lookt at the
sadys home grnils
a whil and then
ate dinner after
dinner we found
a picture book with
pictures of little
choldren in it and
mis swone said she
thout she had a
nother won up in

her atic and she
woud send it to
me if there we lookt
at the wone down
stase a little whil
then mis swone gav
me some fotergrafs
to look at a frew
minits and then
we went home and
i sead good by.
nov 1, 1905

5   6

one night a big flok
uf little farys came
croding into are land to
live here they hade bin
bin in the north and
they thourt they woud
rather settle down here
wher it wos wormer
there wer men farys
and lady farys and
choldren farys and they
all wanted to get hiden
before moning so no
wone woud see them
they wer gust about
as big as papas hand
so they woud mede a
hole gust as big as a
crows hole if he had

32

a hole some bilt over
in nat heads woods. and
some down in the meodo.
and some out in the
oched. and they all said
isint this luvly we will
stay here but there is
one thing that we must
not do is not to go
near that house and
thats whot we must
do so ceep yore mind
on it and you must.
or you will get cort
said one and dont go
      tord the house go
a way forom it you
can think about the pretty
things to but when

you go out to wark
you must think of the
house and you must
keep thinking it to
or you will run a
gentst it and get
cort.
nov 2, 1905

34

Jack o' Lantern

every night a gobler cames
and starts in are window
and three nights we
havl not seen him a
round but two nights
we have i guess the
outher three nights we
didint happen to look
out and didint see
him he proble was
there becase he had
bin there the other
two nights he coudunt
look in long becase
wed put down then
i spose he went of
in the woods and
went to bed but if
there were eny farys

around hed gump
right up and run
becase goblens no
that farys can get
rid of them right
off and they do too
farys hat goblens
becase they try to
sell them bad friet
but i shud think
they shud make
them take the bad
friet and get rid uf
them if the farys
wanted to get rid
of them shudunt
you yes but he dount
dus he no.

nov 3, 1 9 0 5

36

last satedy lena gay
came to see me i
was craking nuts
when she came i
cract her a few
nuts and then we
went out to play
we playd hop scoch
i do not no how
but lena gay shoud
me how we make cross
lines and put numbes
in them then you
throw a little stone
in the number one
then in the number
too then in the number
thrll you throw the
stone in the little

scwares first you
hop too feet then
one foot and pick up
the stone on won
foot and it is
kindove hard to
do it becase it
pretty near nocks
you down and some
times i did
get nockt down
then lena gay wanted
to look at toy and i
gave her same and
by and by i put
them away and
playd in the barn
with the swing then
we went down the

34

stone steps to see
papa feed the hens
then we went to
self there were eny
eggs and there was
one and i took it in
and then we playd
with the swing
agan then we went
over in the ferns
and i climbed a tree
then we went down
by the nut tree and
played on the rocks
then i hamerd her
some more nuts and
she went home and
carid them with
her. nov 8, 1905

yesterday mama and i
went down to esthers school
we had a nice ride but
we did not see much in
the school because we
came there gust the time
school was over so we
gust saw ester clean up
so i did not see much
but one little girl read
to me and speld to me
she was named laura
she was very cut and
was five years old
and while we went in
the school we left yunys
untide and while we were
in looking at the school
she ran away but sombody

40

stopet her and we brot
her bak and this time
we tide her ester is
the techer she teches the
children and when lora
speled she spelld sotedy
and carige and esther showed
me the words they had written
and they were awful big and
not round. And Laura's mama
carried her to school and
brought her home every day.
And then we went home.
Esther locked the door, and we
took her to Mrs. Palmers; and
stayed until almost six. On the
way home it was very cold.
1905

the first snow storm
last night when we
came out of the store
from going over to derry
it was snowing the strets
wer wet with it so
we wanted to get home
pritty qwicly the snow
was not soft it was
hard with shape ponints
on them. i had to pull
my cap down over my
face so the snow would
not get on me
and when we wlnt
in the yard the
the snow was thick
on the hen house
and in to a raen
storm.

42

the snow man

Soon winter will be here,
and the snow will be on
the ground. Then the
boys can make snow-balls
and snow-houses.
once some boys made a laerge
snow-man, and put
a hat on his head, And
put a gun in his hand.
but they could not make
him shout any thing.
he did not seem to know
what the gun was for.
1905

desember _ threshing wheat
there was a piksher of
some men cuting wheat
that was in ingland
where they were doing
it. and in the piksher
they were whiping
it with stikes to dry
it. and they cary
it out and pore it
on the ground to
klen all the chaf
and little bits
of hay out of
it they have to
to it on a pretty
windy day becase
if you didint it
woudent klen all the
chaf and little bits of

44

hay out of it.
then they take
it in and put it
away, and leave it.
1905

it will be fore weeks
before crismas will be here
and irma and carol
and i are going to have
these things, a horn
and o and a little
table and a little chair
for a doll and a little
play house and some
strore berry and three
crismas books with
picshers in them and
a stove handle and
some stove covers dount
you thingk all those
things will be nice,
" yes very nice it coms
on the 25 of december,
and it is not santer

46

clase that givs me
the things it is
my mama and papa
that give me them
why they call him
santer clase is becaus
they do it gust for
fun.
1905

dear mildred.
you live down
south. dount you,
you never see winter
do you. ~~and~~ what is
winter lik. well in
winter there is snow
on the ground and
after a very cold
day you hove a sled
in winter. and when
the snow gets hadend
in to ice you tack
yore sled and go out
and slide down hill
and its great fun.
and if you lick it
you can come up here
but i dont think

48

you would lick it
and too it would
be cindove had
to because after
being down in that
warm state it would
shile you cindeve
after beaug down
in a warm state
and after comeing
up in this cooler
state it would be
cindove curus at
first but you would
get yust to it but
it would be funy
to you quite a while
and now i will tell
what dusunt grow

up here. oring trees
dount grow up here.
nether do benaner
trees. nor do parm
trees. becaus it is
toocold for them.
and one thing that
never gros down
there that gros up
here is alder trees
    yore frend.
      lesley frost.

50

gingal bell gingal
bell gingal all
the way o what
fon it is to ride
in a one hourse opon
slay. when i went
to ride to day there
was snow on the
gronb and it has
been on quite a while.
this is the first slay
ride carol and i
and irma and mama
had to day and
papa had one to
all alon.

1905

BOOK III

December 25, 1905 to July 9, 1907

(Aet.: 6 years, 8 months to

8 years, 2 months)

FOREWORD TO BOOK III

ONE of my presents on Christmas Day of 1905 must have been a new composition book, inside the cover of which I immediately wrote my name and the date. Six of the first seven entries in this new book are simply dated, "1905." The next entry is dated March 2, 1906 — as though at least two months had passed without my writing anything here. Thereafter, the dated entries continue with some regularity until the one which seems to mark the end of the school year for me: it is on page 49, and it is dated June 6, 1906. It would seem that when our school-at-home started again, in the fall, I made my next entry, on page 50. It is entitled, "playing school," and it is dated October 4, 1906.

For reasons which I do not remember, I seem to have been given another new composition book on or about July 4, 1906. On page 2 of this new book (which became Book Four, in this series), my father apparently gave me a topic for an essay, by writing this question: "Why do we fire guns, on July 4?" If he planned to have me use Book Four as part of an intensive summer-school course, something must have happened to spoil the plan. I did make entries, thereafter, which are dated July 8, July 10, July 20, and July 25; I made three other very brief entries which may have been written in July. But my next entry in Book Four (pages 12–13) bears a date in my father's handwriting — October 4, 1906 — and this is the identical date which I wrote on page 50 of Book Three. How or why I happened to be making entries in two notebooks, on the same day, I do not know.

During the next six weeks and more after that date, I seem to have made no other entries in Book Three; but during that same six-week period I made at least twenty entries in Book Four. My next entry in Book Three was dated November 20, 1906; my next entry in Book Four was dated December 5, 1906. Thereafter, it would seem that I used the two notebooks indiscriminately, although I showed a tendency to write more in Book Three than in Book Four. The last entry in Book Three is dated July 9, 1907; the last entry in Book Four is dated August 9, 1907. Then I must have been given a vacation. My first entry in Book Five is dated October 16, 1907.

As I have said, I do not know how to explain why I used Book Three and Book Four in such a way that they overlap. I am merely describing a mystery.

BOOK III

CONTENTS

NOTE: *Lesley did not write on pages 126–127 of Book III.*
These pages have not been reproduced.

the cow got out.
one day my doll was
in the kichin and she
heard the cow
getting out and
she skremd for us
we were up on
clins hill and we
heard her and came
runing home and
we sow that the
cow was out we
ran up staesl and
calld papa and
papa came runing
down and by that
time the cow was
down by berus cane
and by the time

2

we were down there
the cow was down
by patisens coner
and the patisens
were just cameing
around the caner
and they stoped
her and brought
her back and
I we were there
and we took her
back and she had
a good spanking
after that and never
went away agan.
1905

the scuingk 3
day befor yesterday
it was warm
and we smeled
a scuingk and mama
went down too miss
pamus she smeld
it from gays to
hear and after that
me and papa went
over to derry and
we smeled it all
the way to derry
but we didunt smel
it on the way
back.
1905

songs

sixty miniits make
an hour sixty seaconds
make a minut.
come little bird i
have a cage that will
keep you warm safe
froom danger and
safe from stom no
little lady we canot
do that not for a
dime nor a brand
new home we are
happy and wild and
free.

the snow birds
day befor yesterday
i was ant in the orchard
and what do you suppose
i sow i sow quite
a big flok of snow
birds and they were tame
i wos right under a
tree and the tree wos
white with them over
my head. snow birds
have white breasts
and blak wings with
white on the tip ends
of them and white
head papa said he had
never in his life seen
a snow bird they
fly very pretty they

6

fly around in a
serced then fly away
then come back go
around then fly away
snow birds have a
very pretty song
i cannot say it but
i can say most of
the birds songs.
1905

my dreams.

one night papa was away
and mama was out getting
marjorys bottle and she was
crying like evry thing and
by and by she stoped crying
and when mama came
in with the bottle there
was nothing there but a
great big paper of needles
and when we took the
children up we hapend
to go into the room where
marjory sleeps and there
we saw marjoory in the
crib and we wonderd a lot
how marjory got up there
so we ran down and got
the bottle and gave it to her.

1905

8

why the cow gumped over the moon
one day our cow got out
and went down the wind ham
raod and papa went after her
and mr. percins was just coming
down from his house and papa
yelled out to him stop the cow
please will you and mr.
percins said yes and he put out
his arms and they came
on tord her and just as soon as
they came on tord her it
came into her mind that
she was going to serprise
them and she looked up in
the sky and there she saw
the moon and she stoopet down
a little and up into the
air she went and they were

so serprised that they burst
into laufing and why she
jumped over the moon wos because
she wonted to serprise them
and because she wouldent hovl
to run so hard to get away
from them.
. 1 9 0 5

10

the fairy and the squirrel,
one night we wer all asleep
a fairy came in and sat
doun in one of the corner
and took a litle box out of its pocket
and opend the little box and took
out foere gold rings and lad
them on the table and took out
foere diamonds and lad them
on the table then in popped
a little gray squirrel and
they began talking together,
the squirrel said what are you
doing in here some one will
get after you.
and the fairy said well if they
do catch me and put me in
a cage i will reach through
the wire and unlock

it. well said the squirrel.
you can do what you think is
best. and i can do what i
think is best, and then they
all disaperd in a moment.
and when we came out
there we saw them on the
table and they gave them to
us and they fited us and
we wondered how the fairy
new our size.
1905

12

carol and his toe

one night when carol was asleep
a goblin came up stais and bit of
his toe. and carol felt it and
jumped up and the goblin was gone
and his toe was gone she jumped up
quike and ran down stais and ran up
the beery road to find out what
bit his toe when he sow it it had
a little white tling in its hand
it, was carols toe but carol could
not cacthe up with it was running
so fast. so carol ran back and
jumped
on eunices horse back rider and
eunice galaped up the road and
just as soon as eunice saw the goblin
she ran after it and goble'd it
and the toe too and carol ran
back and told papa and mama abort

it. and just then a fairy came
in and said to carol i thought i
herd you say that your toe was
gone and carol said why yes and the
fairy asked what toe and shoud
him and she put one of her fingers on
carols shoulder and in a minute
carol looked up and the fairy
wasgone and he looked down
at his foot and his toe was
on.

     march 2
  1906

14

Falling in the water

day before yesterday i was playing
in the little pasture and i was lening
over a little edge of rocks and there
was a little water below me and i
was reching for something in the
water when splach i went into
the water i pulled myself out
again and i looked like a skarecrow
running down that little hill
i ran into the house and had to
take every thing off except my
waist and shurt and put on
my nightgown and ly on the sofer
carol crild he was afraid
and carol and inma gave
me lots of things

march 7
1906

the chestnut tree

there is a very big chestnut tree
out in mr gays woods and in the
fall there are piles of chestnuts
under it and on it last fall papa
got more then too full pockets of them
we liked them very much and soon
ate then it is the bigest tree out
there and has more chestnuts
then any of the others.
in the spring i and mama think
we could hove a picnic out
under that tree in the spring when
marjorys big enough to todle
around.

march 9 1906

16

Odysseus left Calypso on
a raft and poseidon found it
out and got angry at him
for puling out a cyoplas eye
and he said head make trouball
for Odysseus and he took a
puh fork that he always had
in his hands and made
a figist wave that ever was
ruch on to Odysseie it
ruched on to him and came
so hard that it nocked the
nudder from his hand and
nocked him into the ocon
and one ov the goddeses
pitted him and came down from
the sky to him and sat on
the raft beside him why is it

she said that Poseidon is so
angry at you take this wimple
and put it about your breast
and swim the rest of the way
to shore it will cep you
from drowning U. dysseus
took the wimple and she said
when he got through with
it to throw it into the water
and she would catch it
then she flew away but he
waited till the raft brock
very soon it frock and he
climbed onto a beam and
took off his cloths and
put the wimple on then
he dived head first into
the scon he went down
but he pulled himself up

18

again he swam on and
on he very soon sow the cost
but when he got near it it
had hiy rocks around it
and a great wave threw him onto
a rock and pretty near
toir him oppen he swam
off and soon he saw
a river and he swam to it,
and praid to it i have forgoten
what he praid and he swam
to the land and lay down
among the reeds and coverd
himself with leaves he was
afraid to go up in the woods
for fear anaimales
eating him and a godes
that liked him waved her wand
over his eyebrows and put him to
sleep   march 30 1906

20

how the chimney got on fire
wednesday our chimney got on fire
i happened to look out of the window
and the yard was full of smoke
i did not no what it was at first
but i soon made out that it was
a fire some Where and i called
out there is something on fire
and we went out doors and
the smoke was just poring out
of that chimney and papa
thinks heknows how it got on
fire he says he thinks a brown
tail morth blew up the chimney
and caught on fire we took
a several pails of water up
stairs and pored it down the
chimney but after papa said
the chimney was on fire

i cried we soon put it
out and since that the children
have been playing fire and
to day irma was afraid the
house was on fire.
   march 31 1906

22

yesterday papa and i took a walk
down to osgoods corner after some
blood root then we came
up and talket with oedood
about chicens he had 2 5 0 of them
they were very quite i pikt
one up and after awhile
they asket us to go in the house
it was sprinkling then
and we said no and went
home and pat the blood root
in some water for mama.
   may 7 - 1906

about the flowers

the first we fond were
inercins and next were
hapaticas and vielets and
singcwafoles and at last
eneminys. the inercins we
soon got tired of becaus
the farm was just white with
them we fond the frst of
them on the wood road to my
little sprius tree that was in
march on sunday.
the hapaticas we fond over
acroes the road papa trans
planted some over there there
is 5 on it this year it is
very pruity they have golden
senters.
the violet it has about the

24

same kind of senter it is the same
color but it hasn't the same kind
of leaf the hapaticer has three
cuts in it like this ♈ and the
violet has a round leaf like this
♈ and the hapaticer has a langer
stem then the violet
i think the hapaticer is best
i forgot the inisins irma
likes those best shegrabs them
up in handsful they are
white and not very pretty.
carol likes singqwafolls best
this year he yells out at them
every time he sees any and
calls me they are yellow
and have golddern senters.
strowberry blooms are white
carol fond one out in the big
pasture.

the orcad that i no
is lady sliper it growes
its an orcad it growes most
anywhere only not in modows.
i call them pink there is anouther
papa said that i don't know it
grows out in berry woods we do not
find it any where els

the cherry blosoms
the cherry blosoms came first
they are white the trees are
just louded with blosoms the
bees come and take the honey
and while they are getting
it the pollin from of the
stamins get on his wings
and work onto the pistal
and it goes down through
the pistal into the seedpod
and if it is to cold for the
bees we won't have any friut
the seedpod won't grow biger
without the pollin and won't
grow into a cherry without
pollin.

may 1 4 1906

k

The quince blossoms

the quinces blossom the same time
the cherry blossoms do they
don't smell a bit but they make
the front yard look luily and red
quince blossoms are red you know
the huming birds fly all around
here they wing go like litining
and they are aful aful tiny little
things they can sand right
stille in the air flaping its
wings to catch a fly it makes
a noise with its wings
like a bee they like the
quince blossoms very much
yesterday i was going through
the gat and a huming bird
lit right on a flower besiderne
but he heard me and flew

28

away quik as winking.
may 15 1906

Our laurel bush:
we have a laurel bush out
in gays woods its flowers grow
in clusters one day we took the
blue handeled shouvel and went
out and sug a peace up
and planted it by the little
oak tree at the corner of the
bars and this spring papa moved it
into the front yard and
sawed the high part off it is
starting to make new leavs
come out on it, and i hope
it will grow and have
flowers on it.
    may 16 1906

30

the thunder shower
we had to to thunder
showers night before last one
right ontop of enouther all but
the litining was on all sides
of us all but the south
and i saw a star like this
⸺ and therewas
a great big thunder after
it. and i saw enouther
one like this ⸺ and enouther
like this ~~~~~ they were
very pretty and when
papa was up stairs
puting marjany to bed mama
and i saw one like this
they are all very
pretty.
may 18 1906

the dolls

mama sent to newyork for
some dolls with metle heads
one for me and one for irma
they are very nice dolls
they can sit down witlout
you holding them mine has
brown eyes and irmas is blue i
want my doll to. have a skirt
just like mine and i want
my doll to have too dresses
one blue and one brown and
want mine to have a waist
just like mine. buttons in
just the same plases and
winter drowers and summ-
er drowers and they sent
some little lether shoues
they are stronger tle outhers

32

the outhers are made of
paper. 19   1906

snider and the woodchuck

one day snider went up
the berry road and he saw
a woodchuck with a rat in
its mouth good morning said
snider good morning said
the woodchuck you've got a
good breakfast havent you
said the woodchuck oh no
said snider i wouldent eat
you for the world you've
got a nice rat to eat
better than an old bony
woodchuck and i am going
to make friends with
you come home and
i will give you a little
table to eat on and the
the woodchuck came and

34

and snider put him and
the rat too in the
oven and when he thought
they were done he took
them out, and ate them.
may 7 1905

putting the calf out

to day papa took the thing we use
to put on the other calf tide it onto
this calf it is a bull calf and
after we put it on we put
it out in the pasture with the
cow he had nails on it the
calf had been down in the
back barn for   sevirel days
and we had to feed it milk
and when we him out he ran
to her to drink but the sharp
nails prikt her so that
she kept running away from him
and the calf kept running
after her that at last the
cow went out in the big
pasture and left the calf and
the calf is still mooing there
may 30   1906

36

the front gardern
the front gardard is just full
of good things and bad things
we've got a riacfillermantoser and
three flowess a gen flox and a
white flox and a purple
flox and two perniss and three
hydrangers one died and the
other to and our ~~and our~~
riacu i think is dead and
a purple clemetis we planted
that down the stone steps
the rain pretty near spoled
it and there is to behind
the fense that are dead
i have forgotten the name
of them we have got some
bulbs miss parmer gave to us
alot of dallyas and alot of

other things we dont no
enything about   nor what
they are ether but they are
all growing nicly   all but a
frew of the dallyas

38

my dream
a few nights ago i
dreamed that we were out
driving and an
automobile came and stoped
beside us papa took out
ten sents out of his
pocket and opend a tling
in the seat and there
was a holle in the
bottom and papa through
the ten cent pees in
and out came a gold
ring papa took it and
put it on and shut it
up and the automobile
went off without any
man in it nor any
sterer. 4 . 1 9 0 5

the   daissess
    the daisses are out day
befor yestuday made of
buds of daisses chain
i like daisses becaus you
can make daissy chains
of them but i dont
like tlem because there are
little bugs in them i
think they are pretty
robins planting and
daissess belong to the
same family i think
robins panting to it.
dosent have any bugs in
it daisses are white
robine planting is light
blue. 6 1905

40

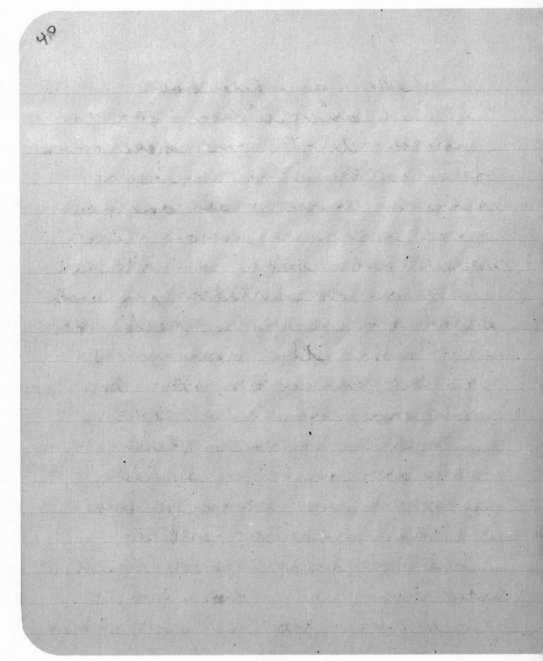

the big white hawlk
we sit and watch for a
hawlk that coms here very
ofen he is a white howlk
with a little blak on his
wings we sit under the
apple tree back of the house
the miscetoes bouther us quite
alot we have to keep them
away and the hawlk to
we scream when we see
him once he came down
right down betwene the
peach tree and the apple
tree and the hens made
a noise and we yelled
before we saw him mama
saw him i didnt he is
very bold he is not ofraid

42

lawrence

about the falls
day before yestriday i and
mama svent to lawrence
and then we went to
andover and we crossed
the merrimac falls tley
werethe longest and bigest
falls i have seen and
on the top there was
a long line of red lights
and on the way back
i saw it too i thoughtthe
bridge would break but it
didn't and i thought
they didnt make any
noise but papa thinks
it was the rumbling
of the car that stopped
it and papa said that

there is something behind
the falls to walk on but
you have to waer ruber
clothes because there is a
thick spray underneath
like rain.
13 1906

44

the consert

to days ago i and mama
and papa went to a consert
we started at seven and it
lasted till eleven i was terebely
tired the song i liked best
was when the man came out
and played on the ponino and
the outher sang and there
was a lady there that i
didn't like the two last
songs she sang very well it
was about Jack and another
dog lots of times they fond
dead sleep on the gurond and
they thought jack did it
because they saw blood and
wool on his head but
one time when they were

up on the hill with
the sheep they fond the
outher dog killed and in
his throut were jacks teeth
marks whisser was his name
so they knew that whisser
had killed them and jack
hadn't i was so tired i
could hardly walk out
of the place but i got
out and went home and
went right to bed

june 27 1906

46

the orcad that i no
i no lady sliper it grows most
any where only not in medows
i call it pink there is onouther
kind papa said that i don't no
lady sliper is an orcad and grows
out in berry woods there is a
hole bunch of it out there we
don't find it any where els
but in one or to places.
and i no ladys tresser there
are to kinds one is thin and
the outher is fat, the fat
grow in modows last year we
picked a pile of it out in
or modow i do not like it
quite as well as the thin
kind the thin kind grows
most anywhere.

and i no snake mouths
they are an orcad to they grow
in our cranberry bog ive got
some day before yestuday they
smell very nice and while
papa was getting them he
ran across some whit ones
to with a little of the pink
around the bottem i cannot
tell you how they are shaped

i hove seen aruthouses they
are the newest fower i hovl
seen sot only a few weeks
ago i cannot tell you how the
flower looked and i can't make
it becauce i have forgotten how it
was shaped i like snake mouth
and aruthouses best i think.
june 28 1906

48

the fire works
night before last papa and
i and mama went to see
some fire works i saw a sky
roket they were this ʌ and
there was a thing like this
☿ and anouther one like this
♉ and anouther like this
∴ a man took a long
thing and dipet it into
some fire and waved it around
and fire balls came out
of it i was a little
afraid of the shy roket
and the valkano a little
there was a bonfire at
the end and mama went
in to see miss maryena while
papa went out to help make

the bonfire and then we
rode home and i went to
bed. june 6 1906

50

playing school

almost every day about ten o'clock
mama calls us in the front room.
and we have to sit up on the
sofa and tell storys then we
have to count 1 2 3 4 5 and then
we sing a song and then read
and then we do a b c d and
when any one says a word right
he gets the word and then we
sing anouther song and then we
do our exersizes and then we
march around the room once
or twis and then march out
into the kichen to show papa how
we can do it. oct 4 1906

the first rubber

once upon a time down
in south amaraka, a man
went into forest and choped
down a tree wich he did
not na anything about and
found out that it had some
strange sticky milk in it
he went home and told everybady
and they o said he was joking
and they said just cows and
goats have milk trees never
have milk they have sap
i gluess you mean sap you
don't no what sap is between
milk we will soon teach
you that.
and the man said i will
soon teach you something

52

you are lazyer then i
am you better come and
look at it before you say
that.
so all the people that he
told came with him and
brout milk to see if it was
any difrent they knew
probably it was difrent but
when they got there they
wer astonished becaus it
wasn't any difrent exepet
a little stikyer.
and the man said sap is
good for some thing and
milk is good for something
and mayby this is good for
something
so they tried and tried and

tried and then they thought
and thought thought
and one man thought
lets put some an a stick
and dry it over a fire
and see what it does so
he did it and when it
was dryed he felt of it
and it snaped and he said
lets call this rubber snaper
and now they only call it
rubber.   nov 20 1906

a thought
in the night something
come after me and in the
morning i tried to make
it come again but it would not.

54

a thought

Up the airey mountain;
Down the rushy glen;
We dare n't not go a hunting
For fear of little men;
We folk good folk;
Trooping all together;
Green jacket red cap
And white owls feather!

Down along the rocky shore
Some make their home:
They live on crispy pancakes
of yellow tide and foam;

Some in the reeds
Of the flack mountain lake,
With frogs for their watch-dogs,
All night awake,

High on the hilltop
The old king sits;
He is now so old and gray,
He has nigh lost his wits.
With a f bridg of white mist
Culumbkill he crosses,
On his stately journeys
From slieveleague to rossees;
Or going up with music
On cold starry nights
To sup with the queen
Of the gay northern lights.

They stole little fridget

36

For seven years long
  and when she came down again
her freainds we all gone

They took her lightly back,
Between the night and morrow;
They thought she was fast asleep,
But she was dead with sorrow.
  They have kept her ever since
  Deep within the lakes,
  On a bed of flag leaves,
Watching till she wakes.

  On the cragy hill side,
Through the mosses bare,
They have planted thorn-trees
For pleasure here and there.
Is any man so daring
As dig them up in spite,

BOOK III · 1905-1907

He shall find their sharpest thorns
In his bed at night.

Up the airy mountains,
Down the rushy glen,
We dare n't go a hunting
For fear of little men;
Wee folk good folk,
Trooping all together;
Green jackat, red cap,
And white owls feather!

William
Allingham.

58

Where the bee sucks, there suck i
I.

the sun comes up at 20
minits past seven
and goes down at half
past foer.
dec 13 1906

getting up the hill after sliding down.
i went out doors and took my
sled and went down the stone
stepes w' the stepes were so slipery
that i thought i was going to
fall becaus the sled was right
on top of my head and
when i got down the shed
came after me and hit my
legs and made my legs week
and, it made my legs joint down.
and when i got to the hill
i slid down and the sled
went side ways i was
a little afriad but when
i got down and looked up the
hill i thought it would be
hard getting up and so it
was first i would toke without

603

falling
~ down and then i would fall
down and when i get up
again slipity go and i go
half way down the hill
on my side before i am
abel to get my foot
in any place where i
had put it in before coming
up, and my rubber came
off twice but i thought it
was fun i did not slid
down but once.
dec 10 1906

how the sunshines on the
snow.
how lpretty the sunshins
in your ieys when the
sun shins on the snow.
but when you look away
off the snow does not
look like snow. It looks
likera glitteuring carpet
of crust. — When you
look out in the morning
and the sun is shining
why you think it is going
to put your ieys out.
It is brighter in some
places than it is in
others. dec 16 1906

62

chrismas time
christmas night i could not
sleep atoll because i was
thinking of christmos.
B but in a little while
papa said the bell woold ring
in a little whele and in a
minute carol gove a little
move and the bell went of
at the same time and i
laghed. Mama went down
and lit the fire and
we come down and dress
ed and come in the
front room. There was
a christmos tree with candles
on it. The children liked
it very much. Carol
had an atomobeel and

and some tules. and Irma some
some dishes and the noars
ark. and i had some dishes
and we both had dolls. and
I had a go-go and a twink.
       Marjory was so astonished
when she came in that she
did not no what to do.
and That night we lighted
the candles again and
manjory ran back and
forth and laughed and
played. till mama said
we better come to supper.
    Jan. 7, 1907

Come, he said, let us go out

64

Stoped By Snowstorms.

day before day before yesterday
we planed we we would go
to walen days day befor
yesterday.
But day befor yesterday it
snowed so hard we could
not go.
I said we we would go
tomorow.
But mama said Tomorow
was sunday and we mustn't
call on sunday.
Then i felt abely discourou
ged and busy.
But mama said we
would go day after
tomorow.
Sunday was a pleasent

day and i thought it
would be pleasent to day.
But i in the morning it was
cloudy and i felt more
discouriged then ever.
And every -body said it looked
like snow.
        But mama said she
thought not and we could
    go.
But pritty soon it began to
snow quite hard.
Then i thought mama
wasn't right and i i felt
        very sorry.
    But pritty soon it it stoped.
then i felt brightnd.
        Pretty soon i looked out
and it was snowing just as

66

hard as it ever was.
jan 14 1907

A

Derry At night

derry at night seems cheerfuler
then at day time.
But every body is rushing
to tlein homes from the shops.
because they have a long way to
go.
the lomps are all lit and once
or twice when you look
at a store a lamp pretty
near goes out.
And you see people hurrying
to get to the stores in time
so the store people wont
go and lock up the stores.
And there is a hole crould
in the post ofice for
mail.
And by anici's there are alot

68

of people untying their
hourses.
    ↲ There are only a few lights
in the shops because the people
are all done working
and only a few people
are cleaning up the
shop.
    The lamps are on the ceiling
so people can not nock
them over.

good

69

9   6

Papa goes To See santa clous

One day before christmos papa
said to us i am going out in
the alders to see santa claus
and i must take the aye.
I tried to make him tell me
what he was going to do
with the aye but he would
not.
After he had gone we went
out on the hill and shouted
about santa claus till papa
could not stand it and
he sent us home. Pretty
soon papa came home. But
he would not tell
us what santa claus
said. And we never
knew till christmas what

70

papa went out there
for. It was a chistmas tree
jan 17 1907

72

A Made-Up Story

One day when i was down to
Hilda and veras.
the house was all changed
and i didn't think it was
the house at first.
there were to or three new
rooms. allan was sick. And
there were to or three new
girls that had come there. I
was quite surprised. Pretty soon
allan said to one of the
girls play that game again.
and the girl brought five
or six long wires with
a curl on one end of it
and at the end of the curl
was a knot so the things
could not run off. At

the other end was a
mashenry to make the
things go along the wire.
the things that i am calling
things are marbles made of
quite soft pearls soft
enough so that it will break
up as it goes along the line
of wire,

And pretty soon she went
away but pretty soon she come back
with three quite big bags all full
of the soft pearl marbles. And
the marbles had a hole in the
the midle so that they could
run along the wire.
there was a little basen in the
midle of the mashenry. and there
seemed to be a little corc in

74

the midle of the basen and
you drop one of the marble at a time
in. you turn a wheel and
the marble seems to sink down
into the mashenry somewhere,
and first you know you
heak the wire make a noise
you look and the marble
is runing along the wire.
As it goes little pieses break
off but they do not fall off
side ways they fall off front
ways onto the wire. But
they do not fall off because
their is some kind of electricity
in the wire that makes
them stay on. then the
people go and get them and
smooth them off all around

when they are soft and then
harden them and they are
auful pretty.

jan 19 1907

76

Out On the cranbeury Bog
this four noon mama said we
might go to derry. But when
we went out to play we said
it was to scold to go. But
papa said he would take
a walk out to the cranberry
bog with us. When we came out
their the cranberry bog was
all frosen over, so we could
walk on it. There was to lares
of ise and just a little water
between them. It cracked a little
with papa, but not with us.
We had great fun sliding
back and forth. carol walk
back and forth over tho ice.
and laghed and shouted and
sang, Papa made a poth

s through the thin snow
on the ice and papa and
me slid back and forth on it.
Papa went clean acros sometimes
because he hadn't any rubbers
ons but i had to slid two or
three times to get acros, but
i liked it. In some places it
was ruf and we could not
slid in only onl spot it
was good to slid in. Irma stood
still and wached and at last
she got so cold we had
to come hoal, and carol
shouted all the way home.

jan 21 1905

78

About Poems

Poems are very pretty soometimes.
I like wordsworth and shakspeare
best. I like it in the very moistain
and obout sleep and edward the
little boy you know. Lucy gray
is a little to sad i do not
like, that so well, thats all
i know of wordsworths. then
of shakispeire under the green
wood tree

8

80

The Pretty Sky

One day quite a long time ago, Papa
and Lesly and Irma and Carol went
to walk way out in gays, and
we found a chestnut. We went
out to the little field and
down the little road that goes
to the mountain loral bush and way out
through the stumps. It was kind
of hard for Irma and Carol to
keep up with us but we walked
kind of slow. That was becauseWhy
we got home pretty late.
Pretty soon we got to the big
chestnut tree, we had to go
in a little way from the
road to get to the tree. That made
the sharp end of the chestnut.
Then we went home to the little

field, and home back to the
house from the gate was the
tail end of the chestnut.
As we got over the gate the sun
was just going down and we
happend to look at the sky and
it was a very pretty pink. And
papa kept asking Carol what
made it, but carol said he didn't
know, and papa would lough.
At last irma i think, Irma
said, i guess mr Pleaves and mr
Beurys bonfire cot it on fire.
But when we got home it had
about gone out and Carol and
Irma said it's all gone out
now, jon 23 1905

82

A Story

The Crow at the Window

A crow was hungry and
could not find any food, he
had hunted a long time but could
not find any. And one day when
he saw a house he happened to
notice some open places in it.
He looked in and saw that there
was no snow in there and
thinking that he might find
something to eat in there he
flew tord it but when he got
there he found glass, And he ran
against it so hard that it cracked
quite badly, he gave to loud caws
and flew away, We heard it
crack and came in and it was cracki
so badly we had to by a new set
of glass, jon 24 1907

Carol Grumpy At Apples

Carol always had to apples a day.
and he wanted more. But, mama
said he couldn't. And Carol said
yes, and mama said no. Then
Carol said i will go and ask
Lesley and Irma and Marjary
and if they say yes then i
can have one. then mama said
go along, and carol first went
to Irma and Irma said yes
he could have one. Then he went
to me and I said What did mama
say and carol said mama
said i couldn't have any. Then
Lesley said i do not no any
thing about it, if mama said
no then you can't have one.
Then Carol went to Marjary

84

and marjary did not no
what carol meant when
he said, can i have an
apple. She said apple apple.
Then carol stampt his foot
and went and tried to
play but he couldn't play
very hard at first because
he felt grumpy. But
when he went in to school
he forgot all about it, and
he didn't think anything
more about it till he bit
an apple again.

jan 25, 1907

Some of Wordsworths Poemes
I like wordsworths poems
about best of all, he makes them
so pretty and gives you such
a pickcure that he sees, and
he likes to have somthing
in his poems that caried
something in his mind.
now the reaper he says at the
end, the mucik in my halrt
i hear long after it was heard
no more. And the dafidils,
and dances with the dofidils.
that is the prettyist line
in the dafidils. Then the
reaper. The prettyist _verse_
in that is, no sweter voice was
ever heard, in spring time from the
coocoo bird breaking the silence of

the seas among the fartherst hebrides.
Then in edward, as we strolld
on our dry walk, is the pretteyest
line in that, i think that is
an awfull pretty one it is
so quiet and nice. And sleep,
the pretteyest one in that is, smooth
fields, white sheets of water and
pure sky, Thats pretty to, it
makes you think of sleep and
makes you want to go to
sleep, when you think of it.
Then, my heart leaps up when
i behold a rainbow in the sky,
The pretteyest line in that is,
a rainbow in the sky, i like
that because you can see a
rainbow in the sky now. I like
wordsworth that way because

you can see and feel things
about them. Jan 26 1907

88

The paths

There is a path to the woodpecker tree.
we use that path to go there because
we play the woodpecker tree is a store
or something, and buy things there.
Then there is another path that leads
to the mail box, thats the most usefull
of all to papa because he can read
papers and i cann't, so you see
its hardly any good to Irma and
Carol and me we hardly run
in it at all. And then there is
another path that goes to the barn.
I that is one of papas quite usefull ones
but not very usefull to us because
there isn't any place to buy and sell up
there, papa uses it to b water the
horse and cow with. Then the one
up to the piazza, thats usefull

to papa to carry water to the house
for us to drink, and its usefull to us
to go to woodpecker tree to buy things
because the only path that goes
to the woodpecker tree is from the
pump. The one that goes to the
woodpecker tree isn't usefull at all
to papa because he doesn't <u>play</u>
buy and sell things. The barn the
piazza and the letter box paths are
the ones papa cares about and
all the rest are ours acsept
one of papas and thats up to
the piazza, thats one of ours to.
Mama likes to walk on all of them just
to take a walk with the children.

Jan 7 1907

90

accidents

Carols Otomobeel Axcidinses

Carols autonsobile has many axcidinses
Every once in a while it will get
tiped over with mamas dress. And
we set up a holler. Then mama says
she did not mean to. Then we begin
scolding eachother, but not her, just
like jason   he rolled a stone
in between the soldiers   that came
up from the firy bulls teeth and
they began fighting with eachother
andnot him. Then he has lost every
man and lady that belongs in it.
The ladys went first then one of
the men not the steerer the steerer
lasted the longest but bee broken
now,   Nobody plays with him
exept - Irma and Irma doesnt play
with him so very nauch so he is

lonly and hurt. And i supose
he is saying, now look at those
s children when they get hurt
people pity them but "none alive
will pity me". jan 30 1907

9v

A War Between two turtles

Once supon a time two turtles
wanted to sleep in the same place.
And they both couldn't sleep, one couldn't
sleep becaus he was truying to think
what to do to the outher one, the
outher one was thinking to and was
teribly afraid the outher one would
com upon him befor he expected
it. But they were so angry at
one anowther, that they could hardly
think. Their was ice on the
bog so they couldn't get through to
get any sticks to fight with. But
the one that was so afraid the
outher one would come upon him
hapend to find a place along the
edg of the bog where it was soft
enouf so he could get through

he went out and got as big a
s club as he 9 could carry. Then
he went back in he didn't feel
so frightend. Then he began thinking
he 9 could think better then
because he wasnt so frighrend, and
this is what he thought. H e
thought when people pick me up
and feel my claws they drop
me. And if i can break the other
turtles shell and get upon his back
and tikle him he womt have any place
to drop me because turtles are so
low he wouldn't have any place to drop
me. So he started off putting his club
up in the water as far as he could.
The other turtle was asleep because
he thought the other turtle would
sleep that night in peace

94

of war, just like mr dooly in
peace and war and he laughed a
little. When he got there he was
tickelled to find him asleep.
He lifted his club and let it come
down on the turtles shell and the
shell broke then the turtle with the
club climed up on the other
ones back and it tickled him so
and scared him so that he never
got angry with the other
one again. jan 31 1907

Carols tools accidents

Carols tools have all been broken exept the saw. The hamer and the malit went first then the screw driver. And when one got broken Irma would go around teleing people that it was broken in such an invited way. But carol he is much difrint, he will say to us, now i want my tools put away now i wont havem from next cismas. And he says it in such a funny way that i cant help laughing a little. We put them away but you will soon see them out again because carol will want to play with. But as soon as one gets broken you wont see them for a iwhile. feb 5 1907

Marjory funny things

Marjary is aufull funny sometimes
but sometimes she's naugty and
we scold her but genvily she
laughs and we have to slap
her to make her stop and that
makes her cry. Now i will
tell you some of the funny
    things she does, sometimes Irma
plays that her doll is sick
and plays that the doornobs
are tellifones and tellifones up
to the play dockter and if
    marjory sees Irma tellifoning
she first trys the nob to
telliffone on but that is a
little too   high for her.
then she runs back and fourth
from one corner to onoither

and telliffonce in the corners
put her head right in them and
it looks so funny that we
all burst out laughing. And
manjary when she hears it
jumpes out of her corner and
scuts across to the outher corner
laughing. And if we are
making a house on the floor
with the blocks she will jenrull
uy witt knock it down and
as she goes we will give
her leg a pound as she goes
by. And as she's not expecting
it the knee ive hit will go
frontward and she will
fall down and kick our house
everyb it to pieces and we
pound her on the legs till

98

she gets up. Then another
funny thing, if she sees us
have any food she wants
she'll say i want tasty i want
tasty and we laugh and
I say it over to her and
she doesn't like that and
rubs her eyes and we
rub ours and she laughs
and she would cry if
we didn't do it. feb 6 1907

The northern lights

Last night just after i had gone to bed,
papa came up with the lantern and
asked me if i would like to see the
northern lights. I said yes, And
what do you supose. When i got
up and looked out the window there
seemed to look look like a dark
cloud over in the north west.
It wasn't a cloud it was the northern
lights that made it and they were
all over the sky these clouds.
    And on the west side of the
cloud were the northern lights.
they streamed right strait up
into the air, and the ones that
were nearer the edge of the cloud
were the smallest. It made a light
all over the sky so you could

100

hardly all the stars it was
owfull qeere and we wondered
and wonderea what made it.
feb 6. 1905

102

The Battle of Sandagargo
This was a war between us and
the spainyerds for cuba. And
this is what we did to drive
them out of cuba, we were afraid
we couldn't beet them but we
beet them easear than pie.
it wasn't much of a battle.
we would not find the sprainish
fleet. Everybody said it had ben
doging back and forth among
some islands around cuba. First
they would say it was in one
bay and another and you
would look, but they wern't
there. at last they found
the fleet in a bay called guantan
amo. They had their canans on
each side of the bay all powdera

and ready to go off any time they
needed them So our ships made
a circle right around the bay
so they couldn't get out. Then
they sent word under the ochen
on tellegraghwires [there are
tellegragh wires under the ochen
there are now]. Take more solders.
And when the soldiers came they
got around thespainerds on
land so the spainerds were all
shut in.
At last one of our men said
he with five other men would
go and sink a ship that they
didn't want and that they
thought would plug up the bay
so they couldn't get out by water
anyway, so they tried it. They took

104

the ship and they sunk it.
But it sunk the wrong way
and so they didn't succeed in
sinking it. And all the time
we were sinking it the spainerds
were shelling bulets on to us.
Then we jumped onto them. They
had brought with them but
the spainerds cant them and
put them in gail.
Well after that on the brightest
sunciest morning on sunday one
of them gave a toot and we
looked out and there were
five or six of the spainerds
ships coming out with the
black smoke pouring out
of them. But we beet them easely
then we sunk most of them

and drove to land. So at last
the spainerds thought they had
enough beeting and at last
they gave up cuba.

march 5 1907

The mild Winter Morning

The sky is gray it is not a very
nice day. But even if you look
at where the sun ought to be it
dazzels your eyes and you have
to take them away. I have noticed
when bieng out alon on a mild
winter day like to day, when you
are walking along thinking
with nothing to hear but
the tramp of your feet on
the snow with your head down
and not tending to much,
your quite startled if you hear
a slay coming in front of you.
And if you get out all right
you genraly can't get the thing
you were thinking about back
and how unhappy you feel.

If your walking in the woods
the only thing you can hear is
~~some and~~ a few chickedees and
bluejays and crows. And the
tramp of your feet and rustle-
ing the ook leaves "was all the
sound i heard".

March 10 1907

A Winter morning

A winter morning so mild and
fine with trees so still, o so
fine. The sun is shining and
shooting a ray across the gray
that makes the gray a little
light so it isn't so bad after all.

108

a True Story
Ears

Ears are very cureus. Carol
thinks he can see with
his ears and hear with
his eyes, I laugh at him when
he says it and try to make him
understand but i can't. He
keeps on saying, yes, each time
I say it, just like that sailor
where he said sail on sail on and
on. he wouldn't give up.
Ears are very queere things as
i speak of. If you pinch yourself
under your ear it hurts but
if on top it hardly hurts at all.
papa genraly pinches us where
it hurts but mama where it doesn't.

A Cold Snap

A cold snap is quite a good deal
diffrant than a mild snap.
A mild snap is geniraly on a
cloudy day and a cold snap on
a suny day. But you want it just
the other way the cold on a cloudy
day and mild on a suny day so
you could have fun, because
this is how confusing a cold snap
is. now the first fault it has is keep
you awake when you want to be
quiet. The next fault is it wont come
on a mild day, but it has some
good things about it now one thing
is it drys clothi when you have a
day like that when you want
to dry them. And it drives
all the clouds away so you cant

110

see one atall ion the sky on a
day like that. But the worst fault
it has is stirring you up when
you want to write or do anything
if you dont want to be disterbed

Then you feel like hammer-
ing it if it had anything on
it to hammer. And if
it would only give up and not
rattle the windows. It can blow
all it wants to though.

March 11 1907

Playing Out Doors To Day

To day we went out doors too play.
It was early after breakfast and
the sun was shining brightly, it was
late after breakfast when we had got
ouer things on, it takes us so
long to get our things on. But
we did at last and wer out doors
after unlocking oue door. We wer at
playing in a minute on two and
how we did play all the forenoon, we
played mud piess. we found all
the thing we could find along
the edge of the house that we had
played with last summer. we
put dirt in the pans and cover
we found and then put snow
on top of the dirt and let it
melt in the sun the sun was so

hot to day that it was melting
the snow fast. well after we
had our things all put out all
cooking and everything I asked mama
if we could go down by the road
and pick up quatz stones and she
said we could. now mama had told
us that pretty soon the blue birds
would come back. When we wer
down there I was quite startled by
a song I jumped up scied it was
a robin but mama called back
no its a blue bird. We went
home and pretty soon the air was
full of blue birds songs. we made
little mud cakes and played try
make the birds eat it and we put
it out on the ground fore them
and and came in and ate dinner.

After dinner we went out again
and made more mud pies.
After dinner the snow was about
all gone and there were great pools of
water evrywhere with leaves in
them. we took sharp stickes
and went fishing sticking the
stick into the leaves and we put
to dry on the piazza then I came
in and wrote my story.
March 17 1907

114

How water ds carried out of the ocean. The water in the ocean goes up in mist to the clouds and then rains down again because the clouds get so full. It rains all over the earth. where there are hills it canot stay on them but runs down into the vally. and makes a brook and flows tarward the ocean. as it goes it carries just a shititof salt with it out of the rocks. and thier are so many rivers and brooks going at oncl that it makes the ocean salty.

may 6 1907

115

116.

getting The First Inicine

The first time we went after inicine
was when papa was strong enough
to go out the gate, where they
come first is out by the cranberry
bog and down the little road to
the laural. The first time we went
we only found one down by the
cranberry bog place. Three
more times we went, but only
got one each time. after that
we let it go for to or three
days, it had been raining
before so we couldn't go
anyway. but the last time
we went it was a nice hot
day and i took whole hands
full. I got one by the cranberry

bog and one going tarword the
laurel, I could hardly carry
them home my hands were
so full and i was afraid
i would cruch them it was so
hot to i had to sit down
on a stone to rest. when
we got home we put our summer
coats on and i have seen a
few inicinc right around
here.

May 9 1907

118

The Jumping Mouse

The jumping mouse is a very slender bodid thing but extremly long tail. In length of head and body is three inches and tail five. In color redish brown above, and white underneath. He is very delicate and will not live long being shut up andse taken good care of the some as he has had out doors, he is the same sise as a house rat. He is found from new york out to california and as far north as lake michagok in alaska.

may 4 1907

Rubber comes from Brissil. The
climit is hot and damp. The
land is hot. where they are
finding the most gold now
is up in canada in a state
called Quebec in the mountai
s. The climit is dry not to dry
its healthy. Beaf comes in
uninted states in a sity called
chaicogo. I think it must be
as wet sity they must have
dams into the sity from lake
mishagan to wash the beaf
and let the water run back
into the ocaen. Caffee comes
from Brissil. Clamit is hot. The
land is low except one little
bunch of mountains called

120

hyland of bresil. Fur is
found up in the north western
Teritories and state yukon they
are both in canada. The
climit is cold. The land
is low except one little
bunch of mountains i don't
no the name of. Bannaners
come from Central america
in bannaner boats. The climit
is hot. The land is low
but a thin lare of low
mountains along the edge
on the western side. Silver
comes from the rocky mountains
and in andean higlands. The
land is rocky. The andean hylands
are on the western side in columbea
and ecuador and puru and chilly

and agentiner. sand in the rockys
uninted stats and canada and
alaska and messico. They are both
hyghland. saltpetter is found in
chilly to in the desert in chilly
o called desert of atacama and
the land is rocky. Rice found
in swamps in south america
along the amason river i think.
The climit hot and damp and
unhealthy. grain comes from
schoicogo, chorcogo is a sity
u ninted state. Tea comes
from china. The climit is
warm. the land is low. Oran
ges come fom the uninted States
in the city of calafornia The
climit is hot. the land
is hy on the western side

122

but low on the eastern side.
Diamonds come from the
sea divers going down after
them and perls too
may 8 1907

My Favorite Poem.

The poem i like best is sir
richard granvil, that's the
one i like best in the poems
that has a high voice and
low voice, is iseults children.
I like sir richard because
it has a war like sound
to it and then it interests
me to think how they praised
him in the end. why i like
iseults children is because
i have never seen a
castal and it makes me
see how lovely it must
be and i wish i were there
playing.

may 12 1906

124

about war

war is a good thing if you
have a good reasen for it,
but if you think you dont
like a country wheather they
like you or not then it
isn't right to go to war
with them. But when thear
s done sonthing to you ar
doiing something to you
then it is right to stope
them. The best reason we have
for a war in this country
was the reasen for the
civel war the reasen to
free the slaves. The one
between the french and
inglish. The french just fort
because they didn't like the

inglish.
bussel 1906

128.

Reseting a lilack and some Rose
Bushes. There is an old house
half way down clins hill
on the other side wich
was furnt down. It was
a kind of an old fashend
house their were old fachened
flowes around it. Tere were
two or three kinds of milkwert.
the flower was Yellow kind
of pretty. Then there was a
lilack, we had always wanted
to transplant the lilack,
nobody cares to dusplant
milk wert it isn't quiet
pretty knough. But one year
as we went past we went
to the stone wall and looked

over and what shoud we
see but a difrant kind of
rosee they were doubele
petteld and they were extra
red and aufull pretty and
papa said he would trans-
plant them some time
and so he did he went and
got six rose bushes and
one lilack bush.

130

a Row between us children
irma said she wouldn't
take carol to ridecars
he said bad things to her,
and carol said he wouldn't
take her to ride, then irma
said i wont take you to
ride but you must take me
to ride. and carol said
he wouldent. Then irma
got mad and hit us with
a piece of cloth, and carol
threw a leaf at her, and
she went and told
papa about it.
   july 9 1907

BOOK IV

July 8, 1906 to August 9, 1907

(Aet.: 7 years, 2 months to

8 years, 3 months)

FOREWORD TO BOOK IV

FIVE of my earliest attempts to write verse occur in Book Four. My father, after exposing me to a variety of narrative and lyric poems (some of which I quickly learned by heart) and after getting me to write brief critical essays — "About Poems" and "Some of Words-worth's Poems" and "My Favorite Poem" — never so much as hinted that he was frequently writing poems of his own, at the table in the kitchen of our farmhouse, long after we children had gone to bed. Even so, he apparently helped me to want to write lyrics of my own: the five in Book Four are preceded by one in Book Three, are followed by five more in Book Five, and by one more in Book Six. An early effort, here, may have been inspired by the many fairy stories he told or read to us. I didn't know enough about poetry, at that time, to separate the lines from each other, and the experiment on page 6 of this book would have looked better if I had set it up in this form:

> *Under the tree we lie*
> *That blows the cool breezes by*
> *And in the night*
> *When fast asleep we lie*
> *The fairies come and dance*
> *Under the tree that blows*
> *And blows the cool breezes by.*

My next attempt, on page 10, is more successful because I found a more vivid set of images for my analogizing, and yet even that one is improved when the spellings are repaired:

In the damp meadows
The fireflies go in and out
And in the sky the stars look down
At the fireflies that look up
At them that never go in and out
Like the fireflies
In the damp meadows . . .

For a seven-year-old girl, these two efforts can pass as respectable trial-flights. I am sure my father gave me no direct help with them, but it is clear that he had already made me understand certain differences between poetry and prose. My journals contain plenty of signs that he was carefully scrutinizing everything I wrote, as soon as I wrote it. One of my "stories" includes this glimpse of his concern for what I was doing:

". . . and play till it is time to right my story and then when i have ritten my story papa and i talk a frew minints and then I go down stairs and go out doors again."

He must have encouraged me to retreat from all the "holabaloo" made by Carol, Irma, and Marjorie — or perhaps I was the one who chose to escape from them by going up to one of the bedrooms when it was time for me to write. And it would seem that I was not allowed to go down again until my father had talked with me about my writing, at least for "a frew minints."

BOOK IV

CONTENTS

1

the baby owl

When the baby owl went
to live at mary's he was one of
the oddest-looking creatures in
the world.

i thought he was very young, and
had just come out of an owl's nest
He didn't look in the least like
a baby, nor was he atill shy.
He was a small bundle of down,
with no feathers where feathers
are expected, and the wisest
look in his face and big staring eyes

9

v.

Why do we fire guns on July 4 ?
because July 4 was the day they
dicided to hove the war with.
ingland we are glad becaus because
we liked to free our contry

the pogonis

the pogonis grow out in our
cranberry bog it is afull soggy
and wet around it they are
very very pretty and have a
very nice smell papa taks of his
shoes and stokings and wads into
the mud the mud goes clear up
to his nees and five weeks ago
i think it was we went out
after some Papa i and carol and
irma and mama ran across some
white ones with a little of the
pink around the bottom of
the flower they are pink you
no that is the first time we
have had them this year
i think they are faded now we like
them very much july 1906

the famly sunday walk
sunday the hole family of
us went out to the big grove
mama thought it was tooearly
for partrige berrys but i thought
it wasn't but when we got
there there were partrige berrys
i was write but they wern't
this years they were last
years they had lasted all winter
carol irma and i brought hand
fulls to mama and some to
marjory too we at some too
and the funyest thing was
dropes of water fell from the
tops of the trees it wasn't stiky
like gum it must have been
sap and anouther thing we
wondered about. there were lots

of buter fliys fliying around
up at the pines mama saw
nerly a dozen and papa just
one marjory troted around
and played and by and by
grandpa began to get chilly
and wanted to go home so we
went home all but irma and
i and mama and we picked a
handfull of partdrege berrys
till mama was all bitten up
by miscitoes and then we went
home. july 10 1906

6

Poem

under the tree we ly
that blows the cool breesess
by and in the night when
fast asleep in bed we ly the
fariys come and dance under
the tree that blows and blows
the cool breesess by.

a bird
a week and a half ago
one day when mama was
racking up the yard and
papa was cutting it with
the sithe and carol and irma
were playing on the hay
cart grandpa came in from
out in the orchard he
had been pilling up brush
for a bonfire and said he
saw a nest with four solid
blue eggs in it the birds
color was brown it was
some kind of thrush but
papa said that he didn't
no that eny kind of
thrushess bilt on the ground
he said it was very funny

8

he did
not no eny kind of thrush
that had blue eggs.
july 2 o first 1906

the lihtning

one day there was a big
thunder storm and several
times we thought it struck
the house and the next day
we went down to osgoods
and that big ock half way
down the little hill by the
wood pille had been struck
with litining and the bork
had slid right off it.
and all the little placies
were scartered around.
and it wos on our land
too it would take quite a few
men to chop it down.
papa thought the litining
had gone down through
the midle of the tree but

10

that stops it becaus there
was a hole at the bottom
where the litining had gone
in. july 25 1905

in the damp medows the fireflys
go in and out and in the
sky the stars look doun at
the fireflys that look up
at them that never go in
and out like the fireflys in the
damp medows fly.

the peepers sing
and the bells do ring
and in the medows the mist blows
fine
but the peepers keep up their singing
and the bells too keep on their ringing

the way to the theunder
blasted ock,
you go up to the bars
go through them into
the little pasture them
through anouther gote
then up through the lane
to the little grove and
then it's only a frew
stepps to the litiming struck
ock

12

a carol and
marjary walk
one day marjory
carol and carol went to
walk and they came to a
brook and marjary said lets
wade in and carol said
i guess we better not because
theres no body near to get
us out if we should get down
under the water and marjary
said no and carol said we
might so theres no yous in
talking about that is there and
marjary said if we musent we
musent lets hunt along the
brook and find some flowers
said carol and marjary said yes
and they found five big

bunches of blue vialets
and four big bunches of
white ones and then
carol looked at his wach
and said it was five o
clock and so they went
home and irma and i
asked them where they got
the vialets and marjory
said by a brook but
not by our brook.

Oct 4 1906.

14

bed time

we were out in the swing
and mama called us
from the door and we come
in and carol said i want
crackers dip milk and irma
said she wanted some and
mama started to give her
some in a glass and irma
scolded out i want some in
my pritty cup and when
they finish mama goes
in and gets there night
gouns and she undresses
irma and papa
undresses carol and then
papa takes them up
to bed and they say good
night good by and tell

him to leve the lamp
in the hall and when i
come up to bed i have to
have the lamp too and
in the morning when
the children come down
stares they always ask
what there going to have
for breakfast and mama
says tost and egs or
tost and cream.

oct 5 1906

16

and i say i want
tost and egg and carol
says he wants tost and cream
and irma says she wants tost
and egg to and then mama
asks carol if he wont take
tost and egg because so
many wanted that but carol
fusses so mama has to give
him tost and cream and
after we eat are breakfast
we all have a peach or
a bunch of grapes and
then we put are coat and
caps on and go out and
play till it is time to
right my story and then when
i have ritten my story papa
and i talk a frew minents

and then i go down stairs
and go out doors again.
oct 6 1906.

18

the leaves are flying
every - where maple and
the wallnut some of the
maple is red and some yellow
and all the wallnut is
yellow the chickens wounder
every where and get caught
in showers sometimes and
the days are geting colder
and it will soon be nutting
time and pretty soon mama
and i will be going to
our big chesnut tree to get
chesnuts out in gays woods.
                    oct 6 1906

our big cheshnut tree
yesterday papa and i
and carol went out to
our big cheshnut tree you go
out to the gate climb over
the gate and go out one
of the little woodsy roadsthat
uset to be a a road that
teams road on and a frew
scatering houses were aloing
it and then you goup
in a little feaild where
my little spruse tree is
growing but not much
though and then go down
anowther little road just about
as long as the one that
cames into the feaild and
then we looket through

20

some bushess and there is
our tree there were piles
on the tree but hardly
any on the ground we fond
a frew and while we were
there carol got scrached an
a berr and fused about it
till he got to the gate and
just as he came out of
the little feaild on his way
home he fond a pink cartrig
and that satisfied him till
he got the rest of the way
home and then we had
three cheshnuts.

oct 8 1905

the hunting story

one day we herd a bang and
we looked up the berry road
and there was somebody
shooting up there and papa
went out there yelling at
them he was mad as a
hatter and he fond out
that he was too mad
because le fond out they were
somebody he knew arnt
Leoner was here and we
had quite a quarel about it
after wards they had shot the squi-
rell and papa told mama to call
the sherif but she wouden't
till she was sure she had to
and outher people have been
shooting there ever sins one

day irma and carol and i went
out in the big pasture and as
we came up through the
grove   we were looking out
into the feaild and bang a
gun went off right up by the
road and i yelled out you
stop now you will have
sombody hurt next you
   no and then   i went
home and told mama.
         oct 31· 1906

the cow story
one day somebodys cow got
into our orched and carol
and irma came rushing
into the house yelling sombodys
cows out and it is running
after us and papa and mama
came rushing out and there
came a bull tering down the
hill by the backbarn there
and pretty soon i came creepping
out with a big stick and got
behind it and gave it nine or
ten big hard whaks and each
time i jumped back and hid
and pretty soon papa went in
and got a red rag and waved
it at him he thought that
might mack it so angry it

2⁴

might mack him galup
away but insted it just made
him angryer to go for you insted
of to go away and we had quite
a scrap there by the woodpecker tree
i in the midle hitting it a whack
where ever i had a chans and
doging back and papaand mama
running around on the outside
and the bull in the, very midle   we
stayed there to hours scraping
and prettey soon i doged out and
went in and took off my dress and
skirt and came out, in my coat
it was getting cold and papa and mama
did so too. i think and carol
and irma were out on the peazer
watching and in the end the
bull gut oway

and papa ran after it
and while papa was after it
the man came that owned that
bull but we did not find it
that day and carol and irma
talked about cows for to or three
days afterwards.

oct 4, 1906

26

marjarys bottle breaking

marjary ever sins five or sixe
days she has been breaking bottles
and now we are all out of bottles
and we have to use one of papas
emty bottles ever sins day before
yesterday she stoped five days ago

looking out the window
the leaves are turning into there
frutifull colors now some are
dark red some are light red some
are leaves with just yellow alone and
the crows are flocking to go south
and and onse in a while a flock goes
by cowing and won day marjary
and carol and irma were up the
berry road and a little flock went
by and marjary prettey near criad
but after they had gone she
brightend up and laghed.
and the leaves are all come fluturing
down on   a showery day in the
fall in the nuting time it is.
and papa has fond an inisens and i
a yellow daisy and carol a butter
cup in the fall too.   and the

28

popel leaves yet are green
and and the ocks are very
dark red and the chesnut
leaves are verey gray and the
wallnut leaves are dark yellow
and the quins leaves don't have
any color atoll and the pine
trees leave there neadles on all
winter and the neadles stay green
too   oct 6, 1906

the front room
i wish the sofa was o

30

the sun and the rain.
i bring thy vialits to sun and i
bring thy asters to rain.
and when it rains thy asters come
and when it rains thy vialits
fade and when tis sun thy asters
fade and when tis sun thy vialits
come and when thy snow and winter
comes it brings nothing bare bare
evrything and when thy spring
does come it brings nothing but water
water evrywhere.

oct 20 1906

for carol
one day a little squirrel came
to carol i am going up to
a new contry where the men
say we musent shoot and you
must come with me carol and
carol said   i will i want to
ofely and they went doun to
       dilly and   they stayed
there five years and then same
home and the squirrel went to his
home and carol to his.

32

for irma

there was a little rabit and his
name he could not say he thought
his name was little eagl but it wasen't
it was rabit r a b i t and wasn't
he a funny little rabit and his
house was down a hole and
made all round with dirt and
what do you think he said his house
was made of he said his house
was made of but why the little
rabit why the little rabit why this
little rabit, what is dirt.
why the little rabit dosn't no what
dirt is.

the marble

One day three years ago i think.
mildrid came here one day and
she brought with her quite
a big white marble and she left
it here when she went and
it's been turning up and getting
lost all the time and it seems
to me just like this when you
are walking aloung half thinking
about it and have not you seen it
right in front of you but
when you are walking along
and not thinking about it
it is probubly right. in front
of you but you don't see it
and i don't no whether that
is true or not it might be
you no.   oct. 19 1906

34

The snowstorm yesturday
while papa was at school yesturday
we felt drops of rain or snow
we thought it was snow but it
wasent it was rain and when
papa came home it was rainning
quite hard but only a few
minuets after papa had got home
that real snow began to fall
mama thought it would snow
only a few flaks but i thought so
to and i felt bad because i
thought it could not snow
alot but pretty soon it began
to snow harder and harder till
it seteld down to be a storm
it snowed till i went to bed
and then it must have cleard
off because it was a nice

35

clear morning cold and windy
and carol and i and irma have
to come in all the time and
warm our hands and feet.
    oct. 19 1906

36

when papa was a little boy
when papa was in salem he
lived in a tent with no
fly to it and when he went
to bed at night he carlesly
through lis clothes agenst the
cloth of the tent and it raind
in the night and it soked
through the cloth of the tent
onto the clothes and they
were soking wet in the morning
so they went out with there
shirts and got some wood and
trid to make a fire but the
wood was damp and it smoked
and prettey soon the tent got
full of smoke till they smutherd
and then they creped out underneath the cloth of the tent

the fire soon went out
and the smoke went away
and the sun came out
and they hung there clothes
out to dry and they dryed.
that was a fire that woudn't
burn.

oct 20 1906

38

our walk
day before yesturday carol and
i and irma went to walk
up around over clins lill and
when we got about half way down
the hill by the brook we were
by the bushis picking wichhased
flowers when fy the out flew a great
big partrig which fritened both the
heroes so they quite forgot there
quorral and i was so fritened my
hair stood on end but when we
had gone a frew steps fearther
on the other side of the brook
came papa yelling no trespsing on
the land which fritened both the
heroes so they quite forgot there
walk but after we fond out it was
papa we were all right and

papa helped us over the
brook and we came home.
oct 22 · 1906

40

deciding on the front room
we desided to put the new bookcase
in the front room
and we brought the red bookcase
from the front room up stairs down
to the sitting room we decidid
to put the new bookcase right
by the door that goes from the
front room into the hall becouse
there was a bad place in the corner there
and when we play school, at recess
i hide in the little corner behind the
bookcase and the children come creeping
up and i jump out on them
just like indeins.
and we decidid to put the new
arm chair in here too we peat
that right by the door that leads
into the sitting room because there

~~becaus their~~ was a bad place there
too the arm chair is very much
nicket up because the childrin play with
it a little.

the cushens are striped with black
and in betwen is green papa _thinkes_
the wood on it is white oak the
bookcase _i_ think is white oak too

we painted the front room too
we painted it white. we desided to
change stoves we put the front room
into the sitting room and the sitting
room one into the front room we come
about every night and to me it
seems to warm up here qick with
this stove.

we have got the sofa in here too
with a new sofa carpet on it the color
is blue yellow red orang green black

42

it is very pretty too and a new
sofa pillow oing and brown and
white and light green that arnt sent
that is pretty too.
then there is an old ragedy arm
chair that mama is going to by
a new ginzim for.
and there is a table that is right
fy the window that looks out
onto the piazzer and a pretty
table cloth on the table with colors
brown green yellow oing and very
light blue.
and there is a new carpet and
a new rug.

   oct, 24 1906

the nuts

we have got quawter of a bag
full of nuts from up along
the lane and down under the
nut tree carol is very lazy he
doesn't want to pick them up
at all but we make him he
grumps a little when you make
him becaus we want to send some
down to Hilda and Vera at
cristmas time.

about every time after dinner
carol and irma and i get
some nuts and eat them we like
them very much when we are
not playing with other things.
oct 26 1906

44

marjory and the children
 some times carol, and irma are good to
marjory but some times they like
to teas her they don't care whether
she crys or not but some times they
play she's sick and pook all sorts
of stuff down her,
but most of the time they
get her in the big roking
chair and plays go to denry
and play teach school with her
she likes that.
some times mama puts one of
irmas things on her and irma
says she can have it all the
day and and then irma
changes her mind and says marjory
can't have it not any day.
and so it gole's on some times

makeing her, and some
times makeing her laugh
and dance and some times
makeing her fuss.
she likes to laugh and
dance but she doesn't like
to cry and fuss at all.

46

about us

we go down into mr berry's
pasture and get big sticks with
lots of branches on one side of
them and bring them home
and play there bulls and rock
them all to peaces with outher
sticks and play hook them we
have graet fun and carol
and irma play with me most
all day but they stop when
i stop genraly.
then after that genrally we
go in and play school and
then we take a walk over
clines hill.

46A

ruth and us

ruth came to see us westurday
and we a had a great time
playing. we played with the
blocks she dosn't no how to
make a house atall she
just puts the blocks out any
where and then she wants
to take them all away from
everybody els and we played
with the doll and tle doll's
bed she huged irma and carol
oufully hard but they
didn't cry at all.

Nov 7 1906

47 A

the new horse

carol irma and i were over across the road
picking up little quitz stones
and we looked in the barn and
there was papa cleaning up
the gig we ran over there
and asked him if he was
going to derry and he said
no he wasn't that he was
going to send it over to
derry by mr percins so that
he could <u>walk</u> over <u>ride</u> <u>back</u>
with the gig and day before day
before yesterday papa went over
to school but he did not come
back at half past one he came
back at pretty near five and
then he came into the yard
with the new horse and gig.

nov 8 1906

48

the snow storm
it was nice and clear
last night but it must
have begun very soon to snow
because in the morning
the ground was covered
with it and it was snowing
hard. we half like the snow
and half dont we like it
when it is coming down
but when it is all down
we dont like it we like
it when it is coming
down because it is so pretty
it makes me think that alot
of hens are molting up there
and when the wind blows
it blows them down here.

we like to sit by the windows and watch the flakes
come down but mama dossen't
let us long but we are
satisfid if we can sit on
the table and play with flakes
till i got tired of that
and went out doors the
snow was too deep so
i went into the shed and
got the big snow shouvel
and went out and shouveled
a path from the barn
to the piazza then down
to the pump then down
to the wood pecker tree
then over to the tree at
the end of the quince vines.
and when i got ready to

50

run around the paths,
my feet were so cold
i had to come in and
we thought it was going
to snow all day but just a
little while after i came
in it began to rain.

    dec 5 1906

the sun

the sun is the most
needing thing in the whole
world if we did not have
the sun it would be dark
and cold all the time
but lucky we have
it it comes to us
foerteen hours and goes
from us foerteen hours
the foerteen hours that
it is gone we sleep and
the foerteen hours we
have it we play and
work so you see if we
did not have it we would
could not work and we
would be poor and would
die of coldness and

52

nothing would grow.
and how pretty it is
it looks like a star
only a great deel biger
it is all on fire
that's why it warms
us and when it begins
to get dank how quik
it gets dork only at five
  o'clock.
  and in winter it goes
down lower than it does
in summer that's what
makes us   colder in winter
.   dec 6 1906

our three hourses
the first hourse we
had was billy we
used to call him
tukup he was an old
red hourse but he
was a plug he went
sloly we sold tukup
to dockter breako
i remember all about
it it was at night
and the wagon was
out in the yard i
was out there to see it
dockter breako with
anouther man had
come up to get some
hens and they said
they would take billy

54

the next hourse we
had was unicl we
got him from
patersin he was a gray
hourse she wasn't a plug
she was a sprinter
she got away from
us when she could
we thought she was
a nice hourse but
one day she got away
when we did not no
it we hunted every whe
re but we could not find
herbut when we were up
on clin's hill hunting
for her we herd a
snort up the berry road
we came home there

was osgood comeing
down the road with
unice patersin had gone
and a man named
osgood had come to
live there.
we sold unice to
mr berry.
the next hourse we
had was a red hourse
too named roy mama
likes that name but
papa is going to call
it billy the second
because he is red just
like billy the first
we bought him of
davis he has gone away
for the winter, too.

56

boston and said we
could have it
this one isn't a plug
eather he goes like any
thing when he fealls
like it we like him
very much
dec 6 1906

how a man found out what
was a mama and papa deer,
a man had to deer one gave
milk and the

58

the man who made some people
amortol.
there was once a man who
thought pilles and pilles
and he was a great inventer
and at last he thought
how can i make people
live for ever he thought
about it and tried and
at last he got to or three
done and they were great
inventers too and it lasted
people called them angels
and the men that were
imortals were called gods
and some beleave that
there are and some don't.
dec. 10 1906

59

christmas time poem

the snow is falling in showers
the children are thinking of
christmas,
not a bird to be seen
but the chickedes.
nobody is sleeping for
fear of santa claus.
nobody is out doors for
fear of the cold.
the snow is drifting and
the wind is blowing.
but we are in the house
so warm.

dec 20 1906

60

An April Fool

One april fools day. Papa gave me
an aful fool. He made some paper
flowers when i did not
know it and stuk them up
over acros the road. Then
he said to us let's take
a walk up the berry road.
When we got up to the old
apple tree, i hapened to look
at the botum of the tree and
there were the colored flowers
I went in and picked one and
they come right up out of
the ground with no roots
on. I went home and showed
every body and they all laughd
and said it was an April
fool. Jan 22 1905

The Sun Spots.

You know i wrote right about the northern
lights. Well, papa said that genrely
when the northern lights come
there were spots on the sun. And
what do you supose, when the
next days paper came it said in
it that there were spots on the
sun, and papa said, that was prob
ably why the northern lights had
come. It said in the paper, too, up
in Pitsberg they had a thunder
storm and it rained worms.

It's funny to have a thunder
storm in winter and where could
the worms come from, worms aint
tiny enough to go up into the clouds
like mist.

That day or the next day i don't

62

no which papa and i blackened
a glass and tried to see if we could
see the spots. Papa said he could
not see any, it was a kind of a
cloudy day the little clouds were
passing over it all the time. But
i thought i saw a little black speck
down near the edge on the left
hand side so papa looked again he
could not see anything it was
a little too cloudy. So i went
in and read a little while,
and pretty soon it cleared off
and i looked again and i saw
the same little dot, and i am
quite sure i saw the spot.

Feb 25 1907

a chuchoo traintrain train the
engineers a whiseling he's a whiselin
a tralalalala.

64

The Sliced cow

there was once a cow. She was fed all the
time, everybody tried to make her fat,
but she was just as thin as a thin pease of
board. She would get behind a tree, and
if there was a cut through the trunk
of the tree and _ib_ she heard anything in
front of the tree, slipety slip right
through the tree she would go and horn
them into the air and be back in her
place before they could see what did
it. She had alot of tricks she could
play on them. People laughed at
her when they saw her, and
they said where can the milk
come from they get out ob her i don't
beleave they feed her, _or_ she would
grow fat. This is the way she
looked, ▭ only one horn

no horn on the other side, just one eye, two legs just like people, She wasn't thick enough to have four as cows genraley have, Everybody thought the cow was imortal and somebody had sent him down to do tricks on us.

feb 27 1907

Our Apple Orchard

Apple picking is very nice when it
comes the time to pick them.
I wish i was up in the tree now,
and i feel if i was, if i shut my
hands i feel if their was an apple
in them but if i open them
there's nothing their. But i can
see it in my mind, i can see
papa ᴜᵖ that bigest tree where
we got most of the apples
off of this year, i see him with
the backet the hook backet hung
around the branch of the tree
reching after apples, i see

myself up the little ladder and
every once in a while papa getting

down to move my ladder, my
basket without a hook is
hung by the handle to the
top of the ladder. and their
i am not picking many apples
so afriad i will fall and of
corse papa gets his basket filled
quicker than i do.

march 6 1907

The may Pole Day I made
To day we went out doors, we
walked up the berry road. When
we got up to the little grove
a thought struck me and this is how
i came to have a maypole day.
We got over the fence and went into
the little grove, the grove was all
bare, and we took off our mittens
and lad them on the ground. It
was all quite except some birds
singing and a cool wind that
came from the south west and
every time a gust came we burst
out laughing. We stayed right
where we were a minute or two
then we ran down the hill and
a wind was just coming up
and pretty near blew us across

the pasture we got back and
began to pick flowers. We picked
the old dryed up steeple heads and
the ferns and some of the everlasting till our hands were full. Then
we went up to the top of the hill
and looked down it a few
minutes and listened to the pine
trees whistling and watched
the steeple heads waving at the foot
of the hill and it seemed like
a picture to me. After we had
seen it a minute or two we
got our mittens and put
the flowers about our faces
and started for home every
once in a while bursting out
laughing. When we got home
we all got in a row biside

70

t front room window and
shouted, up the airy mountou,
and papa and mama and marjory
came to the window and after we
were through they all clapped
their hands and we came in.
march 17 1907

(9 Turned 8 on April 28 - 1907)

the deer

One thunder storm we were all in
the front room all but carol and
irma they were out in the shed. i
and papa were at the window
that looks down toward berrys
bars. Papa was just stepping away
from the window, and what
should i happen to see a deer
came out of berrys woods it
went to our fence, i called papa
and mama quick they came
and it jumpt right over the fence
without touching it a bit.
Papa has seen them before
but i haven't, papa has
never seen one come so close
to the house before.
It went down through the

72

garden and over the fence
into ferrys pasture.

july 24 1907

The young marsh hen

Papa was going over to derry
with mr percins, and sunndenly
mr percins said their is a
marsh hen biside the road
papa looked and couldent beleave
it was he thought it was a
stick it was standing so strate
up. But papa got out and picket
it up but sure enough it was
a marsh hen. mr percins put it
in a bag and brout it home to
show to us. It was a baby one, and
it picked at our fingers. mama
thought it was pretty but mr
percins didnt very well, the children
did and i did. mr percins said
he was going to take it home
and show it to his folks and

74

then let it go.

Papa fond a marsh hen in the
bird book, the one in the book
was a full grown one. The full
grown ones arn't as pretty as the
young ones i don't think.
any way i don't think old people
in one way are   as nice as
children are.
july 2 5 1907

Two nights in the woods
First night
When the famley went home and
fogot me i was left in the bushes.
But when she didn't hear us talking or moving she came out and
began to meow. But we didn't
hear her we were allmost home.
Irma and carol and i were
afraid that night about it it rained
so hard. Papa and i were the lest
skared papa thought it would
come home the next morning
by the smell, but it couldn't
come by the smell because the
rain would wash the smell all
away. But i thought it would
get up into a brush pile
and keep out of the rain

76

as much as it could and
could hunt its way home tomorrow
but it didn't.

our kitten

august 2 1907

Two nights I in the woods
I he first night
when the famly went home
and left me in the bushes
I came out and began to
meow, but they didn't hear
me I waited a long time and
a few drops of rain began
to fall and i got worried.
pretty soon it began to rain hard,
I ran around a few minutes
but soon i found out i couldn't
find my way home to night.
so I got in the best sheltered
could and thought of house. I couldn't
sleep much I was so worried. I
caught a squrril and it squeald
so when I caught it that it
made other animals run i

herd them. I wanted to catch
them, but the squrril was trying
to get away so that i couldn't
and they all got away before
i had killed the squrril. That
stopped me worring a little and
i went to sleep a little till morning
and i wanderd around till the next
night, and caught a few squrrils
that day. when the next night
came I began to feel so bad
again and want some fresh milk.
But nobody called. Pretty soon
I heard a noise, at firs
i thought it was somebody
calling but it came again
and louder i said that is none
of my folks. In a few minits
it came again awfull

loud, and it began to rain.
I got into my best shelter and
stayed there all night, but i was
awfull afraid. next morning
it was a good day and i
had a pretty good time that
day. That day half of the
famely come out they went
down, they went down the hill
without thinking about me at
last one of them turnd
around and saw me they
took me home and fed
me and i have been there
ever since.

august 4 1907

80

Our war game

Papa and i have a game
of the civil war, we are in
blue ridge mountaines
where jakson did his famos
fighting, and we have the
shanondoir river. and
we have richmand and
washington, and we have
the rapahanick and the
rapadan and the permonky.
and then we have bridgs.
and then we have rules
about crossing things and fighting.
we have a rule about crossing
moutains and forgls, it takes
three turnes to get across a
mountain or ford. and we
have a rule about fighting

each company that toches the
ather sides companys countes
one because its strongist. and
if i had three toching one
of his i would have more
companys and be the strong-
st. and we have sitys like
warronton manasses culpeper
and fredrickberg chancelevil
and port-republick, and
ether one side on the other
side has four sitys and holds
them or the capitil has won
the game.

aug 6 , 1907

82

about mars

Raha and i make beleave
we can see people on mars,
andchildren and houses
and everything ells on
the earth. we say these things
when we go after the cow
at night, we say we will
no more than the astronom
ers do with tellicopes . we
say o what are those things
climing those trees they
look like snakes but they
must be children. o there
comes a man to tell them
to come down because their
mama said they might
tear their stokings and when

we go in we are interrested
in taulking about mars and
teliscops and things.
                    August 2 1907

84

about mars.

When papa and i were bringing
the cow home last night i looked
up at mars, and there were houses
children and people and every
thing elle on the earth. o,
what are those tlings climbing
those trees they look like
snakes but they must be children
. . o their comes a man to
tell them to come down
{ because their mama says
they might tear there stokings,
and because they were their
best stockings.

August 2 1907

Haying this year.
Haying time we diden't
have such a nice time
as last year. Because the
haying men put on so much
hay that we couldn't ride
in one the shouds. and then
the piles of hay weren't so
hy up and it was too
easy to clime the piles
and they weren't so strat
down and hy so you
could have more room
to climb up and run
down. aug 9 1907

BOOK V

October 16, 1907 to May 25, 1908

(Aet.: 8 years, 5 months to

9 years, 1 month)

FOREWORD TO BOOK V

ANYONE who has just finished reading my fourth notebook, which ends on August 9, 1907, will notice a decided improvement in the spelling and handwriting of the first "story" in Book Five, written on October 16, 1907. It would seem that either my father or mother had found a way to make me take more care. The next few stories contain very few misspelled words and show that I was giving special attention to shaping the letters.

The secret of these changes is revealed at the end of my long account of "Meeting a Fairy," on page 29, where my father wrote, "(Copied)." What seems implied is that I was now being required to write two drafts of each entry, and that the second draft could not be copied into the notebook until my father had spent considerable time going over each first draft with me, to help me correct misspelled words.

He must have relented immediately after I wrote "Meeting a Fairy." The next story, "Bed Time for Me," is better written than anything in my previous notebook, but the mistakes in spelling and in hyphenation seem to imply that this version is the first draft. In fact, at the end of the next story, my father added the notation, "(First draft)." At this phase of my writing, the progress was consequently uneven. In the very next story, "Christmas in the Year of 1907," I have returned to my phonetic spelling: I use "anxures" for "anxious," and "espechily" for "especially," and "pichures" for "pictures." Even so, the leniency of my parents in supervising my work enabled me to enjoy my almost-daily story-writing throughout Book Five.

BOOK V

CONTENTS

The Two Deer in The Corn.

We all were dressing one morning,
and papa was washing the milk pail
by the sink window that looks out
toward the corn. In a few minutes
papa said rather supprisingly what
do-d-isee, then he paused a minute,
and then said, a Deer. a Deer. We
all rushed to the window and
sure enough stood a deer beside the
corn eating grass. We all looked
at it, it was so quiet, and in a
few minutes I said there is another
deer behind the corn. We all looked
closly and yes there was another deer
— They both were faun coler exsept one
was a little bit darker then the other
They slowly walked to the fence

we wanted to see them jump, but
the wire was broken, where they
had come along, so instead of
jumping they went right through
the wire and we didn't see them
jump. They went out into the road
and sniffed around a minute or
two, and then trotted off down the
road. I went down the road. I
went down a few minutes
afterward and saw four of their
foot tracks. I didn't see many
because they didn't show unless
it was in very soft dirt. The
tracks were about as small as a
rats track in snow, though shaped
like a cows foot.

Oct 16 1907.

The woodchuck.

The children and I were walking
out into the orchard trotting
along and talking to each other.
We were sudinly startled by some
gray thing running along in
the grass. It was running
toward us from the old garden
we were scared, bor we didn't
expect it. The children looked at
it with great surprise, and
marjorie was awfully scared.
She was trotting ahead of us
and iff she had taken a step
farther she would have stepped on
it and I could have reached
over and picked it up iff I
had wanted to, but I was too

6

scared.

It went into the black
berry patch and went down
its hole. The woodchuck was more
scared then we were. I don't
see why it came so near us.
I should think it would have
gone out around us, but I
suppose he thought cc I might
as well run as fast as I can
and go strate ahead, because
if I went out around they
might run forward and
catch me, so I might as well
go strate, for that's the way
to my hole anyway, and
then if they catch me it
wont be my foult. cc

we went into to the
black berry patch and found
his hole. It was among the
thickest of the grapes for the
grapes for the grapes were on
both sides of its hole. I thought
he made his hole there on
purpose to make his home
pretty.

Oct 18 1907

8.

Hitting The crow with a Stick.

I was out back of the house
by the fence, and a crow flew out
of the birch tree by the sink window.
It wanted to go across into the
woods right up above where I
was standing. It didn't want
to go out around, and it stood
right still in the air deciding
which way to go. I wanted to get
under the fence, but I was afraid
the crow might fly away while
I was getting under, so I stood
still a minute and watched him.
I had a stick in my hand, and
just for the the fun of it I threw
it up in the air, I didn't expect
it to do anything, but what do

you suppose it did, it went
right into the crow's wings.
It looked so funny, but I
was too surprised to laugh,
but then how quickly he
decided which way to go. For
he went out around as
quickly as he could, and into
the woods.

                Oct 27 1907

10.

The Leaves Coming Down In The Fall.

It was beginning to come fall and
the leaves were slowly coming down on
windy days. After a while it began to
grow colder and colder, and pretty
soon there came an awful windy
day and how the leaves did come
down then. It was a cold and
windy day but sunny and a clear
blue sky. We children dressed up
nice and warm and went out
doors to catch the leaves coming
off the trees. First the wind would
blow hard and then die down.
When it blew hard in gales like
that the leaves would come off
the birch trees back of the
house in swarms, and we

would try to catch them. There
were so many and we wanted
to catch them all at once,
and we got so excited that
we got hardly any. But we
laught and had some fun. most
of the leaves came off the woodpecker tree that day and it
looked as if winter would be here
in a few days.

november 10 1907

12

The Two Loveliest autumn nights.

Last night and night and night before last were the two loveliest nights we ever saw. The moon was all-most a whole moon, and it was just about as light as day. If you wanted to you could take a chair and sit out there and read a book and think it was a hot summer day. It was very still: you couldn't see or hear a leaf move on the oak trees or a twig move on the other trees. It was so lovely we all wanted to go out doors and stay out there all night.

nov. 15 1907

What Happened This Morning.

Carol and I were in the barn
today playing. After a while
carol said, there is a wagon
out in the road. we couldn't
make out what it was. at last
we saw the men feed the
horse and go to the back of
the wagon and get out some
chains and ropes and plenty
of other things I don't know
the name of and sling them
on their backs and go up the
telephone pole. They couldn't have
climbed the pole if they hadn't
had some spikes that were strapped
on their feet to catch onto the

sides of the poles to keep them from slipping. They tightened the wires and changed the inulators that hold the wires. The telephone poles kind of bent when the two men that went up got on one side of the pole on those cross pieces and the cross pieces kind of bent down when the men stood and leaned their weight against them. There were three working men and one to boss them. One of the working men fixed one telephone pole by himself and the other two fixed the other. The boss stayed down on the ground and watched

and told them what to do.

At last they come down
and went up in the ferns to
have a lunch. After they had
there lunch they got in the
wagon and drove away.

novem. 17   1907

18

An Approaching Thunder Storm.
One very hot day in July, it
was clear and pleasant for us
children in the forenoon, but in
the afternoon it began to cloud
up with heavy black clouds
like castles and it looked as
if there was going to be a
thunder storm. We all shouted
and had a good time for we
knew we couldn't go out much
more that day

We frolicked around
out there for quite a while,
as the black clouds came
rolling out of the west.

Then we went out
on the front steps in the

front yard. Just as we got there
down came a shower of rain,
but there was a roof over the
piazza so we didn't get wet.
            Pretty soon mama
came to the window and
told us to go right into
the barn. We hurried as fast
as we could for we were
afraid before that we would
have had to stay there till
it stopped raining.
            The lightning began
to flash and the thunder
to rumble, "for there was
lightning in yon horned moon
and thunder in yon cloud,
but hark the music mariners

20

The Approaching Thunder Storm.
The clouds came rolling out of the west
The edges looked like the ocean shore
The mother bird sat close on her nest
Far off the the thunder began to roar
The yellow lighting shot through the sky
The clouds rolled on and darkend it below
The new green leaves together sigh
The rain fell like pebles very slow.

the wind is piping loud?"

after a while it stopped
raining and the clouds passed
over into the east, but it was
too late to play out any
longer for supper was ready,
and we had to come in.

november 30 1907

22

Meeting A Fairy. — A Story

One day I was walking out into the
woods. Pretty soon I heard a rustle
on the east side of me. I looked
around, not expecting anything,
but what do you suppose I saw? I saw
a little golden dressed fairy; I
was too surprised to move or say
a word. The fairy smiled when she
saw me turn around, but I just
couldn't smile. In a few minutes
the fairy walked up to me, and
asked me where I was going. I
stepped back a minute without
saying a word, and thought it
all over. At last I thought, "well
she smiled at me so sweetly

and asked me where I was going
so sweetly that I guess I will
tell her though there might
be some magic in her kindness
for there is in most fairy's
kindness and unkindness". So I
walked up to her trying hard to
smile, but still kind of timid and
shy, and I said in quite a low
voice, I am going after flowers, golden
dressed fairy of the woods", though
I thought she might turn angry
at that name. The fairy stood
still a minute smileing and
looking at me sweetly though
with a kind of twinkle in her
eye that made me think that
she might turn against me any

24

minute though she wasn't thinking
of that at all. At last she said, "I
will go with you and show you
where there are some lovely flowers.
So we walked off together without
saying a word, and I hung a
little behind, because I thought if
I tried to keep up she might notice
that I was taking long steps and
trying hard to keep up and that
I was too unlike her to walk
with her because I didn't take
such light steps as she did. So
I just hung behind a little and
took my usual steps rather shyly.
After quite a
long time, we came to an open
place in the woods where

it was bright with every kind
of flowers in the world. I was so
surprised that I had been out
to walk in these woods about every
day, and hadn't found this place.
As soon as we got to the edge of
the garden, the fairy looked around
and smiled and said. "There are
all the kinds of flowers here in
the world, but you can only
choose twelve that you like best,
and you can only pick those
and no others. Then she smiled, and
bowed her head and disappeared in
the woods. There were paths in and
out of the garden. I walked through
the garden thrying to choose which
kinds to take. I had just chosen

26

three kinds, when the fairy appeared
again from the same place where
she had disappeared, with a little
golden box in her hand. As soon
as she got close to me she held out
the box and said "I will show
you what's in this when you
have chosen what kinds you
want." I stood still a minute
I was so surprised to see a
real fairy with a gold box in
her hand. But pretty soon I
went to work again, looking
at every flower carfully. After
a long time I went to the fairy
and said "I have finished," and
she said "what are the names
of them" and I said, "there is star

grass and yellow violet and rose
pettled butter cup and ladys slipper
and butter and eggs, and blood
root and rue enemone and wood
enemone and star flower and
bell wort and mountain laurel
and pipsissewa and clintonia and
ladies tresses." Then the fairy looked
at every side of the box, in a
few minites she took the
smoothest side of all and
took a little golden rod out
of a pocket she had in her
dress and touched one side
against the side of the box
and it seemed to me that it
opened it self. Then she took something
bright and shiny out of it it was

28

all made of differant kinds of valbole
things, like pearls and gold and silver
and emeralds and things like
that. It was another littler sqware
box, but it wasn't like the other,
for it was carved all over with
differant calored rings and hos
ses and animals of diffrant kinds on
it. after she had given it to me,
she said "I want you to keep the
for any night I might come and
see if you had kept it". Then she smiled
and said good by and before I ha
time to say good by she had
disappeared in the woods. I stood
still a minute thinking about it
and looking at the present she
had given me. Pretty soon I

walked along home, but I didn't
tell my papa and mama that
I had seen a fairy I just
showed them a present and
when cristmas time came
I told them about the fairy
and the garden and the thing
s I saw.

(Copied.)   Dec 14 1907

30

Bed Time For me

Last night there was a graet
snow storm outside, but insi
it was nice and cosy. It was
my bedtime, but I didn't wan
to go to bed because you
could here the wind outside
whistling arönd the corner of
the house and coming in
every crack in the windows
and the fine sharp flakes bang
ing against the window pane
and then I was such a bad
dreamer that I was afraid
I might dream that thousa
nds of little men were break
ing in to carry me off but
I was tired and I didn't think

31

much about it. After I got to
bed I stayed awake and thoug
ht a little about how deep it
might be in the morning and
I guesst it would be ten
inches deep and I guesst
just right. Once or twice
I heard a block of soft
snow blow against the
window, but I soon fell
asleep and didn't dream
nor think any more
about it.

Dec 15 1907.

32

Making Blocks Of Marble Out Of Snow.

Day before yesterday there was a pile of snow on the ground for it had snowed the day before very hard and it was deep. Papa hadn't shouveled any paths. After he milked the cow, mama wanted a pail of water, but papa couldn't get it unless he shouveled a path clear down to the pump. After he got the water pail and laid it on the piazza, he went in the barn and got the shouvel and begon shouveling, but he didn't hurry and make

the path, just the width of the shouvel,
he made it three times the
width of the shouvel, this
is the way he cut it [□], he
took the squarse out and that
showed the bare ground, he made
it this way clear down
to the pump. When he took
the squars out he didnt
break them, he piled them up
against the piazza and under
one of the kichen windows, he piled
them every which way, side
ways and upside down and
the right way and it looked
very pretty, it looked like
blocks of marble, mama wanted
to see how long they'd stay

34

square, but yesterday they melted
some and today they weren't
square, but round, and they only
at all
lasted two days

(First draft.)   Dec 18 1907

Cristmas dn The year of 1907.

This year all the children were anxures to know what they were going to have for Cristmas, espechily drma. Every time mr. Pirkins came into the yard drma would ask mama what he had brought us for Cristmas, but mama wouldn't tell. When Cristmas night came we children

hung up our stockings and went to bed. we were expecting santa claus to come in the front room that night and give us things. We went

36

to sleep as quick as we could.

The next morning we woke up early to see what we had for Cristmas, but mama wouldn't let us go down untill the sun came up. When we came down stairs we ran to the kicken door to go out and dress. As soon as we got out there we found that santa claus had come out there instead of in the front room. After we had looked at all the things there was a rocking chair and doll and a dog with a little bell tied around his neck and pichures for drma, and there was a train

of cars and and a pig and a
pig's trogh and a pig pen
and a little boat and a ball
and some pichures for Carol
and a ball and a doll and
a rocking chair and a kitty
and some pichures for
marjorie and some domin-
os and some dice and a
ruler and a little tracing
and drawing book and two
dolls and a robbit for
me, and there was a black-
board and some candy for
all of us together. After
we had looked at them all
a minute we dressed and
ate breakfast and had a

38

happy time all day playing
with are toys. That night
papa played dominos with
me and Carol, then we had
supper and went to bed very
happy.

Dec 29 1907

(First Draft)

The Sun Comming up.

There is a little hill just in
front of our house, we call it
cline's hill, it isn't our land, we
keep saying we are going to name
our farm liswyn farm but
we never have.

One morning
we came down very early,
the sun had not come up
yet, in december it peeks over
cline's hill at about twenty
five minutes past seven in
the morning. It was kind of
a windy day and there were
small clouds flouting over
cline's hill, the sun was just
getting ready to come up

40.

from behind the hill, its light
shot up into the sky and made
the clouds look awful pink and
pretty at once or we would see
a long thin cloud all solid red
gold color from top to bottom.
As soon as we children got dressed we ran to the window
to watch the sun come up.
We waited a few minutes and
then we began to see the least
least little bit of it over the hill
about like this ⌒ and then
we all jumped up and down
and clapped our hands, if
we looked very closly we
could see the sun move up
as the earth moved around

it, the sun doesn't move but
it looks as if the sun moves
as the the earth moves around
it. If clines hill didn't have
so many stones and and
fern bushes on it but had
a few more big trees on
it it would look a good deal
prettier when the sun shone
on it but now it looks
rough and bare.

jan. 6 1908

42

The End Of The Ice World.

There was once a big
ice world, and I was one of the
people on it. But one day I was
out on the ice, and I saw great
long cracks spreading out from
under my feet, I stood still a minute,
and then the ice all over the
world began sinking down. It
sunk and sunk, till pretty
soon it came to a great round
open place, and then everything
began to whiz through open air,
After a while we came bump onto
a smaller and slipperer ice
world, it was so slippery that
we couldn't bild houses on
it so we all took hammers

and began to hammer the
ice with all our strength,
every once in a while almost
slipping off. After we had hammered about three hours or more
we began to sink down again.
After traveling for about
twenty or thirty meters we
came to a little ellipes all redish
brown color and shaped like the core of an onion. There
and red hot
were lots of pieces of ice floating about in open air with
people on them. There was one
little piece of ice with only
one man on it, and he
threw a rope that he had
around that little ellipes
and drew himself up to that

44

ellipes, but when he got there
the ice that he was on melted
and he went right down as far
as the rope would let him. we
all had watched him and we
all did the same thing forwe
wanted to see what would happen
after we all were hanging down
we looked up and the ropes were
all on fire, we didn't know
whether to let go or hold on
but we decided to let go so
we all let go at once and
went down down down for
a long way. But the ice that
we had fallen through first
had closed up so we didn't
go to nowhere. One day when

we had got all settled down
and wern't thinking of anything to happen that little
ellipes fell down ~~and melted~~
~~all the is~~ and melted all
the ice we were living on
and burnt all of us and
our houses in a second
till there was nothing
left.

     jan. 16 1908

46

How Four Children got Scared On The Ice

One day four children named marjorie and drma and carol and Lesley, (besley is the one that is writing this story) well these children were out on the cranberry bog that is near our house sliding around without skates. We were having a good time on the side nearest our house, but on the other side it wouldn't hold you. We were having a good time but every once in a while hearing a little noise over on the other side, but at first we didn't take any notice of it, we thought it was a

rotten branch breaking or a
rotten tree falling, but pretty
soon they came so often that
we looked up and listened, but
we couldn't see anything so
we went on sliding again. After
two or three days we came
out again, and we were sliding
around there When we heard
an awfull noise and we all
gave a jump and ran to
the shore where we always
got on and off and ran
for home. That was four day
s ago; but today I got up
courage enough to go out there
again, but still we heard
that sound, but this time

48

I made up my mind that
I would find out what it
was, so I walked over to where
we heard it from, and wasen't
I surprised that it was only
that thin crackilty ice that
kept falling through and made
that noise.

jan 23 1908

What The Telephone Buzzed

One day I was out stroling
about up and down the road,
thinking. Pretty soon, after
I got through thinking
about that, I looked around
for something else to think
about. I had not looked long before
I heard the buzzing in the
telephone pole, and I thought
just for the fun of it I would
go in the bushes and listen
to the buzzing a minute, so
I stept into the bushes and
put my ear to the telephone
pole and I began to think what
that buzzing ment, I thought
a minute, and then said

50

its saying that we are going
to have a war with japan
in three weeks, this mesege has
come from the ship connecticutt
from california, they have just
arived at at the mouth of the
river sacramento and one of
the ships has gone in that
river to tell the capital of
california so tell all the
trains to come as fast as
they can and not take
any passangers but pile on
all wood and coal you can
on your way down that's all.
                    when I heard
this I ran   home to papa
and mama about it for

I knew that we couldn't
get enough battle ships and
coal and wood   in ordor
while they were fighting
for we wern't in fighting
ordor at all and we all
were very much excited.

                    Jan 24 1908

52

going To Church.

yesterday I went to church
the first time. mama and I
walked over. As soon as we got
allmost to the church, I was
kind of afraid to go in. for
I had never been before. When
we got there we had to go
through a hall and an outher
little room before we got to
where the church was going
on. we got there just when
mr. mariam was coming in.
When we got into the room
all the seats were full in
the back part. We had got
in there just in time for
the begining. We sat in the

seat with mrs. mariam. It
was very pretty bor^{it}, had not
been changed since cristmas
There were three big pine trees
on each side of the plateform
where mr. mariam stood
and there were pine bran
ches on the plateform.
        The first thing
we did was to have all
in church stand up and
sing something out of the
bible all at once, but
mama and I didnt
sing. Then we had the
prayer and o how tired I
got. I allmost wished I
hadn't come and when he

54

stopped
how glad I was. After that
we sang a few more things
till church was done. After
church was done mama
spoke to mrs. mariam a
minute and then we went
home.

jan 27 1908

The Snow storm

About every day a long
long ring. rings on the telephone and if you want to hear
what the wether is going
to be just go and listen. Friday. the wetherreport said
that " it was going to be
warmer and rain in the
afternoon saterday ".

Well she didn't get
it acxactly right for it began
the next morning and instead of raining it it snowed
terribly. It came on harder
and harder every few minuts but
it didn't snow long enough
to get very deep. Once in

56

a while when it was snowing
you couldn't see the woods
over past Mr. Sows house
the snow was so thick. The
snow blew around the house
like a hurrakane and when
carol and'd went out to
get some wood in so it
wouldn't get covered up with
snow it almost took our breath
away.

  Right in the midst
of the storm willy white came
with some wood for us. His
face was all red with cold
for the snow had been coming right
toward his face. Papa was
sorry to have him stay.

Willy white ?

out all alone and in cold, but
papa was just on the edge of
catching cold so he didn't go
out. we watched willy white
take the wood off as much
as we could from the window,
but every time mama saw
us she told us to go away
from the window for we
might catch cold. when willy
white got through he took
the broom and swept off
his wagon and then
went home.

just before dinner
there was a little hail storm
and after dinner as the
wether report had said, it

58

rained, though it didn't rain
as hard as it had snowed. We
all were glad it had come to
rain for we hoped it would
rain long enough to take the
snow away. It didn't take
it all away, but it took
some.

     This winter it has
been very warm and rainy and
here it is the first of februa
ry and there hasn't been but two
very small snowstorms
yet. Mama said that this was
the storm in the middle when
it was going to change into
snow and grow cold.

The Old Stove

There is an old stove that we have. It is very old and worn out ~~and~~ and rickity, but it is the best stove for ~~war~~ warmth that we have got. It isn't a very high stove, for it isn't as high as any of us children when we stand beside it. We think it is   very pretty for it has little carvings all over it like little chains and wreaths of leaves and things. The chimny is all tippity and rusty it's so old, but we don't care so long as it keeps us nice and warm in the evenings.

Papa used to (when we had the stove in the front room) to light the fires at an

60

open draft in front and when
papa went out to get some wood
with the lamp and left me
in the dark I used to sit on
the floor by the draft and
watch the flame witch almost lit
up the room as much as a
lamp and it seemed so nice, I
would have liked to stay there all
night if only the fire would stay that way.

feb   14   1908

Climbing a Tree.

The trees that I like to climb best are two of those down the stone steps. One is a gravenstine tree and the other is a boldren tree. I like to climb them because they are very low trunked trees and I can climb them easly. Both of them have nice seats in them to sit in, in summer, but not in winter because it is too cold, but when the snow isn't too deep I go down and climb them once in a while. The branches are so near together in one of them that I can climb it awful fast and go clear to the top of it, but it makes me feel trembly.

62

        One thing in the climbing tree business that stops us from climbing the trees as much as we would like to, is that mama won't let us climb them only once in a while for it tears our stockings and she hates to mend them and that almost makes us cry sometimes. The one that she lets us climb the most is on the right hand side (down the stone steps as you go down) for it has got such a small trunk and you don't have to pull yourself up and tear your clothes. She always scolds us if we come in with a hole in some new stocking that she has just put on as we do alot in summer for we climb trees alot then.

My faverit reson for
climbing trees is to go up and look
into old birds nests in winter and
in summer is to take a book and
sit. in one of my old seats in
the trees and read till I get
tired. Why I like to climb the
trees and look into the old birds
nests is not because I expect to
find bird's eggs, because I surly
wouldn't find any, its because
I want to find out how they
make their nests, for if I do
find out how they do it, I will
make an april fool to the birds
by making a nest and puting
in some hens eggs and puting

64

it on a tree; and if a bird came
to sit on it wouldn't she be surp
rised when she saw the little
chickens runing about, for baby
birds can't run nor walk when
they are young and the chickens woud
nt be the same color and that
would fool her awfully.

My next reson
for climbing trees is as I have
told you is to read a book and
why I like to is because its a
change from sitting in a chair
all the time. When I don't read
I sit there and try and think
out what the birds are trying
to say as they fly all around
me. These are my two best resons

for climbing trees.

march 2. 1908

66

A Mussed Up Room

More than once a day the room gets into a terrible mess, for there are so many playthings, and so when the room gets so thick with them that there isn't any more room to play, then we begin to ask to go out doors, but mama never lets us till we have cleaned it all up. After that we go out doors and stay thirty minutes and then in we come again and out come all the playthings again, as usual. First out come the loud noises and then the trains and blocks and black-board and all the other playthings, and before night the room is all in a mess again. We have so many

playthings it would cover the floor
of two of these rooms put together,
and the noise is enough to fill
two houses, it is just like a steam
engine.

march 3 1908

68

The Phoebe

The birds came rather early this
year. The blue birds and robins
began to come before the middle
of march, and after that the song sparrow
and now the phoebe has, just day before
yesterday.   The day before day before
yesterday papa and I were on our
way to derry, and we heard some
birds in the woods saying phoebe.
I thourght that the phoebes had come,
but papa said "he could hear
chickidees among them and sometimes the chickidees say phoebe
so probobly they all are chickidees",
but it would have been just as
surpriseing if they had come
then for they came the very

next day and were singing
on the maples and bobing their
little tails up and down like a
fan.

The phoebes color is a rather
black on top, but there is a little
brown topnot on his head. He is
pretty, but not half as pretty
as the blue-bird nor the the robin
nor any other bird.   He is
cuter in habits and interesting
in his ways. I always like to
look at his topnot which
gives a sassy little nod once in
a while. His breast is white — here
he is now out on the maple tree
in front of the house singing,
bobing his little tail as happy

7°

as can be.

I like to watch the phoebe
build his nest. He builds it mostly with clay and hardened mud
and then he puts hairs and grass
inside to make it soft and warm
for the yong ones. When mama cuts
our hair we take it, after she cuts
it off, and throw it
over the grape vine for the birds
to use for their nests to make them
soft. I have only seen the phoebe
build his nest twice for he uses
the same nest about every year, but
its under the barn and no snow
or rain gets in it while he has
gone south.

If only the phoebes weren't

quite so timid and the nest was
a little lower down   I would
go and watch them all day.
I haven't seen the young ones
but once and I want to see
them again before they leave
here if they ever do and I
supose they will.

It is very puzzil-
ing to know whether it is the same
phoebe or not that comes here
every year.   He looks just
as yong as when he first started
to come and just as lively too. I
shall watch every year to see if
he comes and if he comes for
four or five more years
I will think he is imortal.

march 30 1908

72

Going Checkerberrying.

We children like to go checkeberring
more than any thing else, in the spring
          though that isn't the time when
most children go getting checkerberrys
in the fields. We go out about every day
that's good, and get half a mitten
full if we don't wander away to play
something else, but we genraly do
not.

          Every morning early after
breakfast as soon as our faces and
hands are washed and our hairs
combed, we get our things right on
and go along out in the yard to
play. Then when we get tired of
playing there we go over across
the road to play on the bars

that lead into the pasture; but
soon we wanted to do something else
and "sombody asks "what shall we play
now", and then some one else says
" let's go get a few checkerberrys in
the field", so away we go down the
hill as fast as we can go with
marjorie way behind, saying " wait
for me   wait for me", but at
last we get there and jump across
a little rill bubles down the
hill. we jump over this and soon
are picking the berrys that cover
more than half the field.
              There are a few
right near the gate as you go
in, but not many, we skipp over
the little that there are, and

74

pick them. Then we go across
the field where there are more
though not so terribaly much. We
pick about half a mitten full
and then get tired of it and
go home to give them to
mama, but sometimes she comes with
us.   March 31 1908

Will And joe go Afishing.

Two boys had thought they would go fishing the next day. They promised to start early in the morning after breakfast. There names were Will and joe. will was the one that thought of going fishing first. They were both neighbors and lived a few miles away from eachother. The next morning after breakfast as they promised they began to get ready. After they were done they walked down the road and met eachother at some corner. Then they walked down to the edge of the water and hired a boat and rowed out on the lake.

After they had

76

got
away out on the middle of the
lake they began to put the bait on
their fishing lines to catch the
fish. Then they threw the hooks into
the water. The fish would gather
around the bait but would not
dare to bite.   Some times they
would nibble a little at it and
sometimes would bite. They laughed and had a jolly time all the
forenoon.

                    In the afternoon
they sailed to a little island
to eat their lunch. They stayed
    there about five hours and they
built a bonfire on the beach to
cook some fish on for lunch. They
sat there and had a very pleasant

time till five oclock.

When they got ready
to go home they had only fourte-
en sunfish left. It was very
pleasant there and they would
have liked to stay a while longer, but
it was getting late and they
thought they would start homeward,
for they were satisfied with what they
had got. When they came to the
place where they had met they
departed and said good by. After
supper they felt very tired, but thou
ght they might like to go again.

April 6 1908

journeys On The Farm

Our farm has interesting places to travel
to, just like the world, though you
do not have to journy so far as
in the world. We go to some place
almost every day that it is good
enough to go and that is only
when it is nice, but when it snows
we sometimes dress up and go
tramping out to the gate.
When it shines we go
everywhere on our farm
though we have been there
a hundred times.
farm though we have been
there a hundred times.

The alders is one
of my favorit places to go, becau-

se it reminds me of the brook
that said "I sparkle out among
the fern to bicker down the
vally," and the brook out there
is just like it, though there isn't
any fern, but it sparkles out
among the woods to bicker down
the vally. The next best journy
I like is going over in the grove.
That doesn't remind me of
anything, but it is best to
play in. You can make little
houses and everything with
the sticks and pine needles
that are over there and we
go there very often, but we
only go out in the alders
once in three or four days.

80

The big pasture
is my next favorite place to
go to, because there is a little round
grove out there of about six trees
and they all touch together at the
top and make a lovely shade to
sit under as soon as it is warm
enough ⚓ and it is very comefor
table. After the big pasture the field
over across the road is next
best. That is noted for its checkerberrys. we go there almost
every day to get checkerberrys
or checkerberry leaves what
ever we find there both just
as good to us. All these places
that I am speaking of we
travel to about every day

and play in each one half an
hour and play that half an
hour is half a year at some
far off place in the world.

              april 9 1908

82

An Imagination

Papa once made up a story,
about being seronded by birch trees
and that makes us imagine that
the birch trees were after us sometimes.
Yesterday we really thought a birch
tree was after us, any way Irma
and carol did, so I pretended I
thought it, but really it wasn't. And
so I will begin the story about
this imagination thing.

Well, in the afternoon
mama brought us out two
cookies apiece and we thought
we would walk up the berry road
to eat them. We started off,
but when we got to the road
we began to think about that

story papa told us once and
to look around to see if we saw
any trees after us.

Then we walked on talking
to each other looking back once in
a while, to see if anyone
was after us, but there
wasn't. The last time we looked back I saw a birch tree
down in the field behind the
house. It was the only one I could
see and it looked as if it was
in the field. The wind
blew it back and forth and
made it look as if it was walking
but of course I knew it
wasn't . I showed it
to the children and they said

84

"let's run home" so we went to
eat our cookies on the piazza
After that we went in the house
but we didn't tell mama. We
kept it a secret till now.

march 11 1908

The yellow violet.
Down below the hill,
Down in the medow,
By the little rill.
A little flower doth grow.
Its color is yellow,
It is it is a violet.
Sometimes, there, I go.

To The Pines
O pines along the river,
How much you seem to difer
From any other pretty pine
Along the long long river rhine
Art thou far from Berlin.
Art thou as old as merlin
Then if you are, live longer,
And beat old magic merlin.

86

My Favorite Books.

In the biggest bookcase in the front room there are a hundred and twenty five books, and there are only six _{that} I read out of. First there is Tennyson's book. Then next mathewarnold and then coldridge's poems and next palgraves golden treasury _{and} then the golden treasury of songs and lyrics, and last of all jean ingalow's poems. So now I will tell you why I like each one. Why I like Tennyson is because all his poems were about things that happened long long time ago, and he made up lovely pictures of castls and old ruins that were made long time ago

x kind of = somewhat
Why ~~I like~~ is because =
I like — because

and then told about the kings
that lived in them. my favorite
one is king ärther now, but
of course I havn't read them
all yet. Still, I am pretty
sure that will be my best.

Some day I will
tell you more about Tennyson,
but if I tell you all I think
about him when I have got
all the others to think
about, it would be terribally
long. So this is enough about
Tennyson. Now ~~why~~ I like Mathewarnold ~~is~~ because he is rather loud
sounding ~~kind of~~ and it is
always about some trouble and
that makes you crazy to hear

88

the end to see whether it is
going to come out all right
or not. I have only read
two of his and they both came
out sadly, but still they they
are aufull interesting so I
will remember him while I
go on with the others.
Now as I
have said that Coldridge came
next, I have only read one
of his, but that is a trouble
too, but his is a differant kind
of trouble, for this is because
somebody did something wrong
and that made them have trouble, its
name is the anceint mariner, the
name doesn't sound as if

there was trouble in it. His
isn't so sad as mathewarnolds
are, but it ends up by killing
and unpleasent things.
After these
three comes palgraves golden
treasury. That is not quite so
interesting excpt it has the
out law in it and that
is interesting, but there is nothing else so atentive as that.
Now comes the
other golden treasury that
I spoke of on the first page.
My two favorite in that book
are the laddins lamp and
the raven. I like those because
they are rather old fashened.

90

and interresting. the laddens
lamp I think is the best, it
is so imaginative and pretty.
now last of
all comes jean ingolour. I like
her just about as well as the
golden treasury, of songs and
lirycs and someday I think
I will put her in the place
where palgraves golden treasury is and put the palgrave one
at the last.

April 15 1908.

Tapping For Syrup

One day we got papa to tap the woodpecker-tree. He bored a round hole in it and hammered a piece of a little tin can into the tree, just below the hole and put in a screw above the hole to put the pail on. He hung up the pail and we watched it drip for a few days.

The first run we drank what there was. That didn't have much tast to it, though we liked it. Now we woke one morning and had breakfast. After that the children went out

92

and came in yelling, that the
maple syrup jug was full of
syrup, I came out and they
were surely right, so I brought it
in and mama said she would
boil it by and by, but it had
a funny pink color and just
as papa laid it on the shelf
I remembered that it had
rained last night and that
all we had was rain and then
we had to throw it away.
After that we put it out again
and got about half a jug full.
We boiled this and we
had a tast of our own syrup
about two tasts apiece and
we were going to get some

more, but the buds came out
on the tree and held the
sap so we didn't get any
more.

April 20 1908

94

Going To The Mountain

Next summer we are going
to the white mountains again. It
will be nice to see the blue high
mountains and the white clouds
sailing above them almost
touching the tips. Papa and I
think we will walk to the top
of mount laffiet next summer,
and look off at the mountains.
We all enjoy the ride on the
train very much, but marjorie
jenraly goes to sleep in mama's
lap on the way. After we get up
there we will be glad to see
misses linch because we
know her so well and she
will be glad to see the children

espeshily drma who is a
little irish herself. After this
we like to take walks. I will
want to walk down to Franconia vally and the children
will want to take any little
walks around in the fields
in front of the house and
behind the house. I always
like to go down in Franconia vally, because papa always
buys some peanuts or candy
for us, and I like to go down
there because I think   the
gale river is pretty going right throu
gh the middle of Franconia
vally. All this is very pretty, but
when it gets time to go

96

home we will be just as
glad to go home as we were
to go up there, for we were
last year I remember.

april 21 1908

Shapes At Night.

In summer we have to
go to bed when it is light,
and I ly on my back and
think till it gets dark. Sometimes I watch the furniture change into diferent kinds of figures as it grows darker. I
remember once when I
slept down stairs in the
front room we had a tall
coal stove then and it was
shapet something like a man
but with no   arms. well,
I woke up one night and
saw that in the dark and
it scared me aufuly so I

98

hid my face in the pillow,
but it is nice to see the
figures on the wall paper
fade away as the light gets
dimmer. Flowers have figures
too, but pretty ones. Many
times I wake up and
think the buero is a big
giant in the room, but soon
faget it by thinking of so
mething else. You watch
these things fade away till
you are sleepy and then
turn on your side and
go to sleep.   May 1 1908

Wishing For Cowslips

This is the time for cowslips
and we children go out to hunt
for them. Sometimes as we go along
the brooks looking for them (those are the places
we find them mostly) we see a bunch
of them on the otherside of the brook
or ditch. We can't get them, but
sometimes I can jump across the
ditch and get a bunch, if the ditch
isn't too wide or too full of water.
It makes you discuriged when
you look across a brook and see
some and can't get them. When
you are hunting for them and
when your not that always
happens and when you try
you get your feet wet in

100

mud or something. Irma is the
one that always wants me to
get them most and tries to
think out some way to get across,
but it genraly proves unsucsesfull.

May 11 1908

The Hobble Bush
*   The flower is white and
is in a big round bunch.
The outside flowers don't have
any fruit on, but they blossom
first, it is what they call sterile.
when the outside ones don't
have fruit and the inside ones do.

The Hobble Bush.

One day papa set out to find things to put in our park named falls bridge. We had gone a long way

and we had found lots of new flowers that we had not seen this spring yet, such as dandilions and sacsafradge and shad bush and cowslips, but, after we got past the corner where _the bloodroot grows_ we found some- thing new that we had never seen before. It's name was hobble bush and it ~~has~~ only had one flower on, but that was a surprise, for even papa had never seen it. *Papa dug it

102

up and rapped it in moss. Then
he said we better go right home
and plant it in our park for
he didn't want to have it
die. After we got home we planted
the things we were going
to plant here. Then we took
the hobble bush and some other
things out in our alders to
plant. We planted the hobble
bush first, because it looked
a little withered and papa
was a ~~little~~ afraid it was
going to die, too. Now it
      looks better, though and we are sure
it is going to live. So this
is the end of one of our plant
exploits. May 13 1908

Going To Get Violets.

I felt like going to walk
this morning, so I thought
I would go and get a boqeu
of violets. It was kind
of cloudy then and a few
drops of rain coming down,
but just the same the children
bothered me worse than I was
afraid so I thought I would go
alone. I started off and didn't
feel afraid till I got there, but
then I thought I heard someone
chopping and that made me
begin to feel more scared than
before though I didn't want
to go home without any
violets so I went on and jumped

104

across the little brook. When
I got across I went over
into a littl field where there
were lots of them and began
picking ~~them~~, every minute
feeling more afraid till at
last I was so scared I
didn't dare to move for
fear something might jump
on me. There was a wood-
chuck hole right near me
and I thought it was a fox
hole and that the fox might
come out and bite me. After
I had got quite a handfull
I jumped up and scooted
for home. When I got to the
turn that goes toward home

I didn't feel so scared, and
went into the bushes a little
way and found the colum-
bine clear out and that
was a very new flower. Then
I went down in the
woods further and found
the rodora and that is new
too but I have found three
more new flowers besides those
today. Mama likes the rodora best.

May 20   1908

Rhodora

106

Finding Papa's Cap. — A Story with a Plot

Yesterday we were moving some chairs and tables out of our bedroom. We had started late in the afternoon and it began to get dark before we had moved them all, so papa thought we better leave them till morning, for he had to go out and get the cow. He went to the place where he hung his cap, but it wasn't there and then he turned around and said, "Why, that is funny I am sure I laid it down somewhere down stairs, for I had it on only a few minutes ago." Then we all took to hunting for it down stairs, because papa was sure it

wasn't up stairs. We hunted
till seven o'clock and it was
quater past six when we started and then we got so tired
of it we had to let the cow
stay out over night though we
hadn't had any supper. We had
to have bread and butter and
cocoa with no milk in it and
mama and papa and grand-
pa had bread dipped in tea
with no milk in it. After that
we went to bed. We still
could see the strange figures
of furniture in the room. They
all looked like men, one paticul-
arly. It had a dark thing on
the top of it. I didn't take

108

much notice of it. I thought
it was something laid on
there. In the morning I
thought of it again and I
looked at the place where I
had seen it and what do
you suppose it was. It was
papa's cap he had laid it on
there and had fogotten it so
we had done all that hunting
for nothing

May 21 1908

A Cross Road.

Papa and I went to walk last night and came to a cross road, which took us right out by the clarks and was shorter than the other way and any way I wanted to go very much. Cross roads are always pretty and this one was very pretty, even prettier than the berry road, but the berry road comes next I gues.

As we went along we saw a very pretty place for a house, that had a fine view of the mountains and if it had only been a nice night we might have seen a lovely sunset; but it was so foggy and misty

110

you could hardly see the mountains.
There was a fine view of derry
too and we looked around at
the mountains
the ∧ and sat on the stone wall
for a little while and then
went on.

        At last we came
to a little hill where the road
turned and you could look
down a long lane as strait
as an arrow with two long
grass ridges that went along
in the middle and I could
see the main road that goes
past clarks way down at the
end of the lane. We went
along talking with all different
kinds of trees on both sides.

of us and all most tucking
at the top it was
like a tunnel. at last
we came out on the other
road and went along
home to tell mama what we saw.

May 23 1908

112

The Atic

It is very interesting
to go up in the atic and
see all the old things that
have been thrown away.
Old pictures that were pretty,
but were so old and dirty
that
  we couldn't use them any
more, but somehow they wern't
too dirty for us and we would
be glad to take some of the
old things down to play with
if mama would let us. Ever-
y time we go up there we
get a look at some new
thing and still we haven't
seen them all yet, All the
things are as new as something

just bought from the store all
shiny and new, to us, for
most of them we have never
seen before, because mama and
papa and other of there relations
                    the other children
had them before I or, were born
so that makes them very interesting.

            may 25 1908

114

The Swallows Home

From behind the hill, the sun doth come
And the bumble bees begin to hum.
While as it slowly peeps over the hill,
And shines upon the old aged mill
The swallows come out and twirl all day
And rise and fall and circle and play.
But when the sun goes down they stop.
They fly far up to their nests in the top
Of the long long roof of the old old mill.

BOOK VI

June 8, 1908 to August 1909

(Aet.: 9 years, 1 month to

10 years, 4 months)

FOREWORD TO BOOK VI

THERE are several experiments, in Book Six, which again remind me of my father's beliefs concerning "the sound of sense" — and of his saying this in 1929:

"A dramatic necessity goes deep into the nature of the sentence. Sentences are not different enough to hold the attention unless they are dramatic. No ingenuity of varying structures will do. All that can save them is the speaking tone of voice somehow entangled in the words and fastened to the page for the ear of the imagination. That is all that can save poetry from sing-song, all that can save prose from itself."

If my father did start me off by encouraging me to write my stories as if I were saying them, that would have been a first step in teaching me to understand what he later meant by "dramatic necessity." He seems to have helped me take another step in January of 1907. On page 63 of Book Three, a notation in his handwriting suggests that he was asking me to try my hand at dialogue. I did try, in the very next story, and I kept trying intermittently thereafter. But here, in Book Six, on page 21, he must have encouraged a step so advanced that I cast dialogue in a formal dramatic arrangement:

Irma. Say, Carol, those apples are ripe. Let's eat some.

Carol. O no. They will make us sick. . . .

A few pages later, on pages 26–28, is a little one-act play entitled "Waking Carol Up," complete with at least one stage-direction. These two experiments seem to have been enough for me. But the stories which follow contain signs that my father had actually succeeded in showing me how to get the speaking tones of voice entangled in the words and fastened to the page for the ear of the imagination.

BOOK VI

CONTENTS

The Pogonias.

Some time in June the cranberry bog is all spotted over with little pink flowers named pogonias. They have a long strait stem with the leaves up on the sides of it. Poeple sometims call it snake-mouth pogonia, because it has a tongue just like a snakes. They are awful pretty pink and papa's going to move some over into our alders. They will grow there, he thinks because he has got a big round wet peace where they can begin to grow. The cranberry is the only

2

place they grow in any where
around here and we are
glad it is so near the house,
but then it isn't very near
We have been waiting for them
to show, but neither buds nor
flower appear yet and here it
is the 8 of June and they gener
ally are in blossom by this time. The
June bugs come in in June and
so do the pogonias and they are
about the same color too. Tomorrow I am going out and
see if the pogonias have started.

June 8 1908

The Three Snow Sisters.

Once upon a time there
lived three snow sisters with eyes
made of ice. They always stayed
near eachother so they would
be strong if they had a
fight with any giant or
any of the immortals. They
liked eachother very much
and never fought nor quar-
reled between themselves, but
generaly killed any one else
that came near them.

They lived in the
cold north up near the north
pole and they had three big
iceburgs to sit on and three
long sheets of ice for clubs and

4

they ate
whales and seals and all
kinds of fish they could
~~finds of fish could~~ find and
shared it among them. They
~~never~~ each tried to have the
most, but each had the same
every meal, for they either
had five seals apiece or
a whale apiece.

Once they only
caught one whale for dinner
in a whole fornoon and
they didn't know how to
devide it for they had ~~not~~ never had
~~to devide it that way~~ to before
so they began to quarrel, ~~though~~ for the first
they ~~had never~~ never ~~disagreed~~
~~before~~. After they had fought ~~a~~

all the afternoon, they got
so hungry they agreed
to take big bites out of
the whale, but one of
them picked up the whale
and slung it with all
her force back into the
sea. when they got ready
to eat they looked for
the whale and couldn't find
it, but thinking the whale
might ~~half~~ alive and ~~had~~ have
crept off while they were
fighting, they took up their
nets and began fishing and
had better luck.

June 3 1908

6

The Big Black Thing.

Tuesday when papa was at
scool, we children heard an
awfull noise down the road. we
went on playing thinking it
was an automobile. after fifteen
minuts had gone by we thought,
why doesn't it come. So we went
into the middle of the road to look, we
couldn't see any thing, but
at last we saw a big black
thing come up over the hill. Carol
thought it was a dragon and
I thought it was a train
and Irma ran for the house
and Marjorie began to cry.
when it got just where we could
see half of it, it stopped

8

while we stood there in the
middle of the road trying to
make out what it was. at last
we went into the bedroom and
looked out the window and
grandpa went out. When
marjorie saw him she began
to cry, "That terrible thing
will run over grandpa". After
a while it started again
and at last got up here.
It stopped here a long time
and what do you suppose it
was. It was just a big steam
roller that they make streets
with.

June 14 1907

9

What I Prophecied

Saterday, evening papa and I
were going to the village. We had
to go to derry village first to
see mr. mariam a minute and
then go to West derry.   When
we were eating supper I proph-
ecied that papa would at last
find out that he had stayed
too long at mr mariam's and would
we to
hurry away, but then he would
get to talking with sombody
on the street and begin to walk
slow so he wouldn't get home till about ten.
now what do you suppose happen
ened? He did stay too long there, He
stayed till nine aclock when he
ought to stay just till half past

10

seven and he did get to
talking with sombody on the
street who walked clear to
websters with us and walked
so slow that we didn't get
home till it was past ten.
now wasn't that a good proph
esy.

June 14 1908.

The Clemetis

Right below the stone steps
we have a white clemitis. It
blosoms every year, but just after
we get up in the mountains so
that we have never seen the
flower at all, for it is faded
when we get home. Papa has seen
the flower before many times.
It is an awful pretty white
flower. Our vine was completly
covered with them, for we could
see where the flowers had been,
afterwood. We are going to try
to have it grow all over
that half of the barn It will
be pretty when it is all
in blosom and it will make

12

the farm look pretty all summer
long, for it will be green. We
have got a purple wisteria down
there and some old fashoned
wild roses too, and it will
take away the dismal look that
there is there.

    The clemetis is like
the moon, It grows up a little way
the first year and then dies back to the ground
and then goes up a little higher
the next year and does that
every year till it is a very
big bush a. The moon does that
every night. The first night it
goes up a little way in the sky
and sinks down to the woods
and then the next night it

goes a little higher than before
and sinks down to the
woods, they are just the same.

June 15 1908

14

The Thunder Storm Last Night.
We have had a long drought
all through June when it hasn't
rained a bit, except a few little
sprinkles once in a while, but
not enough to do any good to
the ground. All the farmers
are having a hard time
without rain. Their gardans
are not growing well and all
their peas are withering all up
and spoiling so that they are
not getting any peas off of
them.

Mama kept thinking that
one of the hot days would
bring a thunder shower. Now
yesterday it was kind of hot

and foggy and it looked quite
a lot like rain, but papa
didn't take any notice of it.
after a while great thunder
clouds began to come up out
of the west and then mama
thought sure that there was
going to be a shower, but
as the clouds came up they
went off an one side, so we
thought there wasn't going
to be one again, we all
stayed up till almost eight
watching the clouds turn
into many difrant shapes.
one of the figures was the
perfect shape of the great
stone face, but it quickly

16

changed into the face of
a dragon. Just after
we went to bed it began to
pour down. It rained almost
half the night, and we all said
it was enough to do some
good.

           June 29. 1908

The children's Ideas about The world.

The children think it is very curius about all the things in the world that I tell them about, they hardly beleave it and keep saying "how do you know" "how do you know". When I tell them how big the world is Irma always says "O I don't beleave that" and then I tell her to go and ask mama but she says no, because she knows mama will say yes and then she will have to beleave it, but she doesn't want to think it is true

18

so she doesn't ask her. Once
after we had taken quite a long
ride carol said "that we had
been clear around the world",
but I told him "that we had
at all" and then he said almo
around it and I said "no" and
he said "yes". Then I told him
that we had only been just
a tiny bit of a way compared
with the world and to wait
till he got older and see if
we had gone around the world
I will ask him when he
gets my age.

June 30 1908

a. Rain at last

This morning we were all woken up by the noise of rain on the tin roof outside our bedroom window. It was coming down terribly hard and making a noise like a steam roller. When I began to wake up I heard it I couldn't beleave it was rain though, but sure enough when I looked up, it was pouring down great guns. I thought sure it was going to be a good storm.

2º

but we only had two
good hard showers that
I think went down to
the wells and did some
good. It makes the grass
look greener and the road
not so dusty, but it
would have been nicer
if it had rained all day.

July 22 1908

Carol And Irma

Irma. Say carol those apples
are ripe let's eat some.
Carol. O no they will make
us sick they're not a bit ripe
Irma. But I am going
to taste one any way now
Carol You better look out
papa won't like it at all.
Irma. I don't care I wont
tell him will I caroll:
Carol. I know you won't
but I will won't I.
Irma. Yes but he won't say
any thing cause they are alm
st ripe.
Carol. O no O no they are not
a bit ripe you naughty

22

drma. now you shutup carol
I am going to taste one an
that is all there is to it.
Carol. But I am going to
tell papa.
drma. I don't care I know
you won't.
           After a while they.
got to talking about
something else and carol
fogot all about telling
papa about it. one day
they got into anoxther
quarrall and and carol
went to tell papa about
it. When he got through
he told papa about the
green apple, but papa

only said O it is so
long ago never mind
about it

July 22 1908

24

Carol and My Bean Garden.

This spring Carol and I
made three or four little
bean gardens. Carol let his
grow till they were full
sized before he he pulled
a weed out of them; they
were just an awful sight.
I planted mine a gooddeal
latter, but I planted them
in rows and kept the weed
out of them. Every time
we went down to look at
them I would tell carol
to pull out some, but he
would say "O never mind
I am too tired now". The

beans are almost ripe
we may have enough
for dinner in a day
or two. Carol seems very
proud of them and
goes and looks at them
every day, but never
cares enough to take
care of them.

July 23 1908

Waking Carol up.

Irma. O dear why doesn't
carol wake up so that we
can talk.

Marjorie. Lets wake him
up

Lesley. O no he will be
mad and tell mama.

Irma. Wake up, carol, wake,
Carol Stop irma stop.

Irma. Then wake up Carol;
mama will call us down
stairs.

Carol. I don't care; I
want to go to sleep. I am
tired.

Lesley. Don't bother him any

more Irma.

Marjorie. O yes do I Irma.
We want to play school.
Irma. Can't we Lesley.
Lesley. Mama wont like it.
Irma. O she wont say any-
thing; she never does; she
just talks to us a little,
but never does
any harm.
Lesley. Alright, but I
won't have any thing
to do with it.

Marjorie. Tickle him some
more, Irma,
Irma. yes I will Marjorie

28

Carol. If you don't stop
Irma, I will tell papa
and mama both.
          Enter mama.
mama. Come down stairs
now, children.
Lesley. Alright, mama

Carol. Say, mama, Irma
woke me up this morning.
mama. O don't be so fussy
she won't do it any more
will you Irma".
Irma, "no"   July 20 1908

Seeing a coon.
Carol and I and
marjorie were going
down by berrys bars
and two bysicles came
along; I backed into
the bushes out of there
way. just as I did so
I heard a growling
noise like a cat behind
me, so I ducked back
to see what it was,
but there was nothing
there.

yesterday morning
I had been reading
a story about how ugly
brown theashers were.

when they had any
young ones any where
you were (in a little
bird book that I have
got) so I thought it
might be one of those
so I turned and watched
the bisicles go along.

      After they had
gone I thought I would
see the nest so I turned
to go into the bushes,
but, just as I turned
right close behind me
ready to bite me was a
coon snapping and terribly
angry. It kind of parilisd
me for a minute, but when

I saw it was a real animal
I turned and shooted. I
yelled to caroll to
come and look but
when we came back
we heard it running
away in the bushes ferns
and we didn't see him
again.

I went to tell papa
about it and he said
that if I had turned
a little latter he
might have bitten
me. He had long fuzzy
brown hair and a
sharp nose just the same
as a coon has and papa

32

was
pretty sure it was
a coon.
                July 15 1908

A Little Lonsome House.
Down on the road to
windham, there is a little
half stone house. It is
very pretty, and has many
flowers around it. Most
of the flowers are in pots
on the piazza and near
it. The lower part of it is all
stone and the upper all wood.
The stone part lookes very cute; it
lookes as if it wos only a
play house made out of
blocks. When I was down
there the last time, just
the frames of it were there.
I didn't expect it to be
half as pretty as it is now.

34

There are
woods allaround it exept
on the side toward windham,
and there you can see
right out over it. There
is kind of a sharp corner
right in front of the
house, which I always forget
as I go driving
past,

and while I
am looking at the house
I almost go off the edge
into the meadow. I wish
I could go by there walking
and have a little better
look at it, it is so pretty,

august 5 190 8.

Flying Machines

It is queer how many
new things are being made
in the world. Now the flying machine that is just begun
to be thought of. It has
wings just like a birds,
but they wont go themselves
just like the birds They have
to have machinery to
make them go and a
steerer. Only one man
can ride on it, but
two can on the baloon.
The flying machine
is more interisting than
the other. They are mak-
ing the flying machine

.36

safer every year so
most people will
feel safer to go out in
them. They cost more
than the automobiles, but
people will want to travel
in the air for a while
and let the autoes alone.
They are finding some
new way of making thing
about every two years; it
makes it interesting for
papa and mama and me.
                    August 9 1908

Scaring Marjorie.

One day marjorie and I were playing in the barn, and marjorie went in to ask mama about something. After she had gone I went and hid from her. When she came out she hunted every where for me. By and by she came upon me so sudenly and I jumped out on _her_ and made such a rackett that it about scared her wits out. After she had come to again, she stood still, curved her lip, frowned, and said, you almost shook my head off.   nov 9 1908

38

My Remembrance Of New York.

When I was almost four years
old we went to New York. Carol was
a baby then and Irma and Marjorie
were not yet born. There are only
a few things that I remember. Papa
took me to many places: to the
zoo, and the theatre, and a deep
well where all kinds of fish were
kept, but we got there and found
it closed. In the zoo I remember
a few animals: the elephant, the
badgers, (the badgers were fighting
all the time over peanuts that
people threw to them,) the giraffe,
the tiger, the hippopotamus; thats
about all I guess. In the theater

I remember seeing cats climb
string and do all sorts of
tricks and dogs climb rope ladders
and jump into blankets down
below.

The place where we lived
was right in front of the
elevated trains, where you could
see them from the window.
They build the tracks up high
now, so as to give the wagon
and people more room to pass
below. I used to spend alot
of the time at the windo watching
them.

In the boat we had two little
rooms of our own, one a bed
room and the other a kitchen

40.

We had berths to sleep in
instead of beds, which is what they
always have in boats. Mama
and I slept in the lower
one, and papa in the top
one, while carol slept all
alone in the kitchen in a sma
berth. The night we got on
the boat it was raining and
papa took me out on the
deck to look at the water.
There was a great big steamer
down below us all lit and it
made the water look pretty and
all the city lights looked
like stars. It was lovely.

Speaking To The Pine

O sweet and breezy pine
That I am under now,
With thy own words, not mine
You talk of things you know.
But every every bough
In Ireland hears you now,
And all the folk who hear
But do not understand,
While home they drive their cows
They talk of on the way
The things that you don't fear,
And wish that they themselves
Could nothing ever fear.

Hallowéen Night (1908)

It is hard to wait from seven
oclock in the morning till six oclock
at night to come for something good
to happen. Now hallowéen night; I
kept watching the clock and wanted
terribly to git up and move the
hands of it, so as to make the
time go by quicker. We were all
very impatient all day long.
for the time to come. At last
the time drew near and the children began to dance up and down
and ask whether it was going to be
after supper or before.

Now the fun began. One
after another in turn went

up stairs and back alone in
the dark to see the lanterns.
There was one in the sitting
room, another in the hall, one
on the top of the stairs, and
one in our room. The one in
the hall carol, Irma and
Marjorie liked best, the one
at the top of the stairs Papa
liked best, and the mama and I
liked the one in our room, as
we children call it, and the
one in the sitting room nobody
liked. The one mama liked had
long sharp paper ears on it.
Papa had one that looked like a
ghost with the eyes nose and
mouth not quite cut through

44.

the skin. That made him look
kind of weird, and the jackolantern
Carol liked had very big and
very curly mouth, as if he
was grinning broadly.

That night we had more
fun too. Papa hung an apple
up by a string to see who could
take a bite out of it alone, but
nobody could untill papa proposed
that two should try at once. In
this way they soon got a bite, because
they would hold it between there
teeth long enough to get one. We
played that for a long time laughing and having great holabaloo,
so that you could hear it
troughout every room in the

house up-stairs and down.

A long time past and the
children began to want something new to play, so Papa
put some apples in a pail of
water to see who could get
one out with their teeth. Papa
got one out and ate it and I
took a little bite out of one,
but it got away without being
caught. You had to hold your
breath and plunge right into
the water to get at them at all.
Marjorie would just put her
mouth in and drink every time,
and so would Irma after she
found out how hard it was.

It was hard to go to

46

bed after so much of a good
time, for we knew we couldn't
have so much fun another night
till Cristmas.

Dec 19 1908

The Lonely Codroy Path.

There is one path out in the alders
that we children have been afraid
to go down ever since we have been
home, now I will tell you the
reason why. Well once we were
playing out there alone, and I
started to run down codroy
path, and when I got to the bridge
down there what do you supose!
I looked into the bushes and there
stood a great big coon. I had seen
a coon before in my life and in
more of a dangerous plaise than
this, so I knew what a coon looked
like. I was so astonished and yet
frightened that I stood still a minute

48

and then (though I could hardly
stand up, I was so scared) I ran
as fast as I could back to the
children and told them about
it. Ever since then, however, the
children have been afraid to
even take a step down there,
and nobody has except papa
one day when he was hunting
for the horse, and so the codray
bathe is left lonely, I am afraid,
clear till next spring.

Dec 21 1908

A little Girls Life.

There was once a little girl
who never wanted to go to bed
whether she was tired or not. It
was a very queer reason why;
I bet that nobody can guess
what it was. It is very strange
that this reason ever came into
her little head, for she was only
four years old, though she was
very thoughtful and intelligent.
She was a very imaginative child
too, and had many day dreams
such a I have had in the last
few days. Her mother let her
wander anywhere she wanted
on their farm, so she would

50

often walk in the fields thinking
of birds and flowers. Now this
is one of the reasons why she
didn't want to go to bed. At
night she always dreamed terrible
dreams; but in the day lovely
half fairyland dreams that
she liked better than anything
else, even better than candy,
which she liked very much too.
All day long when there was
nothing else to do she would
dream. As she was doing it
she would pick up sticks and
make all sorts of playthings,
such as slingshots bows and
arrows and little ornaments
to play with; she wouldn't find

this out though untill she come
again from fairyland. All
these things she loved and hated
to leave at night and go into
scary ones. There was not a
night for twelve years but
what she refused in going
to bed. This little girl as I
have said was very imaginative
and thoughtful and all her
life she beleived religeous things
from the bible that werent true
and at last became a nun.

Dec 22 1908

52

The Unkept, But Tame Squirrel

The berry road has a good many
squirrels in it, for there are a alot
of nut trees to get nuts on; and
so the hunters come there a good deal
in the fall. Most allways when I go
up there I see one squirrel anyway,
but generally two or three.

Well this morning I happened
to be strolling up there for a little
walk, and I saw a squirrel dodge
down from the top of a tree and
sit on one of the lower branches
with his tail up against the trunk
as if he was trying to keep it
warm. As he was sitting there
on the branch it looked as if he

had a pocket on one side filled
with nuts; I suposed though that
it was only some white fur,
and I know now anyway that
the only thing in America that
has a pocket is the aposum.
I had frought an old handle
of umbrella up on my sholders,
the way I had seen gunners carr
y thiers, to play shoot a partridge or squirrel or anything I
happened to see. The minute I
saw him it was off my sholders,
and I laid my hand on a
little peice of iron I had put
on there for a trigger. Snap
it went; not a bedge nor a move;
he sat just as still as it dead.

I did this two or three more
times, and stampt the ground
with my feet and hit the snow
crust with my gun, but not
a stir nor turn of his head.
I only noticed that his tail
began to shake rather nervously
as if he was getting rather disterbed

In the end I began pelting
him with snowstorms. He looked at these a little more
seriesly, but never paid any
atention of me, At last one
came so near her that she jumpt
to another branch, though she
took care to keep her tail up
against the trunk of the tree,

as she did before, so that
it wouldnt breeze to death.
.   After I had thought
it over a minute I let anouther snowstorm drive. This time
it would have hit her I
beleive, if it had not hit a
branch an scattered the snow
in every direction, as well
as all over her. I almost
burst with laghter as she
ran down the branch shak-
ing herself so as to get the
snow off her pretty red
silky fur. After she got near
her hole in the tree she stood
still and looked at me as
if to say, "How would you

like to be teased like this
if you were helpless like I
am and couldn't pay it
back?" This made me laugh
again, and I said half to myself,
"if you could understand me
you little rascal I would tell
you that my feet were getting
cold, and that if I went away
and left you out here you might
do something that I would want
to see, so I thought I would drive you
into your hole, and anyway
I want to save my feet just as
much as you do your tail.

　　　　　Drop! sudenly she
was out of sight down her hole
in the crotch of the tree.

I wish I had a camera
to take pictures of the squir-
els when they sit like that or
get where I have time to snap
the camera before they are
out of sight in the stone wall
I have seen many a time two
squirrels fighting for a nut
or sitting on a branch eating
a nut or runing along a
stone wall. Squirrels and
chipmunks are the only things
we see around here very often.

58

Chestnuting This year.

It has been very good chestnuting this year papa and we children have got seventeen or eighteen quarts. It is good wallnuting too, but we have been too lazy to get very many so that the squirrels got most of them. There is one tree out in Gay's that we got most of them on, but it isn't the great big tree that we generaly get most on.

This year seems to suit the chestnuts, for they are very big too. The first time we got many we got two quarts under one tree down here in Berry's; papa went up and knocked them off

with a stick and they came
down in showers, that proved
that it was. We intended to
pick apples but picked chestnuts
instead.

Another time we went out in
gays and got eight quarts. That day
it was very cold, and when we started
off, we didn't feel very much like picking up chestnuts, but when we got out
there the woods sheltered us, so that it was
nice and warm. That day Marjorie came with
us, and we filled her pockets so full that
she thought she couldn't walk home.

Then yesterday we went again and got
four quarts, though when we started off we
only expected to get a quart or a half a
one; but when you come across a good tree

60

your pockets are filled before you know
it. I guess the chestnuting is about over
for the year, but there will be enough nut-
nuting to keep us busy a little while
longer, if we want any.

Nov 1 1908

Dear Woodchuck

We have talked alot about
the things you have done this summer. I
have seen you many a time, but I supose you do not
remember. Once I scared you like everything, but
you frightened me just about as much as I did
you. I have seen you run up the paths
and dodge into you tole under the peach tree
where you steal peaches like a little fox

62

Tithonio's Secret.

Long long ago there was a little boy,
whose name was Tithonia, and everybody, from
far and wide, thought he was about the greatest
boy that ever lived. The day when his four
year old birthday came he said he had a secret
that he wouldn't tell untill he was thirty.
Everybody tried to guess, but nobody could,
so they just settled down to wait.

Every day, from when he was four,
he grew stronger and stronger untill
people thought there must be something in
him that they didn't have, and there
curiosity grew and grew and grew untill
they began to pleg him to tell.

At first he didn't notice
this at all, and told them they could

have to wait or he would never tell
it to anyone exeept to those in his
own family, but they would have to
wait till he was thirty. The more the
people bothered him though, he began
to want to tell it and get it off his
mind, and the people saw this and
offered him things if he would tell
it untill all he would do night
and day was to think whether he better
or not.

They kept on teasing him
till he was twenty-nine, and that
night they got a great banquet
where they made him stand up
and tell it. He got up and said,
"It was no secret," and sat down
again.

64

Going Down Cellar In The Dark

There is a little cellar that goes in under
the kitchen on one side of the main cellar
stairs. Always when I go down there in the
evening after an apple it makes me feel
trembly and I get as near the other side
as I can, but on the other side there is a
hole so that I don't know where to go. The
only thing I have to do is (for I don't
want to go back and say that I am too
afraid to go down) pull up my dress and
go by very carefuly watching on all sides.
When I get into the cellar I am glad, but
on the way up it is the same again and
worse, for I can't hold my dress watch,
so I just hurry by as fast as fast as
I can. When I get to the top of the stairs

there is another disadvantage like the other,
for my hands are so full that I have to
wait till someone opens the door, and then
I rush in as if I were being chased
by a tiger or lion. When it is over
I am glad, and sit down by the fire
to eat my apple and calm my
nerves.

66

The Goods and Bads of a Snowstorm

After the snowstorms have held back
clear into December, it is very disappointing
to have a big one come, and if there is alot
of ice to skate on, cover it all up, though
snowstorms have their pleasures too.
This winter there has been but one, and
here it is December 11. We have a little
skating rink, as we call it, down in
the brook below the hill, and we have
had a nice time on it for two or three
days, but to-day it is snowing so hard
it will spoil it all
Now I will tell you the disapointing
things of a snowstorm. I have told you
about skating and here are two others:
One because if it snows too deep papa

will have to dig a path clear out to the
alders so that we can get water; and
another because it seems too bad to see
winter come, for we have to huddle under
the blankets to keep warm at night

But the main things are the good things
of a snowstorm. These are some of them:
snowballs, snowmen, houses, paths, and
so on. When you see a snowstorm first
start, these good things don't pop right
into your head, but after a while, when
you are trying to forget the disappointing ones they do.

These sorrows and good things are
only such for children. Some grown
folks like winter just as well as summer,
and better, but not as well as children
I guess.

Dec 11 1908

The Monster Everyday.

There was once a monster by the name
of everyday, who lived in Europe. It was a very
hideous beast, something like a hippopotamus,
though very much larger and stronger. It
was born in the Japan sea, but some-how
got around to the White sea, where it
is now living on people and everything it
can find. It has been the terror of Russia,
for Russia would rather have a war with
England or United states than be bothered by that thing forever. These animals are now
growing very much more numerous than ever, and
I am afraid they will conquer Russia and drive
the people out, and that will mean war too,
because nobody will want to take the Russians in.
I would like to see a war now, because I would

understand it more. The war between Japan
and Russia didn't interest me very much,
for I was too young. These animals may
spread over all Europe, Aisa, and Africa,
if people don't kill them out now. People
have tried it, but never come back alive,
so nobody cares to try it at pesent, though
they may in time.

Dec 13 1908

70

The First Turkey For Thanksgiving

And now the joy began. The children
danced up and down and whispered an
talked about secrets; but when the dinner
came they were too excited and timid
to surprise anyone with them. All the
forenoon all we could do to put it out
of our heads. When the table was being set,
Irma would pull her dress and wriggle
and wriggle, and smile until the ends of
her mouth most touched her ears and
hop up and down like a baby rabbit
playing in the grass beside its hole.

The turkey didn't turn out as we ha
expected it to; by the way mama and
papa spoke we thought it was going
to be better than a chiken, but instead was

a little. Anyway it was all right. We
had so many things to eat we could
hardly finish the last thing: mince pie,
squash pie, grapes, candy, nuts, cranberry
sauce, and then the turkey. The candy was
the last thing we ate, but it would
hardly go down. We got up from the
table in good spririts and lay down
on the floor.

This is the first thanksgiving since
we have been here that we have had a
Turkey, and it seems nice to see one on the
table, though it is a little worse than a
chiken. [I joked you'd like it just as well
as a chiken].

72

A Woodchuck's House

We would all like very much to see what a woodchucks house looks like inside, but as long as we canot we will have to guess what it would look like if we could.

I will take the one out in our orchard where the woodchuck lives that I wrote a letter to once, but he didn't answer, because he was sound asleep for the winter and didn't know that he had such a thing as a letter from children.

His hole is rather crooked, becouse he tries to avoid the peach tree roots, but even then there must be quite a few of them going through his house, unless it extends out beyond the roots.

It must seem cozy and nice

to run down his paths underground;
all his very own, and just his size. no
other paths seem to join it or the house, and
each family has his own house and tunnel
and I never knew them go calling on each
other, even.

The house inside, probably, is very
warm and cozy, for there are no cracks
to let in air like in real houses, and
I should think the little ones would about
smother in summer.

I would like to live in one if
it were not for that smothering, and
then the smell of dirt all around you
would make you go crazy and perhaps
die after a while.

74

A walk Alone.

Once when we were playing by the stone-
steps, I jumped up, said goodby, and ran for the
alders. The children did not follow me, and so
I will tell you what I saw instead of the
things I would have encountered with
them. After I had been in the alders for
a minute or two I went up on the hill
and was going home when I heard a rustling
in the bushes. I looked and there was a
pretty brown rabbit running away
into the woods. I walked on and come
to the little old garden on top of the further
knoll, and there a great flock of juncos
they flew away right in reach of my
hand. I am always taken too much
by surprise at the time to reach out,

but afterward I wish I had, so I could
tell the rest.

The First Snowstorm.

We children were playing out of doors this morning when it began to rain little fine drops; in a few minute it turned into half rain and half snow. The children began dancing up and down and calling to mama to look out of the window to tell her that there was going to be a great big storm, and that Christmas would be here soon. They danced around in it and looked to see if they could see any flakes on the ground or piazza. It realy did show a little on the roof; it made it look a tiny-bit white.

After a while it stopped and the children almost cried. It is very funny it snowed even that little because it is hardly cold enough and when I told mama she would hardly beleive it.

A Storm

First the clouds come sweeping ore the
sky, and darkness covers the earth. Then
as minutes fly by there springs a wind from
out of the east driving before it rain
and sleet. First comes the sleet ~~first~~ slow
then fast, and upon that comes rain in
torrents, and the wind now is raging
to the height of a huricane. Around
the house whirls sleet and rain driven
by gusts of wind, and around about
the fragments of leaves and paper are chased,
till drenched with rain they sink to
the ground.

But now the storm has abated and
the the earth is covered with pools of water;
Roads, hollows, and drains are filled with

rain, and clouds have rolled on to
the Pacific ocean,   and the wind
has stood still in the air, and the
only sound that stirs the air is the
drip, drip, drip of the water from the
roof to the ground.

Our new Playmates.

Since we have moved over here we have two new playmates, Roseina and John. Roseina is almost nine, and John almost four. Marjorie is almost four too, but she can talk twice as plain as John; you can hardly understand a word he says. He is very cute though, and likes to laugh and play. Roseina is older and about my age, so we have more fun in playing games together like checkers and and jackstraws and so forth. The out-door games we all can play exept Marjorie and John, and they play somtimes, though we always see them the first thing when we are it. In summer we have more fun, for we can sit on the ground, go bare-footed, and such things that are fun

for children. We will still have more
fun in a year or two, for John and
Marjorie will then be old enough to
play games right, too. They live up here
at the next house so that we can
get to eachother easily.

Derry Village –

81

How White Violets grow.

Down behind the old bars, that
lead into our pasture, there is a little wet
place where the first white violets show their
heads above the ground. The grass and blue
violets start there first, too. It seems to me
the first day we take the cow out to pasture
we see the white violets poking their heads
above the earth and green grass that comes
just before they do. Whenever you are near
some, whether you can see them or not, you can
smell the perfume plainly just the same as
you can with yellow ants, whether they are
under a stone or way in the ground, you can
smell them as if they were in your hand.

It is there the children go more
to pick them, but of course there are some

in other places, like the cranberry-bog
and at one end of the big pasture, where
they push their slender stems and delicate
petals above the soil into the air air and
sunlight to send forth thier fragrance
into the still summer, and wave in the
breeze, like poppies on an April day.

The End

NOTES

THESE journals provide subtle views into the girlhood of Lesley Frost and the manhood of her father at a time when he was just beginning to discover those rural images, characters, scenes and subjects around which he built the most important part of his poetic career. No other sources of information concerning these years begin to approach the value of these journals in heightening and deepening our knowledge of this crucial phase in the life of Robert Frost.

One purpose of these notes is to clarify the obscurities caused by Lesley's youthful ellipses and quaint spellings. A more important purpose is to sharpen the sense of immediacy and intimacy, in these journals, by giving useful background information concerning her father's relations with his children, his wife, his neighbors, his farm, and the countryside within easy walking distance of it.

Lesley's flower-gathering stories suggest that her father spent more time botanizing than farming while he lived in Derry, and that many of these experiences were later used as raw materials for his poems. These notes make reference to twenty-seven poems which he wrote in Derry or which he remembered as being rooted in the soil of his Derry farm. Titles of these poems are indexed twice: separately, in the alphabetical arrangement, and all together under the heading FROST, ROBERT LEE, POET.

Another purpose informs these notes. Now that the State of New Hampshire has purchased the Robert Frost farm in Derry, and is restoring it as the central feature in a Memorial Park, many of his admirers who make pilgrimages to it will want to retrace on foot some of the picturesque travels made by Lesley with her parents on this farm and in this neighborhood. Some of these notes are designed to help anyone who follows them in fact or in the imagination. References to geographical features, landmarks, stone-wall boundaries, roads, brooks, ponds, lakes, neighbors, and the homesteads of neighbors, are here indexed primarily under the topical heading, LANDMARKS. Further assistance is provided by the accompanying maps which serve as endpapers.

The editors take pleasure in acknowledging the many forms of assistance given them by so many individuals during several visits to Derry and to the Frost farm. Special gratitude goes to Mrs. Lesley Frost Ballantine, with whom the editors have explored the house (from attic to cellar), the shed, the barn — and with whom one of the editors has walked the entire boundary-line of the farm. Mr. and Mrs. J. A. G. Theriault were the occupants of the farm during these first-hand researches, and the cheerful hospitality of these occupants, throughout repeated intrusions, is deeply appreciated. In these notes, many specific acknowledgments are given to Mrs. Harriett Chase Newell, who had become acquainted with all of the Frosts when they had visited the home-office of her husband, Dr. Charles E. Newell, in Derry Village. Mrs. Newell's books on houses in the township of Derry have given many valuable details, here used and cited. Mr. Ralph I. Miltimore, who was a boy when he played baseball with Robert Frost and with other neighbors in a pasture on Miltimore Road, has accompanied one of the editors — sometimes on foot — in helping to identify abandoned roads, old farms, woods, fields, streams, and other landmarks near the Derry farm. He was, during these researches, the owner of six acres which surround the one cellar hole described by Lesley in her journals as the place where she found, with her father, those "old-fashioned flowers" which she helped him transplant to their own front yard. Mr. and Mrs. John Pillsbury of Plymouth, New Hampshire, have played a very significant part in developing plans for the Robert Frost Memorial Park. They continuously and generously helped the editors in many ways. On their own initiative, they secured and made available an aerial map showing the Frost farm and the region immediately surrounding it. All of these collaborators, and many others here not named, are warmly thanked for the ways in which they added the flavors of adventure and friendship to conscientious research.

In these notes, the abbreviations are few. Each note begins with numerals which refer to the number of the journal, the page-number in that journal, and (where pertinent) the line-number (or numbers) on that page. For example, "I, 1, 1" refers to Journal (or Book) number one, page one, line one.

BOOK I

I, 1, 1: Carol Frost, Lesley's brother, born May 27, 1902, was not yet three years old when he suffered the embarrassments amusingly described in this first story.

NOTES

I, 1, 5: Paraphrase may remove the obscurities. Lesley seems to imply that one of Carol's shoes had gotten wet, perhaps because of puddles caused by rainy weather; that it had been placed in the baking oven of the kitchen stove, to dry out; that someone had accidentally shut the oven door; that the shoe had become damaged through too much drying.

I, 1, 10: The five-year-old Lesley, having heard her mother address Robert Frost repeatedly as "Rob," had obviously fallen into the habit of using that name for her father, and had been permitted to continue the habit. It will be noticed from later journal evidences that she soon outgrew this habit.

I, 1, 10–11: When Lesley writes that "rob went ofu to derry," her echoing of the customary preposition implies that he went "over" to Derry Depot, or West Derry as it was also called, rather than "down" (that is, largely downhill from the Frost farm) to Derry Village.

Derry Depot, or West Derry, was and is the largest of the three once-separate communities in the township of Derry — which, in turn, was until 1827 a part of the township of Londonderry.

Back in 1718, some of the Scotch-Presbyterian settlers who came from Londonderry in northern Ireland began to build a cluster of dwellings in the region which is now called East Derry.

The second settlement was made at what is now called Derry Village. It began to develop in 1806, when the partial completion of the Londonderry Turnpike from Concord, New Hampshire, to Andover, Massachusetts, made an important crossroad at the point where the Turnpike intersected the important local road from Londonderry to Chester, New Hampshire.

The third settlement began to grow in 1848, when a railroad was built from Manchester, New Hampshire, to Lawrence, Massachusetts. This railroad passed through the western part of Derry township, and the local station was placed near the boundary line between Derry and Londonderry. A gradually expanding cluster of shoe factories, stores, and homes developed near this railroad station, and the new community quickly outgrew the two older settlements. It was commonly called Derry Depot, even though the postoffice address there was West Derry. It is now officially called Derry, while the older settlements still retain their first names: East Derry and Derry Village.

The Frost farm is on the old Londonderry Turnpike, two miles southeastward from Derry Village, and roughly the same distance from Derry Depot. The Frosts did most of their shopping in the larger business center, Derry Depot.

NOTES

I, 1, 16:   Lesley attempts to find phonetic spellings for Carol's baby-talk. He apparently called his new shoes, "Tuni day too." Not to be worn on rainy days, they were to be kept for sunshine-days. Lesley seems to indicate that Carol, using "t" sounds for "sh" sounds, thus tried to call his new possession "shiney day shoes."

I, 2, 6–12:   Quite early, Lesley's father shared with her the pleasures he derived from watching the stars. This first reference to stars clearly shows that before she was six years old she could already find and identify several important stars in the winter sky. She mentions Venus, the Dog Star (Sirius, brightest in the constellation Canis Major); also "the stars in the giant" (presumably those in the constellation Orion, including the first magnitude stars Rigel and Betelgeuse) and the constellation Big Dipper, or Ursa Major.

According to the present recollections of Lesley Frost, her father heightened the interest of his children in the stars by "giving" each child a star to "own." Lesley was "given" Arcturus, the brightest star in the constellation Boötes. Her father used a brass-bound telescope, about three feet long, which he propped on a window sash in any one of the three upstairs bedrooms whenever he let the children take turns looking at those stars for which they were "responsible."

(For background concerning Robert Frost's delight in astronomy, starting in his own childhood, see Lawrance Thompson, *Robert Frost, The Early Years* [hereafter cited as *The Early Years*] [New York, 1966], pp. 90–92.)

I, 6, 16:   The Collie dog, referred to by Lesley as "snider" or "Snider," was given to the Frost family by a Derry man who spelled his name Schneider, and the Frosts named the dog after him. Lesley's father, in the sixteen imaginative prose tales he wrote out for his children in Derry (see *The Early Years,* pp. 302–303, 557), uses the correct spelling for the dog's name. The first of these sixteen stories begins, "Schneider met a squirrel . . ." The second begins, "One day Schneider chased a woodchuck . . ." The third begins, "Schneider was asleep on the piazza . . ." Nevertheless, the simplified spelling of the dog's name, as given by Lesley, is editorially preferred here and even in the "Index," where other misspelled words are usually corrected for purposes of clarification.

Lesley Frost currently recalls that more than one of the children in her family learned to walk by holding tightly to Snider's luxuriant hair. Her stories about Snider occur only in her early journals, however, because he died as the result of a fight with a stranger-dog, in the Frost farmyard, in February of 1907. During that fight, Snider drove the stranger out of the yard, taking some wounds in the process. Lesley's father, fearing that the strange dog might be suffering from rabies, confined the wounded Snider to a pen in the barn and personally attended to him. Only a few days after the fight, Snider died, and there seemed to be evidence that he was not the only victim of the intruder. The *Derry News* for February 19, 1907 (p. 5) carried a brief article entitled "Dogs Are Dying," as follows:

"Whether it is a result of the mad dog epidemic of a few weeks ago or not, no definite statement seems to have been made, but it is known that several dogs have taken sick and died of late. Among the number are those belonging to A. [i.e., R.] L. Frost, Peter Cole and F. T. Rogers. The heads of the two first have been sent away to laboratories [at the University of New Hampshire, in Durham] by the selectmen to be examined to ascertain if there are any traces of rabies."

One week later, the *Derry News* for February 22 (p. 5) carried a follow-up report to the effect that in these two laboratory tests no evidence of rabies had been found. This official claim provided no consolation for the grief-stricken Frost children, who were still convinced that their pet had died of rabies. Snider's headless body was given tender burial in a flower-garden near the front steps and inside the quince-hedge in the front yard of the Frost farmhouse. His grave was marked by a little spruce tree, transplanted to that spot from the nearby woods. It seemed significant to the mourning Lesley that even the spruce tree died.

I, 8, 1:   The word, "apples," added as a correction for Lesley's "apools," is in the handwriting of her father. He also wrote, at the bottom of p. 5, "finished on page 8," to indicate that Lesley's imaginary story about the wolf was continued out of normal pagination: apparently she had accidentally turned two pages of her journal at once.

I, 10, 9:   Irma Frost, Lesley's first sister, born June 27, 1903, was almost two years old when this entry was written.

I, 10, 10–14:   In writing that her father will take her to find the faraway flowers, off in the meadows, Lesley names these: anemones (or windflowers), violets, cowslips, daisies, buttercups, dandelions, goldenrod, and innocence (or bluets).

At the age of six, Lesley is already reflecting the ways in which she has begun to share with her father his exceptional pleasure not only in stargazing but also in flower-gathering. She devotes more words, in her journal, to describing her own delight in flowers than to discussing any other topic. One specialized statement occurs in her little essay entitled "The Orchids That I Know" (III, 46–47).

NOTES

I, 14, 7:   For Lesley, the Derry Road is that part of the old Londonderry Turnpike which continues in a northwesterly direction, past the Frost farm, toward Derry Village. Elsewhere, she calls the other part of the Turnpike (the part which goes in a southeasterly direction from her home) "the Windham Road." In III, 8, she writes, "One day our cow got out and went down the Windham Road and papa went after her and Mr. Perkins was just coming down from his house . . ." Mr. Perkins lived on the Londonderry Turnpike, near the top of Ryan Hill, less than a mile southeast of the Frost farm.

(For background on Mr. Perkins, see the note to IV, 47, 11; for the location of what was officially called the Windham Road, see the note to I, 19, 4–5.)

I, 14, 12–13:   A not-intimate neighbor of the Frost family was the elderly Mr. George A. Webster, whose fine set of buildings still stands, in 1969, on the northeast corner of the crossroads (still known as Webster's Corner) formed by the intersection of the old Londonderry Turnpike by the Island Pond Road, six-tenths of a mile toward Derry Village from the Frost farm.

Lesley seems to be implying, in this account, that a small road through woods led off the Turnpike to the bars at the entrance to Mr. Webster's cow pasture (probably to the southeast of Webster's Corner) and that she tracked her own runaway cow to these bars.

(A photograph of the Webster house may be found in Mrs. Harriett Chase Newell's *Houses of the Double Range and East Derry, N. H.* [hereafter cited as *Houses of the Double Range*] [n.p., 1954], p. 18.)

I, 16, 4–5:   As Lesley's description almost implies, a democrat wagon is a high lightweight horse-drawn vehicle with two rows of seats fastened forward of a flat-bed enclosed area used for carrying supplies.

I, 19, 4–5:   As soon as Lesley tells how she "started up the Berry Road" with her dog Snider, and then came back and "turned the corner by the bars" of the gate leading into the "little pasture" of the Frost farm, she is beginning the first of her many stories about her wonder-filled "travels" on and near her farm. Those "travels" can be followed more pleasurably (on foot or in the imagination) if the follower acquires a basic historical and geographical awareness of certain names, landmarks, and boundaries mentioned. (The endpaper maps are obviously helpful.)

The Berry Road, which has its beginning directly opposite the Frost farmhouse, proceeds in a southwesterly direction from the Londonderry Turnpike for a little more than a mile until it connects with and ends at the road officially named the Windham Road.

The gate to that part of the Frost farm known as the "little pasture" was almost directly across the Turnpike from the Frost barn.

At present, this "little pasture" is largely overgrown with brush, weeds, and trees; but on three sides of it the stone-wall boundaries can still be found. In dry weather, it is also possible to follow the stone-wall boundaries on three sides of the "big pasture." Lesley, in her journal, hints at the fact that these two pastures were separated from each other by a shared fourth side: a barbed-wire fence, containing a wooden gate which gave access from one pasture to the other. Her cryptic reference to this shared fourth side occurs in I, 27: "You know that wire in the little pasture with no stone wall and there are lots of violets beside it . . . ."

The property boundaries of the original thirty-acre Frost farm are given in the records of the Office for the Registry of Deeds of Rockingham County (in Exeter, New Hampshire) as follows:

"1900, Sept. 25: the record of the warranty deed of sale, Edmund J. Harwood of Manchester, N. H., to W. P. Frost [paternal grandfather of Robert Frost; bought the farm for the use of his grandson] of Lawrence, Mass., for $1,725.00. Two parcels of land, the parcel on the east side of the Londonderry Turnpike containing house and barn, bounded on the south by land owned by Joseph Klein, on the north and east by land owned by Sarah J. Upton; the parcel on the west side of Londonderry Turnpike, pasture land bounded on the northwest by a road [Berry Road] leading from the Turnpike to the dwelling house formerly of Marshall Merriam, at a corner of the wall, then down in a southerly direction to the land owned by Millard F. Miltimore, being the same premises described in the deed of Robert C. Brampton to Charles S. Magoon, Aug. 30, 1894, and assigned by Magoon to Harwood in a deed dated Feb. 27, 1895." (Book 578, p. 160)

Some of the names in this record are closely bound up with the history of the Frost farm. Shortly after the Civil War, Mr. Marshall Merriam owned almost all of the land which later became the Frost farm. He also owned many other acres of meadow and woodland in the neighborhood. His earliest homestead in this vicinity stood on a shoulder of Klein's hill, at the edge of the Londonderry Turnpike, only a short distance below the stone wall which later marked the southerly boundary of the "big pasture" on what is now known as the Frost farm. While Mr. Merriam was attending Fast Day services in the Congregational Church at East Derry, in 1867, his house caught fire and burned down. The cellar hole, still easily located, gradually became surrounded by lilac bushes and double-petal red-rose bushes, some of which Robert Frost transplanted to his own gardens at the front of his farmhouse in 1907 (see III, 128–129). The same cellar hole may have provided inspiration for Robert Frost's early poem entitled "Ghost House."

In 1867, shortly after Mr. Merriam's house was destroyed by fire, he bought or built the fine farmhouse which still stands as the first dwelling on Miltimore Road, not far to the westward of the pastureland on what is now known as the Frost farm. Hence the later reference to the northern boundary of that pastureland as being along the [Berry] road leading from the Turnpike to "the dwelling house formerly of Marshall Merriam . . ." When Robert Frost's grandfather bought the Derry farm, in 1900, the Merriam farmhouse and land to the westward of the Frost pastureland had long ago passed into the ownership of Mr. Frank O. Berry.

In 1884, Mr. Nathaniel G. Head had purchased from Mr. Merriam most of the land now contained in the Frost farm. Mr. Head, having worked for years in a fruit nursery, set out an exceptional variety of fruit trees on his new farm: a scattering of cherry, pear, quince, peach, plum trees, and a good-sized apple orchard behind the barn. He also set out six sugar maple trees: three in line near the Turnpike and parallel to the front of his house; three in line below and parallel to the retaining wall flanking the driveway from the Turnpike to the barn. In this second line of maples, the one nearest the Turnpike became known to Lesley as "the woodpecker tree" — probably because at least one part of a good-sized dead branch had been drilled and hollowed out for use as nest-holes. All six of these maples are still alive, although some of them are near the end of their usefulness. When Robert Frost's grandfather bought the farm from a later owner, in 1900, several acres of woodland across the Turnpike and to the northwest of the farmhouse were still owned by Mr. Head. Lesley, in her journals, repeatedly imitates her elders and neighbors by making reference to "Nat Head's woods."

Mr. Millard F. Miltimore, whose name is mentioned as the owner of land forming part of the boundary for the southern side of the Frost pastureland, owned a neighboring farm and lived in a large house (which burned down, long ago) on Miltimore Road, a half mile south of the Merriam-Berry homestead. Next door to the old Miltimore homestead, and slightly nearer the Berry farm, lived a younger brother of Mr. Millard Miltimore: Mr. John A. Miltimore, one of whose six children (Mr. Ralph I. Miltimore) studied for two years under Robert Frost at Pinkerton Academy, in the Class of 1913.

(A photograph of the Merriam-Berry homestead may be found in Mrs. Harriett Chase Newell's *Outlying Districts of Derry, New Hampshire* [hereafter cited as *Outlying Districts*], [n.p., 1965], p. 156; photographs of the homes of the Miltimore brothers may be found in *Outlying Districts,* p. 163.)

I, 19, 13–14: After Lesley's word, "sqrale" (squirrel), the words "lived in the tree" are in her father's handwriting.

I, 20, 5–6: Lesley's obscure statement, "one day we hanist up unis and went to see mr. clack" may need clarification: "One day we harnessed up Eunice and went to see Mr. Clark." (One description of the frisky mare, Eunice, occurs in IV, 54.)

The Clark family which was best known to the Frosts lived in Derry Village, near the start of the road to Chester. The elderly Dr. David S. Clark was family physician for the Frosts during their early years on the Derry farm, and assisted at the births of Carol, Irma, and Marjorie. Dr. Clark died on December 7, 1907. Thereafter, the family physician for the Frosts was Dr. Charles E. Newell, husband of Mrs. Harriett Chase Newell. (A photograph of the home of Dr. and Mrs. Newell, to which the Frost children were taken for office calls, may be found in Mrs. Harriett Chase Newell's *Houses of Derry Village, N. H.* [n.p., 1951], p. 47; a reference to a gift or loan of a tent to the Frosts, by Dr. Newell, mentioned in one of Lesley's journal fragments, may be found in the preliminary note to Book VI.)

Dr. Clark's daughter, Miss Sylvia Clark, had studied at Wellesley College and had already demonstrated her literary gifts in the writing of prose and poetry before she began teaching English at Pinkerton Academy in the fall of 1905. She became a colleague of Robert Frost's when he started teaching at the Academy in 1906. Dr. Clark's son, Mr. Lowell M. Clark, was a well-informed and enthusiastic amateur botanist who knew many choice stations of rare wild-flowers in the region. Robert Frost occasionally went bog-trotting with him in search of wild orchids.

(A photograph of the Clark home may be found in *Houses of Derry Village,* p. 28. Miss Sylvia Clark's reminiscences, "Robert Frost: The Derry Years," appear in *The New Hampshire Troubadour* for November 1946, pp. 13–16. For an account of how Robert Frost was prompted to write for Miss Clark, at Pinkerton, a satirical poem which he teasingly entitled, "An A No. 1 Sundown" — and for the text of this poem — see *The Early Years,* pp. 569–570.)

I, 22, 1: Marjorie Frost, Lesley's second sister, was born on March 29, 1905. Mrs. Frost gave birth to three children in less than three years while living on the Derry farm. For convenience in reference, all the birth-dates of the Frost children are given here:

1896, September 25:	Elliott (died July 8, 1900)
1899, April 28:	Lesley
1902, May 27:	Carol (died Oct. 9, 1940)
1903, June 27:	Irma
1905, March 29:	Marjorie (died May 2, 1934)
1907, June 18:	Elinor Bettina (died June 21, 1907)

I, 24, 1: Lesley's mention of pears and cherries may serve as a reminder that her father was extremely fortunate in acquiring a farm which had first been owned by a former nurseryman, Mr. Nathaniel G. Head. (See note to I, 19, 4–5.)

I, 26: Lesley gives another account of this fire, on p. 31 of this journal. The same event provided her father with the central metaphor in his poem entitled "The Bonfire." For further details on the fire and on the poem, see *The Early Years,* pp. 301, 533, 557.

I, 29, 2–3: Lesley's sixth birthday fell on April 28, 1905.

I, 30, 5: The reference to "clins woods" is partially clarified by one detail in the record already quoted: ". . . bounded on the south by land owned by Joseph Klein . . ." Mr. Joseph Klein, a German immigrant who was prominent in Derry — prosperous and well-liked — owned a good-sized farm which was only four-tenths of a mile to the southward of the Frost farm, on the easterly side of the Londonderry Turnpike. Although he sold his farm to a French Canadian farmer, Mr. Napoleon Guay, soon after the Frosts moved to Derry, Mr. Klein and his name continued to be associated locally with two landmarks which are mentioned repeatedly in Lesley's journals: Klein's hill and Klein's woods. At times, she seems to use the terms, Klein's woods, and Guay's woods, interchangeably; but she never calls Klein's hill, Guay's hill.

(For more information on the Guay family, see notes to I, 38–39; II, 2, 3–4; II, 36, 1. For a photograph of the Klein-Guay farmhouse see *Outlying Districts,* p. 133, where it is shown with the name of a later owner, Mr. David W. Chism.)

I, 33, 1: Lesley's choice of title, "the lefes" (the leaves), apparently refers to her disappointment in finding only the leaves of columbine and lady's slipper when she had hoped to find blossoms.

I, 33, 2–3: The context suggests the probability that Lesley is referring to the old Merriam cellar hole (see note to I, 19, 4–5) when she mentions "the brnt up house." When she writes, ". . . we went out in beris wood," she refers to a woodlot then owned by her neighbor, Mr. Frank O. Berry. This woodlot nearly surrounded the two Frost pastures on the western and southern sides. It extended downhill from the Berry Road to the southwest corner of the Frost "big pasture." Then it extended more than halfway to the Turnpike along the southern boundary of the "big pasture. One part of Mr. Berry's pasture (either rented or bought from Miltimore) completed the act of surrounding: it had a common boundary with the "big pasture" from Berry's woods to the Turnpike.

Lesley makes several references to Berry's woods and pasture. In IV, 46, she writes, "We go down into Mr. Berry's pasture and get sticks with lots of branches . . . and play they are bulls." In IV, 71–72, she writes, "I and papa were at the front room window that looks down toward Berry's bars [one entrance to his pasture]. . . . A deer came out of Berry's woods. It went to our [pasture] fence . . . and it jumped right over the fence. . . . It went down through the garden and over the fence to Berry's pasture." (Lesley's father may have had a "garden" fenced off in the southeast area of his "big pasture," but the "garden" reference is now obscure even to Lesley Frost.)

(For more details on the Berry farm, see the note to I, 19, 4–5.)

I, 34: Lesley's account of how she "went out the lagus rod" suggests that she may have heard her father or someone else mention this particular road as one used by "loggers" in hauling or dragging felled and trimmed trees out of the woods. (Her later mention of a nearby field of stumps would seem to support this guess.) Although she does not again refer to it as a loggers' road, she is describing an ancient thoroughfare which became so important to her, and to her father, that it deserves to be identified as a landmark.

The record of boundaries quoted in the note to I, 19, 4–5 states that the eastern side of the Frost farm was bounded by property which Mrs. Sarah J. Upton owned. This eastern boundary was (and still is) marked by a straight line of stone wall, approximately 450 feet long. Just beyond the wall, and running close beside it, may still be seen the remains of what was once called the South Road: it extended south from Island Pond Road to the Londonderry Turnpike for a distance of one mile and one-tenth. As early as 1781, this road was already being called "old" when mentioned as a boundary in a deed of gift. Quoting from this deed of gift (in *Houses of the Double Range and East Derry, N. H.* [n.p., 1954], p. 25), Mrs. Harriett Chase Newell adds, "This byway started a few rods west of the road from the cemetery [officially, Cemetery Road, and so listed on current maps of Derry] at Island Pond Road, and ran in a southerly direction to the South Range, and it may still be traced in part by the old walls." As Lesley's journals indicate, she and her father frequently walked this old South Road, occasionally following it all the way up to Island Pond Road (see note to II, 20, 4–6), but more often turning the other way. The southern part of it is marked by a stone wall which crosses the farm once owned by Mr. Joseph Klein and then by Mr. Napoleon Guay; it apparently joined Featherbed Lane not far below the Klein-Guay farmhouse.

I, 35, 4: Lesley's story about getting lost while going to "the pamers" (the Palmers) provides her first mention of a Derry family and a Derry region with which she later became well acquainted. Several landmarks are suggested by her account of this adventure.

On the Londonderry Turnpike, one mile and seven-tenths southeastward from the Frost farm, Clyde Road crosses the Turnpike and continues east (as Kilrea Road) only a short distance before Stark Road branches off it, to the north. Approximately one mile up Stark Road from this corner stands a granite marker which was erected in 1897 to indicate the birthplace of General John Stark, hero of the Battle of Bennington, in the Revolutionary War. (Robert Frost made artistic uses of the Stark family in his poem entitled "The Generations of Men.") Approximately one-tenth of a mile from the same corner stood the homestead of Mr. Herbert S. Palmer. His wife, Mrs. Hattie Kilborn Palmer, had lived in Salem, New Hampshire, before her marriage, and her mother (Mrs. Elizabeth Kilborn) had been a friend of Robert Frost's mother while the latter was teaching in Salem — from 1886 to 1889. The Palmers had four grown children living at home when Lesley made this entry: two sons and two daughters. One of these daughters, Esther, had been graduated from Pinkerton Academy in 1904. At the time of this entry, she was teaching elementary grades in a nearby district school in the township of Windham. For an account of Lesley's visit to this school, see II, 39–40.

As a result of the previous Palmer-Frost association, the Frosts frequently visited in the Palmer home, and they kept in touch with the Palmers long after the Frosts moved away from Derry. Recently, in a letter addressed to Lesley Frost and Arnold Grade under date of April 22, 1968, Miss Esther E. Palmer wrote,

". . . We were always happy whenever we looked out the window and saw Mrs. Frost with her children entering the yard, driving her beautiful grayish brown pet horse, Eunice. This often meant a picnic lunch in the cow pasture. When the farmhouse, surrounded by the lovely maple and elm trees, burned in 1934, Mrs. Frost wrote that she felt as much sorrow as if it had been her own."

If Mrs. Frost had taken the shortest route to the Palmer farm, she would have driven straight down the Turnpike to Clyde or Kilrea Road, (a distance of one mile and seven tenths), then east on Kilrea Road for one tenth of a mile, to Stark Road, then up Stark Road for one tenth of a mile — a total distance of not quite two miles. This time, however, she apparently wished to give her children a longer excursion. Starting out from the Frost farm, she apparently drove over the Berry Road to the Windham Road, then down the Windham Road to North Windham (at Windham Depot), then eastward along Clyde Road toward the Turnpike — a total distance of roughly four miles. It is probable that the lake and house "we did not no [know]" were Ezekiel Pond (named after one of the last Indians living in the region) and the nearby ramshackle house known as the Paul Otis Clyde place. At this unfamiliar point — when she and her children, having almost reached the familiar Turnpike, were roughly three-tenths of a mile from the Palmer farm — Mrs. Frost apparently felt so "lost" that she turned around and returned home by retracing her course.

(Photographs of the Palmer homestead — "burned in 1934" — and of the old Clyde place may be found in *Outlying Districts,* pp. 149 and 142.)

I, 36, 2–3: Lesley's ". . . i went down the stone stepes" refers to a landmark which may be traced back to Mr. Nathaniel G. Head's decision to erect his new house and barn on sloping land: the pitch is to the southward, toward the stream which the Frosts called Hyla Brook. While house and barn were being constructed, the exposed foundations must have accentuated the downhill tilt of the side yard. In order to make a level approach to the barn door, from the Turnpike, it was necessary to use fill (perhaps from the excavation of the cellar) for grading. Held in place on the northern and eastern sides by the foundations of house and barn, this fill was buttressed on the southern side by constructing a substantial retaining wall of flat stones, built at a gradually increasing height, from near the Turnpike all the way to the corner of the barn. Along this wall, Mr. Head planted Concord grapevines which were still bearing well in Lesley's girlhood. Her father mentions them in his poem entitled "October," when he pleads, half-seriously and half-humorously, that the freezing weather will delay its arrival "for the grapes' sake along the wall." Lesley mentions them (I, 31) when she says that the grassfire in the meadow spread until it "birnd are grap vine . . ."

This retaining wall created an obvious inconvenience which was foreseen and overcome during the original construction of it. Through the highest part of this wall, and only six feet from the corner of the barn, Mr. Head built a flight of seven granite steps, thus giving a short-cut from the graded upper level of the barnyard to the southward-sloping part of it. On the lower level, the exposed downhill side of the barn had (and still has) a door which gave (and still gives) ground-level approach to what became the cellar of the barn. In this cellar, Robert Frost kept, fed, and milked his one cow. An inside flight of stairs, for winter use, led (and still leads) up to the main floor of the barn from the rear of the cellar.

Near the foot of the stone steps, in the retaining wall, there grew two apple trees — a Gravenstein and a Baldwin — which were favorites of Lesley's, for climbing. (See V, 61, 1–5.)

I, 37:   This evening walk "in the feald" was a little journey into the two Frost pastures, across the Turnpike from the Frost farmyard. Each of these pastures had its own spring of water, but the reference here is to the spring in the lower or southwestern corner of the "big cow paschur." Lesley's ellipses merely imply some of the words which are given in the following paraphrase of the most obscure lines: her father went down to the corner of the big cow pasture to see how much water was in the spring, there. He said he found a good flow of water.

One of these springs inspired some part of the well-known poem entitled "The Pasture":

> *I'm going out to clean the pasture spring;*
> *I'll only stop to rake the leaves away*
> *(And wait to watch the water clear, I may):*
> *I sha'n't be gone long. — You come too.*
>
> *I'm going out to fetch the little calf*
> *That's standing by the mother. It's so young*
> *It totters when she licks it with her tongue.*
> *I sha'n't be gone long. — You come too.*

I, 38, 6:   The words, "first part," are in the handwriting of Lesley's father.

I, 38–39:   This long walk in search of flowers can be mapped, at least in part, by means of the landmarks which Lesley mentions.

The "gate" to which she and her father first went is still visible as a ruin in the previously mentioned stone wall which serves as the easternmost boundary to the farm. It was a hinged gate, made of boards. Just beyond the gate is Lesley's "loggers' road" or "old South Road" (see the note to I, 34) which runs parallel to the wall and relatively close to it.

Instead of choosing to follow this largely overgrown road northward, toward the Island Pond Road, Lesley and her father this time chose to turn right or southward, beyond the gate, and thus to follow it downhill a short distance to Hyla Brook, where Lesley got one foot "a little bit wet."

She next mentions another landmark which is repeatedly named and variously spelled in her journals: ". . . we went clere up on clinse hill." As already noted, the record states that at the time of the Frost purchase this farm was "bounded on the south by land owned by Joseph Klein." (See note to I, 30, 5, particularly for reference to the next owner, Mr. Napoleon Guay, who was the nearest neighbor of the Frosts during the years they spent on the Derry farm.)

The stone wall marking the boundary between the Frost farm and the Klein (or Guay) farm provided Robert Frost with the central images and actions in his poem, "Mending Wall." For more details which have bearing on this poem, see note to II, 2, 3–4.

Klein's hill rises quite sharply beyond the stone wall. In a later journal entry (V, 41, 4–11), Lesley writes that she wishes it were not so rough and bare: "If cline's hill didn't have so many stones and [sweet-] fern bushes on it but had a few more big trees . . . it would look a good deal prettier . . . but now it looks rough and bare." Today, the top and sides of Klein's hill are covered with pines. There must have been at least a small stand of young trees just beyond the wall, even in Lesley's days there; enough, at least, to suggest to her father the line, "He is all pine and I am apple orchard."

According to Lesley's pleasant story, this "long walk" in search of flowers was continued from the top of Klein's hill in a direction which was almost certainly to the southeast: she says they followed a path which led them into a big upper field and "then we went out in the deep woods [this must be beyond Klein's (or Guay's) woods] and then we came to a gate and gut under it and came out in the est derry road . . ."

What she refers to as the East Derry Road can be identified quite easily. It is probable that she and her father had not yet left the Guay-farm property when they briefly came out into the "big upper field." It is also probable that when they returned to the woods and went through the "deep woods" to a roadside gate, they reached a familiar and lonely continuation of the Old Lowell Road; a continuation which makes an almost straight progression (for approximately one mile) from the Londonderry Turnpike to the Island Pond Road.

Today, what remains of that old road is locally called either Lovers' Lane or Featherbed Lane; it has only one farmhouse on it, at a point which is roughly two hundred yards southward from the Island Pond Road. Below that farmhouse, still further southward, most of the road is no longer passable except on foot; but the entire road shows very clearly on the most recent aerial map of the region. Back when this "Lane" was usable (as it was in Lesley's girlhood), it did indeed serve as a road to East Derry: it provided the shortest route to East Derry from that point where the Old Lowell Road (and this continuation of it) intersected the Londonderry Turnpike.

Lesley, relatively short-legged when she was only six years old, had her own reasons for calling this adventurous and random prowling over hills, through woods, into fields, and onto back roads, a "long walk." Her zig-zag searches for flowers, with her father, may have covered more than two miles from the beginning to the end of the walk. But as one of her crows might have flown — in a straight line — from the Frost farm to whatever point she was at, when she came out on the "est derry road," she was not more than half a mile from her home.

Her father, long before Lesley was old enough to be his walking companion, had certainly become familiar with the best stations of wildflowers in this neighboring terrain of hills, woods, and fields. His most intensive flower-gathering expeditions seem to have been concentrated primarily in the more-or-less triangular area bounded by Featherbed Lane, to the eastward from his farm; Londonderry Turnpike, to the westward; Island Pond Road, to the northward. Each side of this crude triangle is approximately one mile in length.

I, 41, 1:   Lesley's "we went danduling" is an account of how she and her father went not far from home to gather dandelion greens. She says that when the whole basketful of dandelion leaves and buds thus gathered was boiled down (as spinach is cooked), it provided servings of only two or three spoonfuls for each member of the Frost family.

I, 45, 1:   Lesley's hoop was probably the favorite of any farm-child: a light metal tire or rim which had been removed from a discarded carriage-wheel.

I, 46, 1 and 4:   The mystery or puzzlement which is at first created by Lesley's "we went to gonhols" is very quickly relieved when she adds that "gonhol had some ducs." Mr. John Amos Hall, a prize-winning specialist in raising ducks, geese, and hens, lived on a small farm on the Island Pond

Road in the nearby town of Atkinson, seven miles from the Frosts. He and Robert Frost first met while they were attending a poultry show in Amesbury, Massachusetts, and they very soon became friends. Frost was charmed by Hall's wit, his laconic way of talking, and his passion for poultry. Because John Hall died on December 16, 1906, when nearly 62 years old, Robert Frost seemed to feel free to mention him by name in two later poems: "The Housekeeper" and "New Hampshire." Hall also inspired Frost's poem entitled "A Blue Ribbon at Amesbury."

(For a more detailed account of the friendship between these two men — and for the text of Robert Frost's published description of John Hall's farm — see Edward Connery Lathem and Lawrance Thompson, *Robert Frost: Farm-Poultryman* [Hanover, N. H., 1963], pp. 16–21, 81–83, 112–114.)

I, 46, 19:   When Lesley writes that her father drove "a pretty way home" from John Hall's farm in Atkinson, and that they "came out by" Webster's farm at Webster's Corner on the Turnpike (see note to I, 14, 12–13), she implies that they returned that far on the Island Pond Road. By contrast, they may have gone to Hall's farm over a longer route: down the Turnpike as far as the Derry-Windham town line, then by way of Goodhue Road to Island Pond Road in Atkinson. (The old-fashioned atmosphere of John Hall's little farm is well preserved by the present owner who appreciates Robert Frost's many associations with that farm: the Reverend Clarke L. Blandford.)

I, 47, 5ff: Lesley's make-believe story, "in the grove," has a setting which is within calling-distance from the shed door of the Frost farmhouse: across the Turnpike and over on the western side of the "little pasture." For more details on this "grove," see IV, 4, 3, and the note on it.

I, 50, 4–5:   When Lesley writes excitedly that "the little paschur is fool of frychys," she is exclaiming, with surprise and joy, that the pasture is full of freesias — plants of the iris family, with fragrant white or yellow flowers.

I, 54, 1:   The bog where the cranberries grew wild, together with orchids, was not on the Frost property. The most convenient approach to it from the Frost farmhouse was eastward through the apple orchard behind the barn, then further eastward through a little mowing field to the gate opening on the old South Road (see note to I, 34), then to the right, or southward, beyond the gate, to the ford of Hyla Brook, and then left or eastward along the stream only a short distance. Hyla Brook drains from this bog and, as

Robert Frost's poem makes clear, sometimes dries up completely in the summer:

H Y L A   B R O O K

By June our brook's run out of song and speed.
Sought for much after that, it will be found
Either to have gone groping underground
(And taken with it all the Hyla breed
That shouted in the mist a month ago,
Like ghost of sleigh-bells in a ghost of snow) —
Or flourished and come up in jewel-weed,
Weak foliage that is blown upon and bent
Even against the way its waters went.
Its bed is left a faded paper sheet
Of dead leaves stuck together by the heat —
A brook to none but who remember long.
This as it will be seen is other far
Than with brooks taken otherwhere in song.
We love the things we love for what they are.

That is, what they are to us. This irregular sonnet (with an extra line) was written on the Derry farm, perhaps in 1906, but certainly not much later. One brook "taken otherwhere in song" by Tennyson, is compared with Hyla Brook in Lesley's 1908 journal (V, 78–79):

"The alders is one of my favorit places to go, because it reminds me of the brook that said 'I sparkle out among the fern to bicker down the valley,' and the brook out there is just like it, though there isn't any fern . . ."

The owner of the cranberry bog which provides the source for Hyla Brook was Mrs. Sarah J. Upton, widow of Mr. George E. Upton, the first Derry soldier killed in the Civil War. The widow, personally known to Robert Frost, lived almost one mile nearer to Derry Village than he did: on the east side of the Turnpike near the place where West-running Brook flows under the Turnpike. Mrs. Upton was in part the inspiration for two distinctly different poems which Frost wrote in Derry and to which he gave the same title: "The Black Cottage."

(The text of the earlier of these poems is given in *The Early Years*, pp. 592–593; the text of the later poem occurs in *The Complete Poems of Robert Frost* [New York, 1949], pp. 74–77. A photograph of Mrs. Upton's ancient house — burned down in 1922 — may be found in *Houses of the Double Range*, p. 16. The name of this Derry stream, West-running Brook, is so old that it may be found on the earliest known map of Derry. That name was consciously and deliberately borrowed by Robert Frost, and used in the poem which he called "West-running Brook." Aside from that title, however, the inspiration for that poem seems to have been derived more strongly from a recurrent and central image in the writings of the French philosopher, Henri Bergson, than from any known image or experience of Frost's, in Derry. For textual evidence, see *The Early Years,* pp. 579–581.)

I, 54, 16–17: Lesley and her father found a considerable variety of wild orchids on or near their farm. She here mentions snakemouth (or rose pogonia) and calopogon. It is probable that Frost's poem entitled "Rose Pogonias" was inspired by one of these experiences recorded by Lesley; that, in his poem, he ideally elevated and transmuted Mrs. Upton's muddy cranberry bog into his "saturated meadow, sun-shaped and jewel-small."

(Robert Frost's delight in the very large family of wild orchids which grow in New England was stimulated by his high school classmate, Mr. Carl Burell, who lived on the Derry farm with the Frost family during their first year of residence there — and who taught Robert Frost how to milk a cow. For background on Burell, see *The Early Years,* pp. 217ff, 270–272.)

BOOK II

II, 1, 8–9: Lesley, in supposing that the "holerbellu" of the crows might be their way of saying goodbye "to all of us," sadly contemplates the end of autumn and the approach of winter. Although she liked bluebirds better than crows (as her journals make clear) the crows did stay around the farm later than the bluebirds. In the fall of 1903, two years before this entry was made, Lesley's father had appropriately chosen a crow as messenger to Lesley, in an imaginary and amusing conversation which was apparently calculated to rally Lesley out of her fall sadness. Her father had originally entitled this poem, "The Message the Crow Gave Me for Lesley, One Morning Lately When I Went to the Well." Here is an early draft of the poem:

> *As I went out, a crow*
> *In the dooryard said, 'Oh,*
> *I was looking for you!*
> *How do you do?*
> *Well, I just came to tell you*
> *To tell Lesley — will you? —*
> *That her little blue bird*
> *Wanted me to bring word*
> *That the north wind last night*

That made the stars bright
And made ice on the trough
Almost made him cough
His little tail off.
He wanted to see her,
But winter's so near —
He just had to fly!
But he sent her, Good-bye,
And said to be good,
And bring in the wood,
And wear her red hood,
And look for fox tracks
In the snow with an ax
(But not catch a cold)
And get five years old,
And do everything,
And perhaps in the spring
He'll come back and sing.
He felt you don't know
How sorry to go
And leave the poor baby
(Her ribbon off, maybe)
As wild as a bear,
And no one to care
And give her her supper
But mamma and papa.
But he told me to say
He would think every day —
Every time he began a
Coconut or banana —
And wonder about her
And cry some without her.'

(The earliest known manuscript of this poem — the original trial flight, with the long title and with only one small revision, making a total of twenty-two lines in process — may be found in the Clifton Waller Barrett Collection of American Literature, University of Virginia Library. This manuscript bears a note at the bottom of it, in Robert Frost's handwriting: "This appears to be the very first of this." A later version — the forty-one-line text here quoted — occurs in a manuscript entitled, "The Blue Bird to Lesley." This manuscript, which was sent to Miss Susan Hayes Ward, poetry editor of the [New York] *Independent,* in 1906, is now in the Henry E. Huntington Library, San Marino, California. The final version of this poem, first printed in *Collected Poems of Robert Frost* [New York, 1930], contains twenty-two lines which follow the originally planned version. It is entitled "The Last Word of a Bluebird.")

II, 2, 3–4: When Lesley writes that she and her father went looking for chestnuts "in gay's woods," she makes her first journal-reference to their nearest neighbor, the picturesque and friendly Mr. Napoleon Guay, whose house and farm (purchased from Mr. Joseph Klein) stood on the east side of the Turnpike only a few hundred yards beyond and below the little height of land known to Lesley throughout these years as Klein's hill. (See the note to I, 38–39.)

Mr. Guay appears in two of Robert Frost's poems. He is first mentioned in the "Mending Wall" line, "I let my neighbor know beyond the hill." He is also the man who actually "caught my ax expertly on the rise" and who arranged for Frost to pay a visit, in "The Ax-helve" — although his name is there changed from Napoleon to Baptiste.

(For more details concerning the close and always cordial relationship between these two neighbors, Guay and Frost, see *The Early Years,* pp. 284–285, 313, 319.)

II, 3: In saying that her dog, Snider, likes to run "up in nat heads woods," Lesley is referring to the large woodlot, previously mentioned in these notes (I, 19, 4–5), as extending uphill on the northwest side of Berry Road, from the point where that road makes a corner with the Londonderry Turnpike. For Lesley, these woods began over across the Turnpike from her front door, and in II, 11, 5, she writes, "over in nat heads woods." At the time when these journals were written, she probably did not know that Mr. Head once owned the land which later became the Frost farm; that he caused her home to be built.

II, 5–6: Lesley's explanation of how her father helped her to overcome her fear of bending birches may serve as one background for his celebrated poem, "Birches," which he later described as a set of memories written in Old England when he was homesick for New England — in 1912 or 1913. He had first learned to bend birches when he was eleven years old, in Salem, New Hampshire, one of the towns just below Derry. His grammar school classmate, a daredevil named Charlie Peabody, had also taught him which birches would (and which would not) bend. (See *The Early Years,* p. 60.)

NOTES

II, 7, 7–8:   Lesley seems to be saying that she finds at least two flowers which are just as pretty in the summer as other flowers are in the spring: the blazing star (or star grass) and the gentian. In the latter choice, her father may have helped or influenced her. His favorite member of the gentian family inspired one of his early poems entitled "The Quest of the Purple-fringed [Gentian]." (For background concerning this poem, see *The Early Years*, pp. 223–224, 270, 530.)

II, 11, 13:   Lesley's mysterious word, "uthus" might be mistaken for the name of a little-known tree on which the leaves are still green even while those on the chestnut and walnut are changing color and beginning to drop off. The context should make it clear, however, that "uthus" is merely her phonetic spelling for "others."

II, 17–18:   In this account of helping her father do his shopping in West Derry, Lesley writes that they "went to Wilson's on the way over" and because "he wasn't there" they "went to Wilson's again" on the way back, "to get some meat." Mr. John Wilson, butcher, had his own small slaughterhouse and meatstore on the north side of the Rockingham Road, less than halfway from Webster's Corner to Shute's Corner. (See note to II, 25–27.) Living within less than a mile of each other, the Frosts and the Wilsons were neighbors. One of Lesley's journal entries describes (I, 16) "Going to See Mrs. Wilson."

II, 20, 4–6:   After writing, ". . . papa and i went way out in noisise land," Lesley goes on to describe certain attractive arrangements on a neighbor's farm which stretches north and west from the corner made by Island Pond Road and Cemetery Road. This farm, held in the Noyes family for eighty years, had by this time been given by Mr. William O. Noyes to his son, Mr. Sidney Noyes.

The shortest route to the Noyes farm from the Frost farm is by way of Lesley's favorite wood road, the old South Road — a distance of not much more than half a mile northward from the eastern boundary of the Frost farm. (See notes to I, 34 and I, 38–39.)

West-running Brook flows through lowland meadows behind the Noyes house and barn. The two little ponds which were originally made by building earthen dams across West-running Brook are still visible, apparently as a result of more recent work. Pines are still growing on the northern and western sides of the Noyes farm.

(Photographs of the Noyes homestead — one of the attractive architectural showpieces in the neighborhood — may be found in *Houses of the Double Range*, pp. 25–26.)

NOTES

II, 25–27:   Lesley's account of going with her father to see the football game played between "the Concord boys and the Academy boys," in October of 1905, contains her only specific reference to anything connected with Pinkerton Academy, where her father began teaching part-time just a few months later — in the spring of 1906. He became a full-time teacher there in the fall of 1906.

Pinkerton Academy still flourishes, just to the north of Derry Village and a little more than two miles from the Frost farm. As Lesley makes clear, however, this game was not being played on the athletic field immediately below the Academy campus. She writes that the game began "gust as we went around shouts cornner," which, being interpreted, means, just as they went around Shute's Corner in West Derry. At that time, Pinkerton played many football games on a public field in the Alexander Playground near Shute's Corner. That playground, or at least a large part of it, later became the site of the Alexander-Eastman Hospital.

Shute's Corner, made by the crossroads intersection of Birch Street and Rockingham Road, is one mile and one half from the Frost farm. Lesley and her father apparently walked to the game by going up the Turnpike to Webster's Corner, then southwest on Rockingham Road, to Shute's Corner.

II, 31–33:   This is the first of Lesley's many original journal-stories about fairies. (One of her original poems, about where the "fairies come and dance," occurs in IV, 6.) Her somewhat fearful preoccupation with fairies and goblins, as revealed in these journals, was very strongly stimulated by her Scotch-Celtic father, who liked to read aloud to his children from books of fairy tales. Lesley Frost still remembers hearing him read a very special one which had been written by his mother, Mrs. Isabelle Moodie Frost, and which had been published in booklet form in San Francisco, in 1884, under the title, *The Land of Crystal, or, Christmas Days with the Fairies.*

(For details on *The Land of Crystal,* and on some of the fairy tales which Robert Frost wrote for his children in Derry, see *The Early Years,* pp. 36–37, 493–496, 302–303, 557–558.)

II, 34:   The title, "Jack-o'-Lantern," is in the handwriting of Lesley's father.

II, 36, 1:   Lesley here makes her first mention of Lena Guay, daughter of Napoleon Guay and one of "the children" mentioned in Frost's poem entitled "The Ax-helve." Lena and Lesley were nearly the same age. Lena had an older brother, Eugene C. Guay, who was born in 1884.

NOTES

II, 39, 2: The reference is to the district school in Windham where Miss Esther E. Palmer was teaching. The next year, Miss Palmer entered the Plymouth (New Hampshire) Normal School, from which she was graduated in 1907. (For background on the Palmer family, see note to I, 35, 4.)

II, 39, 16–20: Lesley's "Yunys untide" is "Eunice untied." The mare ran away after it had been left untied, but didn't get far.

II, 40, 7–17: These lines are in the handwriting of Lesley's mother, who seems to be offering the child a fresh sample of well-rounded letters and well-shaped words. There are times in these journals when Lesley's handwriting approaches the gracefulness of her mother's handwriting. See, for examples, V, 1 and V, 62.

II, 41, 16–18: Lesley writes that snow was falling when she and her father drove back home from Derry Depot; that as they drove into the farmyard they noticed the "snow was thick on the henhouse [roof]." In her retrospective "Introduction" to these journals, Lesley Frost mentions the henhouses behind the barn — buildings not visible to anyone driving into the farmyard from the direction of Derry Depot. This apparent discrepancy is easily explained.

Robert Frost built at least two small henhouses on wooden runners so that a horse could be used to drag them into new scratching-places. One such movable henhouse was apparently somewhere on the slope below (but not behind) the barn on this occasion when they drove into the yard and saw the roof of it covered with snow. Two entries earlier, Lesley gave hints concerning the location of this small henhouse (II, 37–38):

"... then we went down the stone steps to see papa feed the hens then we went to seef [see if] there were eny [any] eggs and there was one and i took it in ..."

(For an account of a dramatic and significant event involving one of these movable henhouses, see *The Early Years*, p. 282.)

II, 43, 8–10: When Lesley writes that the English threshers of wheat were "whip[p]ing it with stikes [sticks] to dry it," she is describing (not too accurately) a process which she might have seen used in some Derry barns near her home: the old-fashioned use of wooden flails, hinged with rawhide and very convenient for threshing small amounts of wheat, oats, barley, on any clean tight haymow or barn floor.

This little essay on grain-harvesting in England seems to be a byproduct of Lesley's study in a book of geography, under the guidance of either her father or mother. Several other essays in her journals reflect similar read-

The Message the crow gave me for Lesley one
Morning lately when I went to the Well.

As I went out a Crow
In the dooryard said "Oh
I was looking for you!

How do you do?

I just came to tell you
To tell Lesley will you
That his little Bluebird

Wanted me to bring word
That the north wind last night
That made the stars bright
And made ice on the trough
Almost made him cough
His tail feathers off.

He just had to fly
But he sent his Goodbye

And said to be good
And wear her wreathed hood
And look for skunk tracks
In the snow with an axe
And do everything
And perhaps in the spring
He would come back and sing.

R.F.

This appears to be the very first of this

A Poem for Lesley
Early draft of "The Last Word of a Bluebird,"
written by Lesley's father, Derry farm, 1903

The Frost Children at the Derry Farm, 1908
Marjorie, Lesley, Irma, Carol

The Frost Family at the Lynch Farm, 1908

Back View of the Derry Farm, 1968

Robert Frost Raking Hay, Derry Farm, 1908

The Lord Protector.

Once there were three little girls who were afraid
of almost everything when they were away from home
engines and electric cars and automobiles and
road rollers and bears and ~~giants~~ and cannons.
But when they were at home they felt perfectly
safe because they had a little brother there just
a little bit smaller than they were who was a
great hero. He always walked about with his
chin close in to his neck and his fists in the pockets
of his new trousers. He kept almost whistling.
All about the yard, like bones in front of a lion's
den, were scattered the sticks and clubs that
none but he could wield and the carts and
boxes and things he had broken by not playing
with them gently enough. When he heard
a wagon coming down the road, he would
come to the barn door to let people see that he
was on guard. As long as they went by it was
all right. He had a terrible smile, a terrible
smile – He made the three little girls feel
perfectly safe ~~perfectly~~ even at night.

Carol As Hero, Age Four
One of sixteen sketches written by Robert Frost
on the Derry farm, for his children

Robert Frost at Pinkerton Academy, 1910

Robert and Elinor Frost, 1911

Elinor Frost at Willoughby Lake, 1909

The Frost Children, 1911
Lesley
Carol
Irma
Marjorie

ing and study in fields of elementary astronomy, botany, geography, history, literature, and physics. Proud of her steadily accumulating knowledge, she later gives a pleasant glimpse of how "the children" in her family challenge her attempts to educate them (VI, 17):

". . . The children think it is very curious about all the things in the world that I tell them about, they hardly beleave it and keep saying 'how do you know' . . ."

II, 48, 1–6:   Some puzzling words in this passage may be translated, with the aid of the context, as follows: ". . . but I don't think you would like it. And, too, it would be kind of hard, too, because after being down in that warm State [Florida?], it [New Hampshire winter climate] would chill you, kind of. . . ."

II, 50:   It is surprising that no story in Lesley's journal mentions an exciting ride she took in this "one-horse open sleigh," when the horse shied in such a way that the sleigh was tipped over and Lesley was catapulted into a snowdrift. That adventure, as described by her father and as told from his viewpoint, is given in *The Early Years*, p. 314.

BOOK   III

III, 1–2:   Lesley's "berus coner (Berry's Corner) is where Miltimore Road branches off Berry Road — four-tenths of a mile from the Frost farm. Her "patisens coner" (Patterson's Corner) is where Berry Road joins the Windham Road, nearly a mile from the Frost farm.

Not far from Patterson's Corner, at the time Lesley made this entry, stood the only homestead on that part of Berry Road which stretches between Miltimore Road and the Windham Road. Back in the days when the owner and occupant of this homestead (and of the farm with it) was a man named Gregg, the present Berry Road was known as Gregg Road — and is still so listed on the current U. S. Geological Survey Map (Manchester Quadrangle). When Mr. Marshall Merriam owned much land on either side of this road (see note to I, 19, 4–5), it was called Merriam Road. When Mr. Fred M. Berry rented and occupied the Gregg farm, at one end of this road, while Mr. Frank O. Berry owned and occupied the former Merriam farm (or at least that part which had not been sold to others), this road became the Berry Road.

During the brief time Mr. Patterson rented the Gregg farm, Lesley may have been the only one who called the corner, beyond his farm from her house, Patterson's Corner. He remained on this farm so briefly that no record has been found of his full name; but Lesley had a particular reason for remembering him, as she explains on IV, 54: from Mr. Patterson the Frosts bought their beautiful and frisky gray mare, Eunice. In IV, 55, dated December 6, 1906, Lesley writes, "we sold unice to mr berry." On the same page she adds, parenthetically and retrospectively, "patersin had gone and a man named osgood had come to live there."

Mr. Albert E. Osgood, who also rented rather than bought the Gregg farm, specialized in raising hens just when Lesley's father was shifting over to teaching. Her entry for May 7, 1906, on III, 22, tells of how she and her father stopped at the Osgood farm to admire 250 newly hatched chickens: "they were very quite [quiet] i pikt one up . . ." Less than two years after this farmyard call — on March 20, 1908 — Mr. Osgood died of cancer at this Gregg farm. Lesley Frost still remembers how miserable, frightened, and lonely she was as she waited outside Mr. Osgood's farmhouse, on the day when her father went there to make his last visit with this dying neighbor.

(At least once in her journals [III, 22, 2], Lesley refers to Patterson's Corner as Osgood's Corner. Although the Gregg-Berry-Patterson-Osgood homestead burned down in 1928, a photograph of it may be found in *Outlying Districts,* p. 155, together with a photograph of the Soly house, which now stands on the same site.)

III, 3, 6–7: When Lesley writes that her mother "went down to miss pamus," she is again referring to Miss Esther E. Palmer. (See the notes to I, 35, 4 and II, 39, 2.)

III, 8–9: Some pleasant background for one of Lesley's father's poems may be derived from these very similar journal entries:

"One day Rob let the cow out doors and she ran away . . . and we had to go . . . after her." (I, 14)

"We took the cow and tied her down by the nut tree to eat grass . . . and she got loose and Rob and I tried to catch her but we could not for quite a while." (I, 49)

"Come here, dog. Go and get our cow. She has gone into the woods." (I, 21)

"One day my doll was in the kitchen and she heard the cow getting out and she screamed for us." (III, 1)

"One day our cow got out and went down the Windham Road and papa went after her . . ." (III, 8–9)

Such recurrences clearly indicate that the poet-as-farmer must have been irked by the amount of time he spent chasing this fractious bovine. No wonder, then, that when he made a mock-heroic farm fable out of these experiences he endowed the fable with some highly moral and even re-proachful overtones:

THE COW IN APPLE TIME

Something inspires the only cow of late
To make no more of a wall than an open gate,
And think no more of wall-builders than fools.
Her face is flecked with pomace and she drools
A cider syrup. Having tasted fruit,
She scorns a pasture withering to the root.
She runs from tree to tree where lie and sweeten
The windfalls spiked with stubble and worm-eaten.
She leaves them bitten when she has to fly.
She bellows on a knoll against the sky.
Her udder shrivels and the milk goes dry.

(For evidence that a convenient "knoll against the sky," for such bellow-ing, might have been Klein's hill, see Lesley's description of it as given in V, 41.)

III, 16, 1:   Only seven years old when she wrote this account of the adven-tures of Odysseus, Lesley here shows how early she heard her father reading from a translation of a work he greatly admired. Years later, in 1936, when asked to make a list of ten of his favorite books, he started as follows:

"*The Odyssey* chooses itself, the first in time and rank of all ro-mances. . . ."

III, 23, 5:   Lesley's "singcwafoles" are "cinquefoils."

III, 27:   All of Lesley's journals dramatically illustrate the ways in which her parents taught her to enjoy "sheer morning gladness at the brim" and encouraged her to make her own individual responses to everyday won-ders. When she says of the hummingbirds, "They can stand right still in the air," the excitement is hers. But the reader can almost hear her father calling attention to this detail. Robert Frost later tried to catch in verse his own sense of wonder over this identical "sleight of wing." His poem, "A Prayer in Spring," written while he was living on the Derry farm, deserves to be quoted here, entire, with special reference to the third quatrain.

A PRAYER IN SPRING

Oh, give us pleasure in the flowers today;
And give us not to think so far away
As the uncertain harvest; keep us here
All simply in the springing of the year.

Oh, give us pleasure in the orchard white,
Like nothing else by day, like ghosts by night;
And make us happy in the happy bees,
The swarm dilating round the perfect trees.

And make us happy in the darting bird
That suddenly above the bees is heard,
The meteor that thrusts in with needle bill,
And off a blossom in mid air stands still.

For this is love and nothing else is love,
The which it is reserved for God above
To sanctify to what far ends He will,
But which it only needs that we fulfill.

III, 35, 1–19: Lesley here describes the workings of a familiar home-made collar-contraption which is fashioned around the neck of the calf to make the mother cow cooperate in helping to wean the calf. (See note to I, 37.)

III, 36, 7: Lesley's "perniss" are "peonies."

III, 48–49: She here describes her going with her parents to participate in a typical small-town New England Fourth-of-July celebration, with fireworks and a bonfire. But there is an obvious mistake in her dating of this account. Her two previous entries are dated June 27 and 28, as she moves closer and closer to July 4. This account of an event which occurred "night before last" should plainly have been dated July 6, rather than June 6.

III, 54: In her retrospective "Introduction," Lesley Frost makes much of the fact that she was taught to memorize many lines of poetry. Here, she follows Allingham's punctuation so carefully that she must be copying "The Fairies" from a printed text. Such copying may have been part of her father's strategy for helping his children to learn a poem by heart. There is a later hint that Lesley was not the only Frost child who memorized at least part (and perhaps all) of this particular poem. She concludes the story of an exuberant walk with Carol and Irma as follows (IV, 69–70):

"... When we got home we all got in a row beside a front-room window and shouted, up the airy mownton, and papa and mama and marjory came to the window and *after we were through* [italics added] they all clapped their hands and we came in."

III, 63, 16: Lesley's father, apparently encouraging her to experiment with the niceties of writing dramatic dialogue, gives her some hints in his own handwriting. Her next effort (III, 64–66) is almost in dialogue form.

III, 68, 12: Lesley's father adds his word of praise, "good," at the end of her "Derry At Night."

III, 72–75: In this "Made-Up Story," the characters are real. Hilda, Vera, and Alan Harvey were Lesley's cousins: their mother, Mrs. Leona White Harvey (mentioned as a visitor at the Derry farm in IV, 21), was a sister of Elinor White Frost. The Harvey family lived on a farm in Epping, New Hampshire, at the time when Lesley made this entry. The Frosts and the Harveys, thus living within twenty miles of each other, frequently exchanged visits. One hint of these visits occurs in a letter from Vera Harvey to Lesley Frost, written in 1968. Reminiscing, and expressing the wish that she could now revisit the Derry farm with Lesley Frost, Vera Harvey continues,

"Do you think we could find the 'Alders' where we used to have picnics when we were children? There was a mossy little brook and the pale pinkish lavender fringed orchis. You walked down the stone steps and way across the field, very hot, and the 'Alders' was cool and lovely. Aunt Elinor would take a milk pail of cold milk with just enough coffee to slightly color it and sugar."

(For other details on the Harvey family, see *The Early Years,* pp. 150, 203ff, 572, 597.)

III, 78: Lesley's comments on poems to which she has been exposed, by her father, throw light on his tastes and teaching methods. He seems to have introduced her to Wordsworth through the brief narrative poem, "Lucy Gray, or Solitude," which Lesley finds "a little to[o] sad." He may have read aloud to her Wordsworth's sonnet, "To Sleep." She had trouble in getting to sleep, on some occasions, and he may have thought she would therefore be particularly sympathetic in her response to this poem. Apparently not satisfied with her brief and cursory handling of Wordsworth in this written assignment, he seems to have asked her to try again, a few days later. He seems to have suggested that she might like to select a few of her favorite lines from Wordsworth's poems, and quote them.

In her second try (III, 85–87), she begins by saying (as though she were anxious to please her father), "I like Wordsworth's poems about best of all." She first chooses the closing lines of "The Solitary Reaper" to quote:

> *The music in my heart I bore*
> *Long after it was heard no more.*

After quoting the familiar last line from "I Wandered Lonely as a Cloud," she immediately returns to "The Solitary Reaper" and quotes four lines from the second stanza — with just enough inaccuracy to suggest that she is writing these lines from memory. Again she mentions the sonnet, "To Sleep," and now she chooses from it her favorite line:

> *Smooth fields, white sheets of water, and pure sky.*

This line, she says, "makes you want to go to sleep, when you think of it." (Her father probably showed her how the nicely sustained vowel sounds help to achieve the lullaby-effect in this line.) She concludes with praise for the rainbow image in "My Heart Leaps Up When I Behold." For the moment, then, and very strongly under her father's influence, she calls Wordsworth her favorite poet. In three months she will be insisting that the poem she likes best of all is by Tennyson. (See the note to III, 123.)

III, 88–89: Lesley's fine account of her travels around her farmyard, in paths dug through deep January snow, gives the impression that the pattern of the paths must have been labyrinthine. She is using her imagination in a way which must have pleased her father. She describes five paths: one to the woodpecker tree, one to the mailbox at the corner of the driveway and the Turnpike, one to the barn, one to the pump, and one to the piazza steps. But it is probable that the path from the piazza steps went past and even very close to the pump from which all their drinking water was obtained; the pump with its tub-shaped trough, mentioned in the poem written especially for Lesley. (See note to II, 1, 8–9.) In fact, two straight-line paths, intersecting each other near the piazza steps, could have included all five of those paths so pleasurably described by Lesley.

Later in her journals, she describes how she herself shoveled a path from the barn to the piazza, then down to the pump and, beyond it, to the woodpecker tree. (See IV, 49.) Perhaps her best account of one extraordinary snowpath-shoveling, to the pump, occurs in V, 32. In her girlhood, the pump and well were located between the driveway and the retaining wall, approximately on a line with the front of the house. At present, the house is supplied with water from another well, newly dug below the retaining wall and not far from the "woodpecker tree"; but the water from this well is now delivered to the house, underground, by an electric pump.

III, 90: At the top of the page, Lesley's father shows her that the correct spelling for "Ascidinses" is "accidents."

III, 94, 1–2: Lesley's reference to "mr dooly in peace and war" reflects her father's great delight in Finley Peter Dunne's first volume about the Irish saloon keeper: *Mr. Dooley in Peace and in War* (1898).

III, 99–100: This account of how Lesley's father "came up with the lantern" after she had gone to bed "and asked me if i would like to see the northern lights" again offers a glimpse of his knack for arousing her excitement over natural mysteries. One of the most revealing touches is her conclusion: ". . . it was awful qeere and we wondered and wondered what made it."

III, 116, 2–3: Much lies behind Lesley's story for May 9, 1907, beginning, "The first time we went after inicinc [innocence, or bluets] was when papa was strong enough to go out [through] the gate [to the old South Road]." Her father, having begun to teach full-time at Pinkerton Academy in the fall of 1906, worked very hard in carrying out his responsibilities during the fall and winter terms. Then he collapsed and suffered a very serious pneumonia illness. At the time, the aged Dr. David S. Clark was ill, and as a result the Frost family made its first acquaintance with young Dr. Charles E. Newell. Frost remained an invalid, during March and April of 1907, recovering very slowly from his first bout with pneumonia. (See *The Early Years,* pp. 334ff.)

III, 123: When Lesley now says that her favorite poem is "sir richard granvil," she is referring to Tennyson's ballad entitled "The Revenge" — the title being the name of Sir Richard Grenville's famous ship. It is noteworthy that she likes in particular the "war like sound to it." Her various and favorable discussions of war, in her journals, further hint at the influence of her father, in this regard. See, for example, "War is a good thing, if you have a good reason for it." (III, 124)

III, 128: The cellar hole of the "old house" which was "burned down" (on Fast Day of 1867) is identified in the note to I, 19, 45.

BOOK IV

IV, 2, 1: The topical question, "Why do we fire guns on July 4?" is in the handwriting of Lesley's father.

IV, 4, 3:   The "big grove" of pine trees stood on the western edge of the "little pasture," across the Turnpike from the Frost farmhouse. Lesley's "big grove" was flanked to the north by a stand of hardwood trees, and it was presumably along the edges of these two groves that she found the partridge berries. Later (in V, 78), she describes her "little grove" of six pine trees in the "big pasture":

". . . a little round grove out there of about six trees and they all touch together at the top and make a lovely shade to sit under."

IV, 5, 6:   Lesley's repeated references to "grandpa" are to Mr. Edwin White, father of Mrs. Elinor White Frost. He lived in Lawrence, Massachusetts, and frequently visited the Frosts in Derry. Several years later, he was with them in Derry Village when he suffered a heart attack and died suddenly — on May 26, 1910. (For further details concerning Mr. White, see *The Early Years*, pp. 135, 151, 211, 308, 571.)

IV, 9, 6:   The location of the Osgood farm is described in the note to III, 2, 3; a more precise location of the thunder-blasted oak is given by Lesley in IV, 11.

IV, 10, 5–11:   It may have been after a conversation with her father concerning the likenesses and differences between stars coming out at dusk and fireflies beginning to appear in the twilight that Lesley was encouraged to build a poem out of these analogies. She does very well indeed, for a beginner. But her father was no beginner when he made something more out of the same comparison by invoking wordplay in which the fireflies are viewed as actors in their attempts to emulate the heavenly bodies:

FIREFLIES IN THE GARDEN

Here come real stars to fill the upper skies,
And here on earth come emulating flies,
That though they never equal stars in size
(And they were never really stars at heart)
Achieve at times a very star-like start.
Only of course they can't sustain the part.

IV, 10, 12–17:   Lesley's poem about the "peepers" is partially related in subject matter to her father's poem, "Hyla Brook," quoted in the note to I, 54, 1.

These two separate names for the same family of little frogs may raise questions as to which name is the more precise in identifying the almost invisible creatures which sang entertainingly to the Frosts, every spring-time, down among the alders. In a letter to his English friend, Mr. John W. Haines, Robert Frost wrote under date of April 25, 1915, "I'll write you out a little poem about the brook on my old farm [in Derry]. The Hyla is a small frog that shouts like jingling bells in the marshes in spring." Strictly speaking, a hyla is a tiny tree frog of the genus Hyla; but there are several subfamilies in the classification. *Columbia Encyclopedia,* in the article on "tree frog," mentions "the spring peeper, which inflates a large throat sac when delivering its familiar trilling call in early spring. *Encyclopaedia Britannica,* in the article on "frog," mentions ". . . *Hyla versicolor,* green, gray or brown, with a loud croaking voice, and *Hyla crucifer,* the spring peeper, having a shrill piping voice." It would seem, then, that both Lesley and her father were correct in using these different names for one and the same frog; but that Lesley's choice was more precise.

IV, 11, 6:   Lesley's "through another gate" refers to the wooden gate in the barbed wire fence between the two pastures. (See note to I, 19, 4–5.)

IV, 13, 12:   The date is in the handwriting of Lesley's father.

IV, 19:   Lesley again seems to echo what she has been told by her father when she describes the old South Road, now, not as the "loggers' road" but as "one of the little woodsy roads that used to be a road that teams road [rode] on and a few scattering houses were along . . ." (See notes to I, 34 and I, 38–39.)

IV, 21, 1–11:   Robert Frost's rage against hunters and hunting, as here reflected, finds oblique expression in some of his poems. Consider, for example, the scorn and impatience not far below the surface in these lines from "Mending Wall":

> *The work of hunters is another thing:*
> *I have come after them and made repair*
> *Where they have left not one stone on a stone,*
> *But they would have the rabbit out of hiding,*
> *To please the yelping dogs.*

Compare these lines with one of Lesley's journal observations which seems to echo her father's practical and farmer-like complaint:

"On the way over to the big grove, we found the stone wall knocked down, in two places, and Carol found a shotgun shell . . ." (II, 14)

Perhaps the best metaphor which her father built around his dislike for death-dealing sportsmen is contained in another poem he wrote while living on the farm in Derry (although he did not publish it until many years later): "The Rabbit Hunter."

IV, 21, 11–12:   Lesley's "arnt Leoner" is identified in the note to III, 72–75.

IV, 23–24:   This "cow story" about a bull is easily recognizable as one of Lesley's "made-up" stories.

IV, 28, 1:   A New Hampshire child, conditioned by colloquial mannerisms, Lesley is regionally correct in referring to the leaves of a poplar tree as "popel" leaves, although the preferred spelling is "popple."

IV, 31–32:   The little stories written especially "for Carol" and "for Irma" suggest that Lesley may have seen in manuscript some evidences that her father was, at this time, writing out many of his own stories which he "made up" and told to "the children" at bedtime. (See notes to I, 6, 16 and II, 31–33.)

IV, 34, 2:   Lesley's "while papa was at school yesterday" is her only reference to his having chosen to give up farming and to devote much time to his teaching duties at Pinkerton Academy in Derry Village. (See the note to III, 116, 2–3; see also the preliminary note to VI.)

IV, 47, 11:   The "mr. percins" who was going to take the two-wheeled gig to Derry was a very agreeable and cooperative neighbor, Mr. George Perkins, who lived near the top of Ryan's Hill, on the Londonderry Turnpike, less than a mile southeast of the Frost farm. Mr. Perkins and his wife, Louella, baked as many as fifty loaves of bread a day, in their kitchen, and delivered them, by means of an enclosed baker's wagon, to various stores in West Derry and Derry Village. His considerateness was demonstrated in his voluntary offers to collect mail at the West Derry postoffice for his Turnpike neighbors, and his delivering the mail to them, gratis, as he passed their farms on his way home. Lesley makes a passing reference to this habit, in V, 35; she also gives another attractive glimpse of Mr. Perkins in her story about the young marsh hen (IV, 73–74).

(A photograph of the Perkins home may be found with the name of a later owner, Mr. Joseph J. Szczuca, in *Outlying Districts,* p. 135. The gig, mentioned by Lesley, figures in other stories about her father's difficulties with the mare, Eunice. See, for example, *The Early Years,* pp. 314–315.)

IV, 53:   Lesley's brief history of the horses owned by the Frosts on the Derry farm is dated, "Dec. 6, 1906." For an account of the wry circumstances under which Robert Frost sold Noah (or Billy-the-Second) only a few months after he bought him, and at a higher price than he had paid, see *The Early Years*, p. 336. After that sale, which occurred in March or April of 1907, the Frosts had no private means of conveyance except shanks' mare. One hint of dependence on others for doing some errands occurs in Lesley's journal entry for July 25, 1907 (IV, 73): "Papa was going over to derry with mr percins . . ."

IV, 53, 8–9: The "docter breako," to whom the first horse was sold, figured in the early stages of Robert Frost's brief career as a farm-poultryman. He was Dr. Charlemagne Bricault, a French Canadian who had been graduated in 1890 as a veterinarian from the Montreal division of Laval University. For several years he bought eggs and "broilers" from Frost, in Derry.

(Details concerning various collusions between Frost and Dr. Bricault are given in *The Early Years*, pp. 251 ff. For other details, and for the text of Frost's published description of Bricault's farm, see *Robert Frost: Farm-Poultryman*, pp. 9–12, 73–77, 109–119.)

IV, 80–81: As was befitting anyone so named, Robert Lee Frost possessed an extraordinary knowledge of the battles and leaders of the Civil War. Lesley Frost recalls that this Civil War game, "probably played with dice," was made at home, for her, by her father.

BOOK V

V, 30–31: This time, Lesley seems to be sharing her father's own sense of storm fear, particularly in the following passage:

". . . I didn't want to go to bed because you could here [hear] the wind outside whistling around the corner of the house and coming in every crack in the windows and the fine sharp flakes banging against the window pane, and then I was such a bad dreamer that I was afraid I might dream . . ."

Robert Frost's poem entitled "Storm Fear" was apparently written soon after Lesley and her parents reached the Derry farm — at least before Carol was born. Internal evidence on this point is at least suggested by what seems to be an oblique reference to Lesley in the lines, "I count our strength, / Two and a child . . ." Here is the entire text of the poem:

STORM FEAR

When the wind works against us in the dark,
And pelts with snow
The lower chamber window on the east

And whispers with a sort of stifled bark,
The beast,
'Come out! Come out!' —
It costs no inward struggle not to go,
Ah, no!
I count our strength,
Two and a child,
Those of us not asleep subdued to mark
How the cold creeps as the fire dies at length, —
How drifts are piled,
Dooryard and road ungraded,
Till even the comforting barn grows far away,
And my heart owns a doubt
Whether 'tis in us to arise with day
And save ourselves unaided.

V, 43, 9–10: In her "Introduction," Lesley Frost speaks of the ways in which her father encouraged her to use analogies and metaphors. In this little piece of science-fiction, after she has described an object as "a little ellipes [ellipse] all red[d]ish brown color and red hot," her father has added a suggestion of how she could make her image more vivid by using this analogy: ". . . and shaped like the core of an onion."

V, 52, 2: Lesley is nearly eight years old when she writes, "Yesterday I went to church the first time." This first time may have been the last, during her years on the Derry farm. Her father, although privately devout, was not a church-goer; her mother was outspokenly a non-believer. The tensions thus created between Lesley's parents over matters of religious belief and unbelief find occasional reflections in these journals. It may be noticed that she never mentions God in any of her delighted exclamations over the beauties and wonders of nature; that her nearest reference occurs in her story about the man who, by means of pills, created some immortal people (IV, 58):

". . . and at last he got to [i.e., two] or three done . . . people called them angels and the men that were im[m]ortals were called gods and some beleave that there are [such] and some don't."

Lesley's awareness of tensions between belief and unbelief is again revealed briefly in the story which contains one of her two references to the Bible (VI, 51, 8–13):

". . . This little girl as I have said was very imaginative and thoughtful and all her life she beleived religious things from the bible that weren't true and at last became a nun."

The other Bible reference occurs in her account of how she and her mother, in church, did not participate in the singing:

"The first thing we did was to have all in church stand up and sing something out of the bible all at once, but mama and I didnt sing. . . ."

V, 52, 13:   The Reverend Charles L. Merriam, pastor of the Congregational Church in Derry Village, helped Robert Frost secure the teaching position at Pinkerton Academy. Additional details concerning the friendship of these two men are given in *The Early Years,* pp. 317–319, 328, 329.

(A photograph of the Congregational Church, much as it appeared when Lesley visited it, may be found in *Houses of Derry Village,* p. 40.)

V, 59, 7:   Between "stove" and "high," Lesley's father has added, "for it isn't as." He has also added the last eight words on the next page.

V, 61, 2–6:   For the location of the stone steps, see the note to I, 36, 2–3.

V, 86–88:   As would be expected, Lesley's "Favorite Books" are some of her father's favorite books. She finds that the bookcase in the front room contains one hundred and twenty-five volumes, among them being separate books of poems by Matthew Arnold, Coleridge, and Tennyson. She implies that her father owned both editions of Francis Turner Palgrave's *Golden Treasury of Songs and Lyrics:* the first, published in 1861, and the "second series," published in 1896. When she says she likes Matthew Arnold because he writes "always about some trouble and that makes you crazy to hear the end to see whether it is going to come out all right or not," she is probably thinking of "Sohrab and Rustum," which her father was then using as one of his texts at Pinkerton Academy. The only Coleridge poem she mentions is also a "trouble" poem; this time one in which "somebody did something wrong and that made them have the trouble, its name is the anceint mariner." As for Tennyson's poems, "my favorite one is king arther now" — presumably the first part of *Idylls of the King.* In conclusion, she decides that of the six books she has sampled in "the biggest bookcase in the front room," her favorite is going to be the *Poems* of the devout Jean Ingelow. Retrospectively, in her "Introduction" to these journals, Lesley Frost singles out Jean Ingelow's poem, "The High Tide on the Coast of Lincolnshire, 1571."

(Some of the books in that front room bookcase were inherited by Frost from his mother, and the chances are strong that he had her copy of Jean Ingelow's *Poems.* Some of these books were gathered by Frost during his student days at Dartmouth — where he acquired Palgrave's *Golden Treasury* — and at Harvard. For many pertinent details, see Arnold Grade, "A Chronicle of Robert Frost's Early Reading, 1874–1899," *Bulletin of the New York Public Library,* Vol. 72, No. 9 [Nov. 1968], pp. 611–628.)

V. 87:   On this page, Lesley's father has given her several kinds of help. He has added a paragraph sign, and in the next sentence thereafter he has made some deletions which tighten up the sentence structure. At the top of the page, he has made several notations, two of which are related to this problem of sentence-tightening. Near the bottom of the page, he has added the modifying word, "rather."

V, 94, 2–3:   A continued story lies behind Lesley's entry for April 21, 1908, beginning, "Next summer we are going to the white mountains again." Her father, throughout his years on the Derry farm, suffered acutely from annual attacks of hay fever — as soon as the ragweed pollen began to dust the air. In August of 1906 he sought relief by going alone to a refuge frequented by many hay-fever victims: Bethlehem, New Hampshire. He stayed there as a paying guest in the home of an Irish farmer named Mr. John Lynch. The Lynch family treated him with such friendliness and cordiality that he asked if he might rent space enough in the Lynch home for his entire family, the next summer. Assured that there was plenty of room, he did bring his wife and children to the Lynch farm in August of 1907, and they stayed into September. As Lesley predicted, the Frosts returned to the Lynch farm in the summer of 1908. Unfortunately, she made no entries in her journal during either one of these visits.
   (For more details on these visits, see *The Early Years,* pp. 342–346, 565–567.)

V, 94, 9:   Lesley hopes that when they get to the White Mountains she and her father will climb Mount Lafayette, one of the high mountains in the Franconia Range, relatively near Bethlehem.

V, 95, 15 and 17:   The four words of interlinear addition are in the handwriting of Lesley's father.

V, 100, 7:   Robert Frost has added the title, "The Hobble Bush," and near the end of the next page he has indicated, with an asterisk, how this trial-flight paragraph can be placed within the longer essay on the same subject.

V, 101, 2–4:   When Lesley writes that she and her father started out to find some flowering shrubs for transplanting to "our park" (Falls Bridge Park), she is mentioning one of the most cherished sanctuaries on the Frost farm:

the shaded area that stretched for more than a hundred yards along the banks of Hyla Brook.

In the spring, when there is plenty of water provided by the cranberry bog (which seems to drain Klein's hill), Hyla Brook flows through the stone-wall boundary line which separated the Upton-Frost properties, then within banks of firm ground for some distance, until it spreads through swampy land and alders as it approaches the Londonderry Turnpike. It passes through a culvert beneath the Turnpike and meanders across the Frost pastureland, on the other side. The firm ground along the banks of Hyla Brook, at the eastern edge of "our park," became a favorite picnic spot for the Frosts when some of the children were still too young to walk far. A few pines which grew on this firm ground provided a brown carpet of pine needles and gave an open space for playing. A thick board, not more than two feet in length, was nailed between two of these pines to provide a seat which was always reserved for Mrs. Frost. The brook flowed downhill near these pines with just enough pitch to invite improvement: Lesley's father let his children help him create a little dam and waterfall, there, by block-ing the stream with heavy stones which are still visible though scattered.

Westward from this little dam and waterfall — near the beginning of the alder grove — Lesley and her father built a small bridge which provided a dry approach across Hyla Brook, from the farmhouse to the "park," in the spring. The approach to that bridge was over swampy land which made for treacherous walking in wet weather; but feet were kept dry there after Lesley's father spanned the approach with a "corduroy path" which she mentions (VI, 47).

The transplanting of the hobble bush to this idyllic park was one of the many decorative improvements. Lesley describes another occasion when her father transplanted some wild orchids (rose pogonias) to "a big round wet place" he had prepared in "our alders" (VI, 1).

Mrs. Frost took so much pleasure in all of these activities within the general area of "Falls Bridge" that she called the little park her favorite retreat. Years later, after she had undergone a cancer operation made difficult by a serious heart ailment, she talked repeatedly of this park near the alders alongside Hyla Brook and said that she would like to have her ashes scattered there. Robert Frost tried to carry out her wish, shortly after her death. In the summer of 1938 he made an exploratory pilgrimage to Derry. He visited the farm, made his request to the owner, and received what seemed to him a crudely unsympathetic answer. As a result, he relinquished the plan. Eventually, the urn containing the ashes of Mrs. Frost was buried in the same plot of ground and under the same flat tombstone where the cremated remains of Robert Frost were later buried: in Old Bennington Cemetery, in Vermont.

V, 101, 11–12: The interlinear words, "the bloodroot grows," are in the handwriting of Lesley's father.

V, 102, 15 and 17: Robert Frost has added three words: "though" and "are" and "plant."

V, 106, 1: After the title, "Finding Papa's Cap." Robert Frost added as a subtitle, "A Story with a Plot." It would have been characteristic of him if he had written this much particularly for the eyes of Mrs. Frost, as a self-conscious and apologetic joke which might turn on wordplay with "Plot." At least, this narrative very subtly reveals some of his temperamental peculiarities which Mrs. Frost learned to take in stride. Another subtle revelation, in which Mrs. Frost is almost completely backstage, occurs in Lesley's account of her mother's request for a pail of water and of her father's tantalizing response (V, 32–33).

V, 110, 7–14: Mention has been made, in these notes, of the many ways in which Lesley's parents helped her to share their contagious enthusiasms. This particular story of experiences involving another walk in the woods contains some nice echoes of the cherishing ways in which Lesley's father expresses himself throughout his poetry. In the following passage, the reader can almost hear Robert Frost's voice through his daughter's record-ing of their shared observations:

"Papa and I . . . came to a cross road, which took us right out by the Clarks, and was shorter than the other way. . . . As we went along we saw a very pretty place for a house, that had a fine view of the mountains. . . . There was a fine view of Derry too and we looked around at the mountains and sat on the stone wall for a little while and then went on. At last we came to a little hill where the road turned and you could look down a long lane as straight as an arrow with two long grass ridges that went along in the middle and I could see the main road that goes past Clarks way down at the end of the lane. . . ."

Lesley Frost can still remember that this walk in the woods began some-where on the Berry Road; that she and her father followed some kind of path up through "Nat Head's woods;" that the path led them up near the top of a big hill; that they walked down the other side to a "little hill where the road turned"; that they turned, at this crossroad, and went out of the woods to the "main road that goes by Clarks" — Rockingham Road, between Webster's Corner and Shute's Corner. (The "other way" to go past Mr. Elbridge Clark's home would have been from the Frost farm, along the

Turnpike to Webster's Corner, then left, along Rockingham Road, toward
Shute's Corner.) She can also still remember that the Clarks lived on the
southern side of this "main road;" that they lived nearer to Webster's
Corner than did the Wilsons (see note to II, 17–18), whose home was on the
northern side of the same road.

Some of these memories are supported by the contour-markings of the
United States Geological Survey Map: in this area, a considerable height
of land is relatively near the Frost farm. Somewhere on the northern side
of this hill, an opening in the woods — across the downward slope of a
pasture, perhaps — helped Lesley and her father discover this "fine view of
Derry." To the north and west could be seen the cluster of houses in Derry
Village, with the red brick tower of Pinkerton Academy visible on its hillside; to the north and east, the community of East Derry, with its hillside
cemetery and the white wooden steeple of the Congregational Church.
Because no other promontory so near the Frost farm could provide so fair a
view, this one may have helped to inspire the sonnet which Robert Frost
sent from Derry to Susan Hayes Ward on August 6, 1907. The sonnet, then
entitled "Choice of Society," was published in *A Boy's Will* under the title,
"The Vantage Point," in this form:

> If tired of trees I seek again mankind,
>> Well I know where to hie me — in the dawn,
>> To a slope where the cattle keep the lawn.
> There amid lolling juniper reclined,
> Myself unseen, I see in white defined
>> Far off the homes of men, and farther still,
>> The graves of men on an opposing hill,
> Living or dead, whichever are to mind.
>
> And if by noon I have too much of these,
>> I have but to turn on my arm, and lo,
>> The sun-burned hillside sets my face aglow,
> My breathing shakes the bluet like a breeze,
>> I smell the earth, I smell the bruised plant,
>> I look into the crater of the ant.

BOOK VI

In this final Derry journal there are some mysterious gaps and silences
which now puzzle Lesley Frost herself. Perhaps these mysteries can best
be represented through a brief summary of the intermittent way in which
this journal was used during the fifteen-month period which began a little

more than a month after Lesley's ninth birthday and which ended nearly four months after her tenth.

She made and dated seven entries in June of 1908; five in July. Only two entries were made in August. No entries were made in September and October. In November, perhaps three entries were made; but only one of these is dated. Perhaps fifteen entries were made in December; but the first date is December 19.

During the next seven months, from January through July of 1909, no entries seem to have been made. The last two entries in the journal are not dated, and yet some internal evidence suggests (for reasons which will be given) that the next to last of these was written in mid-August of 1909.

A few explanations can be guessed at. Lesley did not always write in her journals during the summer months, and this fact may account for the diminishing number of "stories" during June, July, and August of 1908. As already stated in the note to V, 94, 23, the Frost family spent the latter weeks of August and the early weeks of September, 1908, in Bethlehem, New Hampshire. It would seem, however, that Lesley did not even start "playing school" when she returned to the farm in September. Perhaps she was being kept busy with other kinds of study, so that she neglected her journal at this time. But there are no known evidences, internal or external, on which to base guesses concerning the bunched entries in December and the complete silence during the next six months.

This much is known: August of 1909 witnessed the end of one way of life, for the Frost family, and a change which profoundly affected all of them. The causes of the change were developing slowly, during all the months covered by this sixth journal. From the time Robert Frost began teaching at Pinkerton Academy, in 1906, he devoted so much energy to the affairs of the Academy that he lost interest, temporarily, even in playing farmer. He was also gradually convincing himself that his children should no longer continue their education under the exclusive guidance of their parents; that they should begin attending public school. He had great difficulty in persuading Mrs. Frost; but after many months of discussion she reluctantly agreed to leave the farm which now meant more to her than it did to Robert Frost, and to move with her family to Derry Village.

This painful move was made in mid-August of 1909. The Frost family rented from a young lawyer, Mr. Lester Russell, the upper floor of a large house on Thornton Street, very near Pinkerton Academy and within easy walking distance of District School Number 2. (A photograph of the Thornton Street house may be found in *Houses of Derry Village,* p. 167.)

Soon after the Frosts were settled on Thornton Street, they made a new hay-fever-retreat to upland country. For botanizing purposes, and for specializing in ferns, they went to Lake Willoughby in northern Vermont. Their first night was spent in the home of a farmer named Connolley (whose wife inspired Frost's poem entitled "A Servant to Servants"; a poem in which Lake Willoughby is specifically mentioned). The next day, they set up their tents in Connolley's cow pasture, with his permission.

(Lesley, soon after her return to Derry from Lake Willoughby, wrote a brief "story" of this adventure. Her account, written in and later torn out of a notebook which did not otherwise survive even in part, is entitled "Camping." It begins abruptly: "We got there at night when it was all foggy over the lake. It looked so desolate. They [the Connolleys] had to fix beds for us. At Willoughby Lake it was. Some of us even slept on the floor. We got up early and went up on the hill to find camping spots. There were cows in the pasture. Papa said we want a place near the trees. We set up the tents, beginning with the big white one that Doctor [Charles E.] Nool [i.e., Newell] gave us. We got the big posts up and pegs put in, then we put the brown tent up. We had a lot of blankets that we had to spread on the ground. Up in the woods there was a spring of cold water. . . . In the night the cows came sniffing around the tent and we had to chase them away. It bothered us. . . . We had noticed that there was a steam ship on the lake. Papa had to go and see what time the ship went. We got on our best clothes and walked down to the wharf. It was ickstrodnery icksiting . . .")

The Frosts continued their camping at Lake Willoughby until school was about to begin; then they returned to their new home in Derry Village. Their farm, approximately two miles down the Turnpike, had been rented. Lesley's next-to-last entry in her sixth journal contains the only record she made, here, of all the changes. Entitled "Our New Playmates," the entry begins, "Since we have moved over here [to Derry Village] we have two new playmates, Roseina [Rosina] and John [Feinauer]." Very soon, of course, they had many more than two new playmates, and it seems probable that this undated entry was written soon after the move from the farm, in mid-August of 1909, and prior to the departure for Lake Willoughby. Nothing else in this journal gives even a hint of all the other changes which were taking place as a result of the move from the farm. When Lesley writes, after the next entry, "The End," she seems to imply her awareness that she is terminating that important phase of her education which had been conducted solely by her parents. Wistfully, she also knew that she had at the same time brought to an end all of her cherished experiences on the Derry farm.

VI, 4, 14–16:   Robert Frost, again trying to show Lesley how to tighten up her sentences, has made some deletions. Then he has added "never had" on line 14, has added "to before" on line 15, and has added "for the first" on line 16.

VI, 5, 12:   Lesley's father offers further instruction, through deleting four words and then adding the single word, "have."

VI, 9, 10–14:   Robert Frost has added "would have to" and "wouldn't" and "till."

VI, 9–10:   In this account, "What I Prophesied," Lesley makes a point which is easily missed by those who are not familiar with geography and distances in the township of Derry. She and her father were planning to walk to West Derry by way of Derry Village; but they never did get to West Derry.

Her prophecy was based more on experience than on inspiration. She knew that her father was a great conversationalist, and that while in Derry Village he would inevitably talk longer than he intended. First, he "got talking" with the Reverend Mr. Merriam — and apparently he talked for two hours. Then he "did get to talking with somebody on the street who walked clear to Webster's [Corner] with us . . ." The walk to West Derry was apparently saved for another day.

(For the location of Webster's Corner, see the note to I, 14, 12–13; for a photograph of the Congregational parsonage where Lesley apparently visited for two hours with her father, see *Houses of Derry Village,* p. 45.)

VI, 47:   Lesley describes some of her father's handiwork when she again mentions the corduroy path through the swampy land, in the alders, to the bridge. At this time, and throughout his later life, Robert Frost was very fond of any such project involving his own axe-work. He always viewed it as "just another kind of outdoor game." (See the note to V, 101, 2–4.)

INDEX

THIS INDEX is made for those who like to browse. Quotations here selected from Lesley Frost's journals are used secondarily for purposes of indexing, and primarily as a means of establishing another dimension. This anthology of excerpts will appeal most to poetry-lovers who know how to read between the lines.

Many of these selections are edited, to clarify meanings: spellings are corrected, punctuation marks are added, and some capitalizations are added.

Particular attention is called to the major topical headings. Details gathered concentrically, rather than alphabetically, under "LANDMARKS, LESLEY'S" provide a cluster of interlocking references which should be helpful to anyone trying to visualize appearances on or near the Frost farm during Lesley's adventures. Some of her most attractive verbal bouquets will be found under these headings:

ANIMALS	FEARS	GAMES	PUNISHMENTS
BERRIES	FIRES	INSECTS	RELIGIOUS BELIEF
BIRDS	FLOWERS	LANDMARKS	TREES
CELEBRATIONS	FRUITS	PLAY	VEHICLES

Another purpose of this Index is to concentrate and intensify the diffuse light shed by these journals on the personality and the activities of Lesley's father during this phase of his life, before he had earned recognition as a poet. The following topical subheads are therefore used to gather some other bouquets under FROST, ROBERT LEE:

ASTRONOMER	COMPANION	IMAGINER	TEACHER
BIRD-WATCHER	FARMER	PLAYMATE	TEMPERAMENTAL
BOTANIZER	HANDYMAN	POET	TRANSPLANTER
CAMPER	HUMORIST	POULTRYMAN	TRAVELER

INDEX

He was a gray horse. She wasn't a plug, she was a sprinter. She got away from us when she could. IV, 54

. . . we left Eunice untied and she ran away. II, 40

One day we harnessed up Eunice and went to see Mr. Clark. I, 20

The next horse we had was a red horse, too, named Roy. Mama likes that name but papa is going to call it Billy the Second. He goes like anything when he feels like it and we like him very much. IV, 55–56

KITTEN. When the family went home and left me in the bushes, I came out and began to meow . . . IV, 77

MONSTER. These animals are now growing very much more numerous than ever, and I am afraid they will conquer Russia and drive the people out, and that will mean war, too, because nobody will want to take the Russians in. VI, 68

RABBIT. There was a little rabbit and his name he could not say. IV, 32

. . . and was going home when I heard a rustling in the bushes. I looked and there was a pretty brown rabbit running away into the woods. VI, 74

RACCOON. Just as I turned, right close behind me, ready to bite me, was a coon, snapping and terribly angry. VI, 30

RAT. . . . he saw a woodchuck with a rat in its mouth. III, 33

The tracks were about as small as a rat's tracks in snow, though shaped like a cow's foot. V, 3

SKUNK. . . . and we smelled a skunk and mama went down to Miss Palmer's and she smelled it from Guay's to here. III, 3

SQUIRRELS. I hit my fists together to see if I could make the little squirrel come out. I, 19

They had shot the squirrel and papa told mama to call the sheriff, but she wouldn't till she was sure she had to. IV, 21

One day a little squirrel came to Carol. "I am going up to a new country where the men say, 'We mustn't shoot.' And you must come with me, Carol." IV, 31

I saw some holes in the trunk of the tree . . . Then I got up and looked in them and do you know what I saw? I saw lots and lots of nuts that the squirrels had put there II, 9

I had brought an old handle of umbrella up on my shoulder, the way I had seen gunners carry theirs, to play shoot a partridge or squirrel or anything I happened to see. The minute I saw the squirrel, it was off my shoulder and I had my hand on a little piece of iron I had put on there for a trigger. VI, 53

WOLVES. Just then came a wolf and I grabbed a chair and hit him on the nose. I, 5

I will go over in the grove and play shoot wolves [with my bow and arrow] . . . and Snider will come over with me and bark up trees. I, 6

WOODCHUCK. We were suddenly startled by some gray thing running along in the grass. . . . V, 5

"The Woodchuck" V, 5

"Dear Woodchuck" VI, 61

"A Woodchuck's House" VI, 72–73

ZOO-ANIMALS. In the zoo [in Central Park, New York City], I remember a few animals: the elephant, the badgers . . . the giraffe, the tiger, the hippopotamus. VI, 38

Arnold, Matthew

Now I like Matthew Arnold because he is rather loud-sounding and it ["Sohrab and Rustum"?] is always about some trouble and that makes

it, and I stopped in the air about three feet [off the ground] and papa caught me. II, 2

BIRDS

BLUEBIRDS. ... in a week we will see the bluebirds ... and the bluebirds will sit up in the woodpecker tree and in the nut tree and sing to us. I, 9

Now mama had told us that pretty soon the bluebirds would come back. When we were down there I was quite startled by a song. I jumped up and said it was a robin. But mama called back, "*No, it's a bluebird!*" We went home and pretty soon the air was full of bluebirds' songs. III, 112

The birds came rather early this year. The bluebirds ... began to come before the middle of March. V, 68

"The Blue Bird to Lesley" (*see* note to II, 1, 8–9)

"The Last Word of a Bluebird" (*see* note to II, 1, 8–9)

BLUEJAYS. If you're walking in the woods, the only thing you can hear is a few chickadees and bluejays and crows. III, 107

CHICKADEES. I thought the phoebes had come [back] but papa said he could hear chickadees among them and sometimes the chickadees say phoebe so probably they all are chickadees. V, 68

CROWS. Our crows are getting ready to go South. II, 1

The crows are flocking to go South and once in a while a flock goes by, cawing ... and Marjorie pretty near cried. IV, 27

A crow flew out of the birch tree by the [kitchen] sink window. V, 8

"The Message the Crow Gave Me for Lesley, One Morning Lately When I Went to the Well" (*see* note to II, 1, 8–9)

"The Crow at the Window" III, 82

"Hitting the Crow with a Stick" V, 8–9

HENHAWK. We sit and watch for a big hawk that comes here very often. He is a white hawk, with a little black on his wings. We sit under the apple tree back of the house. The mosquitoes bother us quite a lot. We have to keep them away and the hawk, too. We scream when we see him. Once he came right down between the peach tree and the apple tree, and the hens made a noise and we yelled. III, 41

HUMMINGBIRDS. I saw four hummingbirds. One was in the currant bushes and two were around the plum blossoms ... They have a very long bill. They stick it way into the flower and get honey out, and even when they stop they keep their wings buzzing. I, 32

The hummingbirds fly all around here. They are awful, awful tiny little things. They can stand right still in the air, flapping their wings to catch a fly. It makes a noise with its wings like a bee. They like the quince blossoms very much. III, 27

JUNCOS. A great flock of juncos flew away, right in reach of my hand. VI, 74

MARSH HEN. Mr. Perkins said, "There is a marsh hen!" Papa looked and couldn't believe it was. IV, 73

OWL. The baby owl ... was one of the oddest-looking creatures in the world. IV, 1

PARTRIDGE. We were by the bushes picking witch hazel flowers when out flew a great big partridge which frightened both the "heroes." IV, 38

PHOEBES. The phoebe's color is a rather black on top, but there is a little brown topknot on his head. He is pretty, but not half as pretty as the bluebird nor the robin nor any other bird. He is cuter in habits and interesting in his ways. I always like to look at his topknot which gives a sassy little nod, once in a while. His breast is white — here he is, now, out on the maple tree in front of the house, singing, bobbing his little tail as happy as can be. V, 69–70

ROBINS. Robins will sing to us and we will like to hear them. I, 9

Two robins decided to build a nest in one of the maple trees here in the yard, and when they got it half built they gave it up and now they are building over in the little pasture. I, 51

SNOWBIRDS. I saw quite a big flock of snowbirds and they were tame. I was right under a tree and the tree was white with them over my head. III, 5

SONG SPARROW.... and after that the song sparrow [came]. V, 68

SWALLOWS. The swallows come out and twit all day

And rise and fall and circle and play. V, 114

TANAGER.... and on the way out we saw a red tanager. He had two black sides and all the rest was red. He was a tanager, sure. I, 38

THRASHER. I was reading, in a little bird book that I have, a story about how ugly brown thrashers were when they had any young ones anywhere. VI, 29–30

THRUSH.... grandpa came in ... and said he saw a nest with four solid blue eggs in it. The bird's color was brown. It was some kind of thrush. But papa said that he didn't know that any kind of thrush built [a nest] on the ground ... he did not know any kind of thrush that had blue eggs. IV, 7–8

WOODPECKER.... and the bluebirds will sit up in the woodpecker tree ... I, 9

"Black Cottage, The"
(*see* note to I, 54, 1)

Blandford, The Rev. Clarke L.
(*see* note to I, 46, 19)

"Blue Bird to Lesley, The"
(*see* note to II, I, 8–9)

"Blue Ribbon at Amesbury, A"
(*see* note to I, 46, 1 and 4)

"Bonfire, The"
(*see* note to I, 26)

Books (*see* note to V, 86–88)

In the biggest bookcase in the front room there are a hundred and twenty-five books, and there are only six that I have read out of. V, 86

Bricault, Dr. Charlemagne
(*see* note to IV, 53, 8–9)

We sold Tuckup to Doctor Bricault — I remember all about it. It was at night and the wagon was out in the yard. I was out there to see it. Doctor Bricault, with another man, had come up to get some hens. And they said they would take Billy. IV, 53

Burell, Mr. Carl
(*see* note to I, 54, 16–17)

C

CELEBRATIONS

BIRTHDAYS. A little while ago I had my six-years-old birthday and I had a nice cake and some banana pudding and we had some candy and Carol and Irma and mama and papa came to it and we had a very nice time. I, 29

MAY DAY. When we got up to the little grove a thought struck me and this is how I came to have a Maypole Day. IV, 68

FOURTH OF JULY.... I was a little afraid of the skyrockets and the

INDEX

volcano, a little. There was a bonfire at the end and . . . papa went out to help make the bonfire and then we rode home and I went to bed. III, 48–49

"Why Do We Fire Guns on July 4?" IV, 2

HALLOWE'EN. One after another, in turn, we went upstairs and back alone in the dark to see the jack-o'-lanterns. There was one in the hall, one on the top of the stairs, and one in our room. . . . Papa hung an apple up by a string to see who could take a bite out of it, alone. . . . Papa put some apples in a pail of water to see who could get one out with their teeth. . . . It was hard to go to bed after so much of a good time, for we knew we couldn't have so much fun another night till Christmas. VI, 42–46

THANKSGIVING. We had so many things to eat, we could hardly finish the last thing: mince pie, squash pie, grapes, candy, nuts, cranberry sauce, and then the turkey. . . . This is the first Thanksgiving since we have been here that we have had a turkey. VI, 71

CHRISTMAS

[1905:] It is not Santa Claus that gives me the things. It is mama and papa . . . They call him Santa Claus just for fun. II, 45–46

[1906:] Mama went down and lit the fire and we came down and dressed and came in the front room. There was a Christmas tree with candles . . . that night we lighted the candles again. III, 62–63

[1907:] Santa Claus had come out there [in the kitchen] instead of in the front room. V, 36

Cellar Hole, Lesley's Favorite

(*see* III, 128–129, and the note to I, 19, 4–5)

Chester, New Hampshire

We went to Chester, yesterday, to see Miss Swan. It was nine miles to Chester and three miles when we got into Chester. II, 28

Children (as seen by Lesley)

Last night, when the children had gone to bed, mama, I, and papa took a little walk. I, 37

We will have to be pretty careful of the children, because they will want to eat them when everything is green. I, 42

At night, when we took the children up . . . III, 7

The children think it is very curious about all the things in the world that I tell them about. They hardly believe it, and keep saying, "How do you know?" VI, 17

Civil War

Papa and I have a game of the Civil War. We are in the Blue Ridge Mountains, where Jackson did his famous fighting, and we have the Shenandoah River. And we have Richmond and Washington, and we have the Rapahannock and the Rapidan . . . IV, 80–81

Clark, Dr. David S.

(*see* note to I, 20, 5–6)

One day we harnessed up Eunice and went to see Mr. Clark. I, 20

Clark, Mr. Elbridge

(*see* note to V, 110, 7–14)

Papa and I went to walk last night and came to a crossroad which took us right out by the Clarks' and was shorter than the other way. V, 109

Clark, Mr. Lowell M.

(*see* note to I, 20, 5–6)

Clark, Miss Sylvia

(*see* note to I, 20, 5–6)

"Robert Frost: The Derry Years" by, (cited in note to I, 20, 5–6)

"An A No. 1 Sundown" written for, (cited in note to I, 20, 5–6)

INDEX

Climbing Trees

I like to climb trees very much, but mama doesn't like me to, because I tear my stockings. II, 5

I was scared to swing with birches, but now I am not so much scared, because it won't hurt me. II, 5

I climb other trees, but they don't swing as the birches do. . . . I climb oak and maple . . . I climb apple trees and those don't swing at all . . . II, 6

The trees that I like to climb best are two of those down the stone steps. One is a Gravenstein tree and the other is a Baldwin tree. V, 61

One thing in the climbing tree business that stops us from climbing the trees as much as we would like to is that mama won't let us climb them only once in a while for it tears our stockings and she hates to mend them and that almost makes us cry sometimes. The one that she lets us climb the most is one the right hand side (down the stone steps as you go down) for it has got such a small trunk and you don't have to pull yourself up and tear your clothes. V, 62

Cline's hill

(*see* Klein's hill)

Coleridge, Samuel Taylor

. . . I have only read one of his, but that is a trouble [poem], too. But his is a different kind of trouble, for this is because somebody did something wrong and that made them have trouble. Its name is "The Ancient Mariner." V, 88

Concord, New Hampshire

There were Concord boys, there, and [Pinkerton] Academy boys . . . II, 26

Corduroy Path

(*see* note to V, 101, 2–4; *see also,* under LANDMARKS)

Cranberry Bog

(*see* note to I, 54, 1; *see also,* under LANDMARKS)

D

Derry Township

(*see* note to I, 1, 10–11)

Derry Village

(*see* note to I, 1, 10–11)

Saturday evening, papa and I were going to the Village. We had to go to Derry Village, first, to see Mr. Merriam a minute . . . VI, 9

East Derry

(*see* note to I, 1, 10–11)

. . . and then we came to a gate and got under it and came out in the East Derry Road . . . I, 39

West Derry (Derry Depot)

(*see* note to I, 1, 10–11)

. . . and then go to West Derry. VI, 9

"Derry [Depot] at Night" III, 67–68

Dolls

. . . sometimes I play cards with my doll, when mama and papa don't have time to play with me, and I think it is nice. I, 3

When I take my doll out of the closet I always play with it. And I took it out today and Carol and I played with it . . . he walked up and down with it and rocked it in my little chair and then . . . we undressed it and put it to bed, and swept up. I, 12

One day my doll was in the kitchen and she heard the cow getting out and she screamed for us. III, 1

Mama sent to New York for some dolls with metal heads . . . III, 31

Ruth came to see us yesterday and we had a great time playing. . . . And we played with the doll and the doll's bed. She hugged Irma and Carol awfully hard but they didn't cry at all. IV, 46

Dover, New Hampshire

One night, long time ago, a little girl came here. She was lost. She was going to Dover . . . I, 43

Dreams

... and then I was such a bad dreamer that I was afraid I might dream that thousands of little men were breaking in to carry me off. V, 30

All day long when there was nothing else to do she would dream.... All these things she loved, and hated to leave, at night, and go into scary dreams. VI, 50–51

One night, papa was away and mama was out getting Marjorie's bottle and she was crying like everything. And by and by she stopped crying. And when mama came in with the bottle there was nothing there but a great big paper of needles. [In Lesley's dream, Marjorie had been stolen by goblins or fairies; but she was found in another room.] III, 7

... the lovely half-fairyland dreams that she liked better than anything else, even better than candy, which she liked very much too. VI, 50

Dunne, Peter Finley

Mr. Dooley in Peace and in War by, (*see* note to III, 94, 1–2)

E

Ezekiel Pond

(*see* note to I, 35, 4)

F

Fairies, on the Frost Farm

(*see* note to II, 31–33; *see also* GOBLINS)

One night a big flock of little fairies came crowding into our land to live here.... they were just about as big as papa's hand. II, 31

At last I thought, "Well, she smiled at me so sweetly ... that I guess I will tell her, though there might be some magic in her kindness — for there is, in most fairies, kindness and unkindness." V, 22–23

["A Big Flock of Little Fairies"] II, 31–32

"The Fairy and the Squirrel" III, 10–11

"Carol and His Toe" III, 12–13

"Meeting a Fairy" V, 22–29

"The Fairies" by William Allingham (quoted, III, 54–57)

FEARS

Papa once made up a story about being surrounded by birch trees. And that makes us imagine that the birch trees are after us, sometimes, and yesterday we really thought a birch tree was after us. V, 82

Every night a goblin [named Jack-o'-Lantern] comes and stares in our window and three nights we have not seen him around but two nights we have. I guess the other three nights we didn't happen to look out and didn't see him. He probably was there. II, 34

I ran around a few minutes, but soon I found out I couldn't find my way home tonight, so I got in the best shelter I could and thought of home. I couldn't sleep much, I was so worried. IV, 77

... there came a bull, tearing down the hill by the back of the barn. IV, 23

... get big sticks with lots of branches on one side of them and bring them home and play they're bulls, and knock them all to pieces with other sticks, and play hook them. We have great fun. IV, 46

Papa takes them up to bed and they say goodnight, goodbye, and tell him to leave the lamp in the hall. And when I come up to bed, I have to have the lamp, too. IV, 14–15

... as we came up through the grove, we were looking out into the field and, "Bang!" A gun went off, right up by the road. And I yelled out, "You stop, now. You will have somebody hurt, next thing you know." And then I went home and told mama. IV, 22

At first, I was scared to swing with birches, but now I am not so much scared because it won't hurt me and I am not scared if it swings down with me — if it goes clear down with me. I don't like it if it doesn't. II, 5

We were scared, for we didn't expect it. The children looked at it with great surprise, and Marjorie was awfully scared. . . . It went into the blackberry patch and went down its hole. The woodchuck was more scared than we were. V, 5–6

But I didn't want to go to bed, because you could hear the wind, outside, whistling around the corner of the house and coming in every crack in the windows and the fine sharp flakes banging against the window panes and then I was such a bad dreamer that I was afraid I might dream . . . V, 30

Once when I slept downstairs, in the front room, we had a tall coal stove, then, and it was shaped something like a man, but with no arms. Well, I woke up one night and saw that in the dark, and it scared me awfully. V, 97–98

Many times I wake up and think the bureau is a big giant in the room. V, 98

Once we were playing out there, alone, and . . . I looked into the bushes and there stood a great big coon. . . . I was so astonished and yet frightened that I stood still a minute and then (though I could hardly stand up, I was so scared) I ran as fast as I could, back to the children, and told them about it. Ever since . . . the children have been afraid to even take a step down there. VI, 48

There is a little cellar that goes in under the kitchen on one side of the main cellar. Always, when I go down there in the evening, after apples, it makes me feel trembly. . . . I don't want to go back and say that I am afraid to go down . . . On the way up, it is the same again, and worse. . . . When I get to the top of the stairs . . . my hands are so full that I have to wait till someone opens the door, and then I rush in as if I were being chased by a tiger or lion. When it is over, I am glad, and sit down by the fire to eat my apple and calm my nerves. VI, 64–65

("Storm Fear" quoted in note to V, 30–31)

FIRES, AND FEAR OF FIRE
. . . and we came out to a burned-up house. I, 33

There is an old house halfway down Klein's hill, on the other side [of the Turnpike, from our house] which was burned down. III, 128

One day there was a big thunderstorm and several times we thought it struck the house. And the next day we went down to Osgood's and [just after we started down Berry Road we saw that] that big oak, halfway down the hill by the woodpile, had been struck with lightning and the bark had slid right off it and all the little pieces were scattered around, and it was on our [pasture] land, too. IV, 9

We had a fire in the meadow and we knew it would not go across the brook and [yet] it set half the field on fire. And it went to the road and it burned our grape vine. And Rob thought it would get across in the other field; that a spark might fly across. I, 31

. . . but I soon made out that it was a fire, somewhere, and I called out, "There is something on fire!" And we went outdoors and the smoke was just pouring out of that chimney, and . . . after papa said the chimney was on fire, I cried. III, 20

INDEX

... and since that, the children have been playing fire, and today Irma was afraid the house was on fire.   III, 21

"Fireflies in the Garden" (*see* note to III, 27.

FLOWERS

I went to the fairy and said, "I have finished." And she said, "What are the names of them?" And I said, "There is star grass and yellow violet and rose-petaled buttercup and lady's slipper and butter-and-eggs, and bloodroot and rue-anemone and wood-anemone and star flower and bellwort and mountain laurel and pipsissewa and clintonia and lady's tresses." V, 26–27

ANEMONE
  RUE ANEMONE V, 27
  WOOD ANEMONE III, 23; V, 27
ARETHUSA (*see* ORCHIDS)
BELLWORT I, 40; V, 27
BLAZING STAR II, 7
BLOODROOT III, 22; V, 101
BUTTER-AND-EGGS V, 27
BUTTERCUPS I, 10, 12
CALOPOGON, (*see* ORCHIDS)
CATTAILS II, 20
CINQUEFOIL III, 24
CLEMATIS
  PURPLE III, 36
  WHITE VI, 11
CLINTONIA I, 40; V, 27
COLUMBINE I, 33; V, 105
COWSLIP I, 10; V, 99; V, 101
DAHLIAS III, 36
DAISIES I, 10; III, 39
DANDELIONS I, 10; I, 41; V, 101
EVERLASTING IV, 69
FREESIA I, 50
GENTIAN II, 7
GOLDENROD I, 10
HEPATICA III, 23
HOBBLE BUSH V, 100–102
HYDRANGEA III, 36
INNOCENCE (BLUETS) I, 10; III, 23; III, 116; IV, 27
LADY'S SLIPPER (*see* ORCHIDS)

LADY'S TRESSES (*see* ORCHIDS)
LILAC III, 128–129
MILKWORT III, 128
MOUNTAIN LAUREL I, 55; III, 29; V, 26–27
ORCHIDS
  ARETHUSA III, 47
  CALOPOGON I, 54
  LADY'S SLIPPER I, 33; I, 40; III, 46
  LADY'S TRESSES III, 46; V, 27
  SNAKEMOUTH (ROSE POGONIA) I, 54; III, 47; IV, 3; VI, 1; VI, 2
PEONIES III, 36
PIPSISSEWA (PRINCE'S PINE) V, 27
PHLOX III, 36
POGONIA, (*see* ORCHIDS)
POOR ROBIN'S PLANTAIN III, 39
POPPY VI, 82
RHODORA V, 105
ROSE III, 129
SAXIFRAGE V, 101
SHADBUSH V, 101
SNAKEMOUTH (*see* ORCHIDS)
STAR FLOWER I, 40
STAR GRASS V, 26–27
STEEPLEBUSH IV, 69
VIOLETS
  BLUE I, 10; I, 23; I, 27
  YELLOW I, 30; I, 40
  WHITE VI, 81
WISTERIA VI, 12
WITCH HAZEL IV, 38

Frost, Carol (born May 27, 1902)
One day we could not find Carol's shoe and all the time we were hunting for it, it was in the oven burning . . . I, 1

There will be lots of flowers, and Carol can pick the very first ones with me . . . and I will tell Carol how to pick the long stems. I, 10

Carol and I played with [my doll] . . . and I said, "Where is the nose?" And he pointed where it was. And I asked where his [nose] was, and he pointed where it was. I, 12

Carol and Irma are such mis-

INDEX

chievous [children] that we don't know what to do.   I, 17

Pretty soon it will be time to put Carol and Irma to bed and it is over quarter of one o'clock now.   I, 18

I and Carol went . . . and got a bouquet of violets . . . and then we came home and we brought some flowers for mama.   I, 23

One day mama and I and Carol we were going to the Palmers' around that way but we got lost.   I, 35

John Hall had some ducks and we thought Carol wouldn't know what they were. And when we got there we asked him, "What's that?" And he said, "Ducks."   I, 46

I do have a nice little store in the grove . . . I do sell all different kinds of dirt to Carol and Irma.   I, 47

Carol and Irma do not like to go bare footed except in the house because it hurts their feet out doors. And it hurts my feet a little . . .   I, 53

Carol found a [shotgun] shell that they empty out after the little bullets have gone out. . . . I wished I had one but I found one on the way home. II, 14–15

. . . and mama and papa and I played puss in the corner a few minutes and Carol and Irma don't know how to play it.   II, 15–16

I found a shell on one side of the pond. It was very fresh. It looked as if it had been shot just a little while ago. Then we went home and . . . I gave it to Carol because he didn't take as long a walk as I did.   II, 21

I am going to haul stones out of the big pasture with Carol's hay cart . . . II, 22

This is the first sleigh ride Carol and I and Irma and mama have had [this winter].   II, 50

One night when Carol was asleep a goblin came upstairs and bit off his toe and Carol felt it and jumped up. III, 12

Carol cried — he was afraid — and Carol and Irma gave me lots of things. III, 14

Carol likes cinquefoil best this year. He yells out at them, every time he sees any, and calls me.   III, 24

When we came out there, the cranberry bog was all frozen over . . . We had great fun sliding back and forth. Carol walked back and forth over the ice and laughed and shouted and sang. III, 76

It was kind of hard for Irma and Carol to keep up with us but we walked kind of slow.   III, 80

Carol's tools have all been broken except the saw. The hammer and the mallet went first, then the screwdriver. III, 95

Carol thinks he can see with his ears and hear with his eyes.   III, 108

. . . and Carol and Irma came rushing into the house yelling, "Somebody's cow's out and it is running after us." IV, 23

This spring Carol and I made three or four little bean gardens. Carol let his grow till they were full-sized before he pulled a weed out of them. They were just an awful sight.   VI, 24

Frost, Elinor Bettina (born June 18, 1907; died June 21, 1907; *see* note to I, 22, 1)

FROST, ELINOR WHITE (MRS. ROBERT LEE FROST)
(born Oct. 24, 1872; died March 21, 1938; *see* note to V, 101, 2–4)

INDEX

INDEX

Frost, Marjorie (born March 29, 1905; died May 2, 1934)

... somebody came with a new baby and I like it very much ... I, 22

We all went out in the big grove. Marjorie liked it very much. She did not have a bottle. She did not cry at all and we were glad because we do not like to hold her very well — she aches your arms so. She is a good deal bigger than she was when she just came — and she is more interested in things. II, 13

... and Marjorie lay very still and looked up in the tall pines, but at last she got fussy and mama had to hold her. II, 14

"My Dreams" [about how Marjorie disappeared] III, 7

... in the spring, when Marjorie is big enough to toddle around. III, 15

... and Marjorie did not know what Carol meant when he said, "Can I have an apple?" She said, "Apple, apple." Then Carol stamped his foot ... III, 84

Christmas night we lighted the candles again, and Marjorie ran back and forth and laughed and played. III, 63

Sometimes Carol and Irma are good to Marjorie, but sometimes they like to tease her. They don't care whether she cries or not ... sometimes they play she's sick and pour all sorts of stuff down her. IV, 44

She likes to laugh and dance, but she doesn't like to cry and fuss at all. IV, 45

So away we go, down the hill as fast as we can, with Marjorie way behind, saying, "Wait for me." V, 73

We all enjoy the ride on the train very much, but Marjorie generally goes to sleep in mama's lap on the way

INDEX

[to the White Mountains]. V, 94

Carol thought it was a dragon and I thought it was a train and Irma ran for the house and Marjorie began to cry. VI, 7

After she had come to, again, she stood still, curved her lips, frowned, and said, "You almost shook my head off." VI, 37

When bobbing for apples, Marjorie would just put her mouth in [the pail] and drink, every time. VI, 45

"Marjorie's Funny Things" III, 96–97

"Marjorie and the Children" IV, 44–45

FROST, ROBERT LEE

(born March 26, 1874; died January 29, 1963)

ASTRONOMER

. . . see who would find the stars first. Rob found Venus first and I found all the rest except the Dipper . . . I found the Dog Star and the stars in the Giant. I, 2

Last night, just after I had gone to bed, papa came up with the lantern and asked me if I would like to see the northern lights. . . . They streamed right straight up into the air . . . it was awfully queer and we wondered and wondered what made it. III, 99–100

The sun is the most needed thing in the whole world. If we did not have the sun, it would be dark and cold all the time. . . . We would die of coldness and nothing would grow. IV, 51

Papa says that generally when the northern lights come, there are spots on the sun. And, what do you suppose, when the next day's paper came it said in it that there were spots on the sun, and papa said that was probably why the northern lights had come. IV, 61

Papa and I make believe we can see people on Mars, and houses and everything else on the earth. We say these things when we go after the cow at night; we say we will know more than the astronomers do with telescopes. IV, 82

BIRD-WATCHER

I thought the phoebes had come back, but papa said he could hear chickadees among them and sometimes the chickadees say phoebe, so probably they all are chickadees. V, 68

Mr. Perkins said, "There is a marsh hen!" Papa looked and couldn't believe it was. He thought it was a stick, it was standing so straight up. . . . Papa found a marsh hen in the bird book, but the one in the book was a full-grown one. IV, 73–74

I saw quite a big flock of snowbirds in the orchard and they were tame. I was right under a tree and the tree was white with them over my head. . . . Papa said he had never in his life seen a snowbird. III, 5

But papa said that he didn't know that any kind of thrush built [a nest] on the ground. He said it was very funny, he did not know any kind of thrush that had blue eggs. IV, 7–8

. . . we looked into the phoebe's nest and found five little white eggs in it. And some time after that, Rob said he heard little ones peeping in it. And I was glad, papa was glad, mama was glad. I, 36

One day papa and I took a long walk. We went to the gate and on the way out we saw a red tanager. He had two black sides and all the rest was red. He was a tanager, sure. And then he flew away and then we went on. I, 38

(see also, subheads under BIRDS)

BOTANIZER

It will be nice when spring comes. There will be lots of flowers and . . . Rob will take me to the faraway flowers, off in meadows — anemones, violets, cowslips, daisies, buttercup, dandelion, goldenrod, innocence . . . I, 10

Rob asked why the colors and smells

came to the flowers and I said it was for us and mama said that it was for the bees to take pollen off the pistils onto stamens; they saw the color and flew to it. I, 25

One day papa and I took a long walk ... and we found a lot of flowers. We found one kind of star flower — there are a lot of kinds of star flower — we found bellwort, we found clintonia, we found yellow violet and lady's slipper. I, 39–40

... we went out to the gate and went down the hill and into the cranberry bog. We took off our shoes and stockings and waded in. We found a lot of flowers. We found snakemouth and calopogon and we got a bouquet and took them up to the gate and then went and got the laurel and came home. I, 54–55

Yesterday, papa and I took a walk down to Osgood's corner after some bloodroot ... and went home and put the bloodroot in some water for mama. III, 22

The first flowers we found were innocence and next were hepaticas and violets and cinquefoil and at last anemones. The innocence we soon got tired of, because the farm was just white with them. III, 23

The pogonias grow out in our cranberry bog. It is awfully soggy and wet around it. They are very, very pretty and have a very nice smell. Papa takes off his shoes and stockings and wades into the mud — the mud goes clear up to his knees — and five weeks ago ... we went after some. Papa, I and Carol and Irma and mama ran across some white ones with a little of the pink around the bottom of the flower. IV, 3

CAMPER

When papa was a little boy ... in Salem, he lived in a tent with no fly to it. And when he went to bed at night he carelessly threw his clothes against the cloth of the tent. And it rained in the night and it soaked through the cloth of the tent onto the clothes ... and the sun came out and they hung their clothes out to dry. IV, 36–37

We set up the tents, beginning with the big white one that Doctor Newell gave us. ... Then we put the brown tent up. ... In the night the cows came sniffing around the tent and we had to chase them away. It bothered us. (*See* note preliminary to VI)

COMPANION

Yesterday, papa went over to Derry and he took me with him. II, 17

We went to the football game, yesterday ... they all shouted and made an awful noise. They had things on their noses to protect their noses from getting smashed and things on their heads and ears ... II, 26–27

We went to Chester, yesterday, to see Miss Swan. It was nine miles to Chester and three miles [beyond] ... and when we got there I had a very good time. II, 28

When I went to ride, today, there was snow on the ground and it had been on quite a while. This is the first sleigh ride Carol and I and Irma and mama had [this year] ... and papa had one, too, all alone. II, 50

Yesterday, papa took us up the lane to see if there were any [chestnuts] up there and we found a very nice tree ... and we've got half a bag full. II, 9–10

Me and papa went over to Derry and we smelled it [the skunk] all the way to Derry; but we didn't smell it on the way back. III, 3

Papa and I think we will walk to the top of Mount Lafayette, next summer, and look off at the mountains. V, 94

I always like to go down in Franconia Valley, because papa always buys some peanuts or candy for us. V, 95

FARMER

Papa uses the snow-shoveled path from the pump to the barn to water the horse and cow with. III, 88

INDEX

Papa was washing the milk pail by the sink window . . . V, 1

One day Rob let the cow out doors and she ran away from us and we did not know where she had gone. And we went down the Derry Road and we saw her tracks up the wood-road and we had to go in the deep snow after her. I, 14

We didn't have such a nice time haying, this year, because the haying men put on so much hay that we couldn't ride. IV, 85

I can see papa up that biggest tree where we got most of the apples off of, this year. I see him with the basket — the hook-basket — hung around the branch of the tree, reaching for apples. IV, 66

Nobody has [been down to the corduroy path, in the alders] except papa, one day, when he was hunting for the horse. VI, 48

(*see* subhead, POULTRYMAN)

HANDYMAN

In three weeks the snow will be about gone and . . . Rob will put up the hammock . . . I, 9

Then the path up to the piazza, that's useful to papa to carry water to the house for us to drink. III, 88

One day we got papa to tap the woodpecker tree. He bored a round hole in it and hammered a piece of a little tin can into the tree, just below the hole and put in a screw above the hole to put the pail on. He hung up the pail and we watched it drip for a few days. . . . V, 91

. . . and the smoke was just pouring out of that chimney and papa . . . took several pails of water upstairs and poured it down the chimney. III, 20

. . papa was upstairs putting Marjorie to bed . . . III, 30

HUMORIST

One April Fool's Day, papa gave me an awful fool. He made some paper flowers when I did not know it and stuck them up over across the road. Then he said to us, "Let's take a walk up the Berry Road." When we got up to the old apple tree, I happened to look at the bottom of the tree and there were the colored flowers. I went in and picked one and they came right up out of the ground with no roots on. I went home and showed everybody and they all laughed. IV, 60

When we had gone a few steps further on the other side of the brook [Hyla Brook] came papa yelling, "No trespassing on this land," which frightened both the "heroes" so they quite forgot their walk. But after we found it was papa, we were all right, and papa helped us over the brook and we came home. IV, 38

Papa thinks he knows how it [the chimney] got on fire. He says he thinks a browntail moth flew up the chimney and caught on fire. III, 20

IMAGINER

Papa and I make believe we can see people on Mars, and houses and everything else . . . IV, 82

One night a big flock of little fairies came crowding into our land to live here . . . and they were just about as big as papa's hand. II, 31

Every night a goblin comes and stares in our window . . . II, 34

One day before Christmas, papa said to us, "I am going out in the alders to see Santa Claus and I must take the axe." I tried to make him tell me what he was going to do with the axe, but he would not. . . . And we never knew till Christmas what papa went there for. It was a Christmas tree. III, 69–70

Papa once made up a story about being surrounded by birch trees. And that makes us imagine that the birch trees are after us, sometimes. V, 82

Our crows are getting ready to go South. They are having a holerbellu.

INDEX

They are getting in a line to go. Papa said that he thought that they had just chosen a king to lead them, or trying to find one who will be it. Then I thought they might be saying good-bye to all of us.   II, 1

PLAYMATE

We have some cards, and when we play with them, sometimes I deal and [sometimes] mama and [sometimes] papa . . .   I, 3

The children began to want something new to play, so papa put some apples in a pail of water to see who could get one out with their teeth. Papa got one out, and ate it.   VI, 45

That night, papa played dominoes with me and Carol, then we had supper and went to bed very happy. V, 38

Papa made a path through the thin snow on the ice and papa and me slid back and forth on it.   III, 76–77

. . . and on the way home I climbed up a high birch and came down with it, and I stopped in the air about three feet [off the ground] and papa caught me.   II, 2

POET

"A No. 1 Sundown, An"
  (*see* note to I, 20, 5–6)
"Ax-helve, The"
  (*see* notes to II, 2, 3–4; II, 36, 1)
"Birches"
  (*see* note to II, 5–6)
"Black Cottage, The"
  (*see* note to I, 54, 1)
"Blue Bird to Lesley, The"
  (*see* note to II, 1, 8–9)
"Blue Ribbon at Amesbury, A"
  (*see* note to I, 46, 1 and 4)
"Bonfire, The"
  (*see* note to I, 26)
"Cow in Apple Time, The"
  (*see* note to III, 8–9)
"Fireflies in the Garden"
  (*see* note to IV, 10, 5–11)
"Generations of Men, The"
  (*see* note to I, 35, 4)
"Ghost House"
  (*see* note to I, 19, 4–5)
"Housekeeper, The"
  (*see* note to I, 46, 1 and 4)
"Hyla Brook"
  (*see* note to I, 54, 1)
"Last Word of a Bluebird, The"
  (*see* note to II, 1, 8–9)
"Mending Wall"
  (*see* notes to I, 38–39; II, 2, 3–4; IV, 21, 1–11)
"Message the Crow Gave Me for Lesley, The"
  (*see* note to II, 1, 8–9)
"New Hampshire"
  (*see* note to I, 46, 1 and 4)
"October"
  (*see* note to I, 36, 2–3)
"Pasture, The"
  (*see* note to I, 37)
"Prayer in Spring, A"
  (*see* note to III, 27)
"Quest of the Purple-fringed, The"
  (*see* note to II, 7, 7–8)
"Rose Pogonias"
  (*see* note to I, 54, 16–17)
"Servant to Servants, A"
  (*see* note preliminary to VI)
"Storm Fear"
  (*see* note to V, 30, 31)
"Tuft of Flowers, The"
  (*see* note to III, 27)
"Vantage Point, The"
  (*see* note to V, 110, 7–14)
"West-running Brook"
  (*see* note to I, 54, 1)

POULTRYMAN

("R. Frost has moved upon the Magoon place . . . He has a flock of nearly 300 Wyandotte fowls.")

The chickens wander everywhere and they get caught in showers, sometimes.   IV, 18

We went down the stone steps to see papa feed the hens, and then we went to see if there were any eggs.   II, 38

I had to pull my cap down over my

face so the snow would not get on me and when we went in the yard the snow was thick on the henhouse. II, 41

... went over across the road in the little pasture to get leaves in bags to put in the henhouse. II, 19–20

Yesterday, papa and I took a walk down to Osgood's Corner after some bloodroot. Then we came up and talked with Osgood about chickens. He has 250 of them. They were very quiet. I picked one up... III, 22

(*Robert Frost: Farm-Poultryman* cited in notes to I, 46, 1 and 4; IV, 53, 8–9)

TEACHER

It is queer how many new things are being made in the world. Now the flying machine... They are finding some new way of making things about every two years. It makes it interesting for papa and mama and me. VI, 36

One day I was walking out into the woods. Pretty soon I heard a rustle on the east side of me. V, 22

Sixty minutes make an hour, sixty seconds make a minute. III, 4

... if we looked very closely we could see the sun move up as the earth moved around it. The sun doesn't move, but it looks as if the sun moves as the earth moves around it. V, 41

After traveling about twenty or thirty meters we came to a little ellipse, all reddish-brown color and red hot. V, 43

I am going to paint after I write my story for papa — and I like to paint pictures if I can find any nice ones. I do not like to write a story when I go outdoors, because I want to paint. And I show mama and papa them, after I paint them. I, 4

... but just then papa called me to write my story. II, 24

I play till it is time to write my story,

and then, when I have written my story, papa and I talk a few minutes and then I go downstairs and go outdoors again. IV, 16–17

Then I came in and wrote my story. III, 113

(*see,* for references to RF's emendations in Lesley's journals, notes to I, 10, 10–14; 1, 19, 13–14; I, 38, 6; II, 6, 11–13; II, 34; III, 12, 14; III, 63, 16; III, 68; IV, 2, 1; IV, 13, 12; V, 59, 7; V, 87; V, 95, 15 and 17; V, 100, 7; V, 101, 11–12; V, 102, 15 and 17; V, 106, 1; VI, 4, 14–16; VI, 5, 12; VI, 9, 10–14)

(*see also,* for oblique hints on RF's teaching methods, subheadings, ASTRONOMER, BIRD-WATCHER, BOTANIZER, IMAGINER, PLAYMATE, and TRANSPLANTER)

TEMPERAMENTAL

One day we heard a bang and we looked up the Berry Road and there was somebody shooting up there and papa went out there yelling at them. He was mad as a hatter and he found out that he was too mad because he found out they were somebody he knew. Aunt Leona was here and we had quite a quarrel about it. Afterwards, they had shot the squirrel and papa told mama to call the sheriff, but she wouldn't... IV, 21

Yesterday we were moving some chairs and tables out of our bedroom. We had started late in the afternoon and it began to get dark before we had moved them all, so papa thought we better leave them till morning for he had to go out and get the cow. He went to the place where he hung his cap, but it wasn't there and then he turned around and said, "Why, that is funny. I am sure I laid it down somewhere down stairs, for I had it on only a few minutes ago." Then we all took to hunting for it... We hunted till seven o'clock and it was quarter past six when we started and then we got so tired of it we had to let the cow stay out over night though we hadn't had any supper. We had to have bread and butter and cocoa with no milk in it and mama and papa and grandpa had bread dipped in tea, with no milk in it. V, 106–107

Papa hadn't shoveled any paths. After he milked the cow, mama wanted a pail of water, but papa couldn't get it unless he shoveled a path clear down to the pump. After he got the water pail and laid it on the piazza, he went in the barn and got the shovel and began shoveling, but he didn't hurry and make the path just the width of the shovel. He made it three times the width of the shovel . . . clear down to the pump. V, 32–33

Papa went up and knocked them off with a stick and they came down in showers. . . . We intended to pick apples, but we picked chestnuts instead. VI, 58–59

TRANSPLANTER

The hepaticas we found over across the road. Papa transplanted some over there. There is five [blossoms] on it this year. It is very pretty. They have golden centers. III, 23

We have a laurel bush out in Guay's woods. Its flowers grow in clusters. One day we took the blue-handled shovel and went out and dug a piece up and planted it by the little oak tree at the corner of the bars, and this spring papa moved it into the front yard. III, 29

We had always wanted to transplant the lilac . . . and the double-petaled roses, red and awfully pretty. And papa said he would transplant them some time, and so he did. He went and got six rose bushes and one lilac bush. III, 128–129

One day papa set out to find things to put in our park named Falls Bridge.

. . . We found something new that we had never seen before. Its name was hobble bush and it only had one flower on. But that was a surprise, for even papa had never seen it [before]. Papa dug it up and wrapped it in moss. Then he said we better go right home and plant it in our park for he didn't want to have it die. After we got home, we planted the things we were going to plant here [in the front yard]. Then we took the hobble bush and some other things out in our alders to plant. V, 101–102

Some time in June, the cranberry bog is all spotted over with little pink flowers named pogonias. . . . They are pretty pink and papa's going to move some over into our alders. They will grow there, he thinks, because he has got a big round wet place where they can begin to grow. VI, 1

TRAVELER

We went to walk yesterday. Papa and I like to go to walk. We went in Guay's woods and we found two half-pockets of chestnuts . . . When we got all we could find we started home. II, 2

One day papa and I took a long walk. . . . We went clear up on Klein's hill and turned [to go on] another path and went out in a big open field and then we went out in the deep woods and then we came to a gate and got under it and came out in the East Derry Road and walked on a little way and then went in the woods again. . . . And we found a lot of flowers. . . . We brought them home and put them in water and mama liked them very much. I, 38–40

Papa and I went to walk, last night, and came to a crossroad which took us right out by the Clarks' and was shorter than the other way. . . . As we went along, we saw a very pretty place for a house, that had a fine view of the mountains. . . . There was a fine view of Derry, too, and we looked around at the mountains and sat on the stone wall for a little while and then went on. . . . At last we came out on the other road and went along home to tell mama what we saw. V, 109–111

Frost, William Prescott
(born July 11, 1823; died July 10, 1901; *see* note to I, 19, 4–5)

Frost, William Prescott, Jr.
(born December 27, 1850; died May 5, 1885; *see* note to II, 31–33)

FRUITS, AND FRUIT TREES
The pears, cherries, apples are all in buds. Won't they look pretty when they are all in blossom. I, 24

On the fruit trees, the petals are all coming off the flowers. The ground is white with them. It looks like snow . . . I, 42

APPLES. We went to that little sweet-apple tree [in the pasture] and picked a bouquet of apple blossoms. I, 37

. . . one is a Gravenstein tree and the other is a Baldwin . . . V, 61

Papa hung an apple up by a string . . . put some apples in a pail of water . . . VI, 44–45

Always, when I go down there in the evening after apples . . . VI, 64–65

I can see papa up that biggest tree . . . reaching for apples. IV, 66

"Carol Grumpy at Apples" III, 83

CHERRIES. The Cherry blossoms came first. They are white. The trees are just loaded with blossoms. I, 24

And now the little green cherries are beginning to grow. I, 42

GRAPES. We had a fire in the meadow . . . and it went to the road and it burned our grape vine. I, 31

It [the hole of the woodchuck] was among the thickest of the grapes, for the grapes were on both sides of its hole. V, 7

PEACHES. . . . and a lot of peach blossoms. I wanted to pick some, but I thought I better leave them to come to peaches. I, 34

After we eat our breakfast we all have a peach or a bunch of grapes. IV, 16

PEARS. "Pears and Cherries" I, 24

PLUM. I saw four hummingbirds. One was in the currant bushes and two around the plum blossoms. I, 32

QUINCE. The quinces blossom the same time the cherry blossoms do. They don't smell a bit, but they make the front yard look lovely and red. III, 27

G

GAMES
CHECKERS. . . . so we have more fun in playing games together, like checkers . . . VI, 79

CIVIL WAR. Papa and I have a game of the Civil War . . . IV, 80

DOMINOES. Papa played dominoes with me and Carol . . . V, 38

HIDE AND SEEK. They play sometimes, though we always see them the first thing when we are it. VI, 79

HOPSCOTCH. . . . we played hopscotch. I do not know how [to play], but Lena Guay showed me. II, 36

JACKSTRAWS. . . . so we have more fun in playing games together, like . . . jackstraws. VI, 79

PUSS IN THE CORNER. . . . mama and papa and I played puss in the corner a few minutes. Carol and Irma don't know how to play it. II, 15–16

"Generations of Men, The"
(*see* note to I, 35, 4)

Geography Lessons, reflections of
(*see* note to II, 43, 8–10)
["Threshing Wheat in England"] II, 43–44

"The First Rubber" III, 51–53

H

I

INDEX

J

Jason, the myth of

He rolled a stone in between the soldiers that came up from the fiery bulls' teeth, and they began fighting with each other and not with him. III, 90

K

Klein, Mr. Joseph

(*see* notes to I, 19, 4–5; I, 30, 5; I, 38–39)

Klein's hill and Klein's woods

(*see,* as subheads under LANDMARKS)

L

LANDMARKS, LESLEY'S (*CONCENTRICALLY ARRANGED*)

HOME: THE FROST FARMOUSE

... and we went home and ate our supper and went to bed. I, 2

... and we made a path over the stone wall and took her over and took her home. I, 15

... and then we came home and we brought some flowers for mama. I, 23

KITCHEN

Papa was washing the milk pail by the sink window that looks out toward the corn... V, 1

When we came down stairs we ran to the kitchen door to go out and dress. As soon as we got out there we found that Santa Claus had come out there instead of in the front room. V, 36

Christmas morning, mama went down and lit the fire and we came down and dressed [in the kitchen] and came in the front room. III, 62

FRONT ROOM VS SITTING ROOM

Almost every day, about ten o'clock, mama calls us in the front room and we have to sit up on the sofa and tell stories... III, 50

We decided to put the new bookcase in the front room... right by the door that goes into the hall. IV, 40

And we decided to put the new armchair... right by the [front room] door that leads into the sitting room. IV, 40

Once when I slept down stairs, in the front room, we had a tall coal stove, then, and it was shaped something like a man with no arms. V, 97–98

"A Mussed-up Room" IV, 66

UPSTAIRS BEDROOMS

(1) MASTER BEDROOM

... and we brought the red bookcase from the front-room-upstairs... IV, 40

(2) CHILDREN'S BEDROOM

Papa takes them up to bed and they say goodnight... and tell him to leave the lamp in the hall. IV, 14–15

This morning we were all woken up by the noise of rain on the [piazza] tin roof outside our bedroom window. VI, 19

"Waking Carol up" VI, 26

(3) SINGLE BEDROOM

... and when we took the children up, we happened to go into the room where Marjorie [the baby] sleeps... III, 7

ATTIC

It is very interesting to go up in the attic and see all the old things... V, 112

CELLAR

There is a little cellar that goes in under the kitchen on one side of the main cellar. VI, 64–65.

SHED

I went into the shed, and got the big snow shovel... IV, 49

INDEX

BARN

One day Marjorie and I were playing in the barn . . . VI, 37

. . . played in the barn with the swing . . . and then we played with the swing again . . . II, 37–38

BARN, LOWER LEVEL OR CELLAR

(*see* note to I, 36, 2–3)

. . . the phoebe . . . uses the same nest about every year . . . It's under the barn [i.e., on top of the foundation-stones and under the overhang of the upper level] and no snow or rain gets in it while he has gone south. V, 70

PIAZZA (or **PORCH**)

Every time papa goes out to get a pail of water, Snider jumps off the piazza, if he is there, and runs . . . II, 3

Then the one [snow path] up to the piazza, that's useful for papa to carry water to the house for us to drink . . . III, 88–89

We took sharp sticks and went fishing, sticking the sticks into the leaves and we put [them] to dry on the piazza. III 113

Carol and Irma were out on the piazza, watching, and in the end the bull got away. IV, 24

After he got the water pail and laid it on the piazza . . . V, 32

. . . so we went to eat our cookies on the piazza. V, 84

BARNYARD

. . . so I went into the shed and got the big snow shovel and went out and shoveled a path from the barn to the piazza, then down to the pump, then down to the woodpecker tree, then over to the tree at the end of the quince vines [the maple tree closest to the northern corner made by the driveway and the Turnpike]. IV, 49

There is a path [through the snow] to the woodpecker tree. We use that path to go there because we play the woodpecker tree is a store or something, and buy things there. III, 88

Then there is another path that leads to the mailbox [at the corner of the driveway and the Turnpike]. That's the most useful of all to papa because he can read papers and I can't . . . III, 88

And then there is another path that goes to the barn. That is one of papa's quite useful ones . . . Papa uses it to water the horse and cow with. III, 88

The barn, the piazza, [the pump,] and the letter box paths are the ones papa cares about — and all the rest are ours . . . III, 89

(*see also*, note to I, 36, 2–3)

FRONT YARD

Then we went out on the front steps [to the front door] in the front yard. Just as we got there, down came a shower of rain, but there was a roof . . . [over the doorsteps] so we didn't get wet. V, 19

Papa moved it [the laurel] into the front yard, and I hope it will grow and have flowers on it. III, 29

The quince blossoms . . . make the front yard look lovely and red. III, 27

FRONT GARDEN (in **FRONT YARD**)

The front garden is just full of good things . . . phlox and two peonies and three hydrangeas . . . III, 36

(*see also*, note to I, 6, 16)

STONE STEPS

(*see* note to I, 36, 2–3)

Once when we were playing by the stone steps, I jumped up, said goodbye, and ran for the alders. VI, 74

[1905:] . . . a purple clematis we planted . . . down the stone steps. III, 36

[1908:] Right below the stone steps we have a white clematis. It blossoms every year, but just after we get up in the mountains, so we have never seen the flower at all. VI, 11

I went outdoors and took my sled and went down the stone steps. The steps were so slippery that I thought I was going to fall — because the sled was right on top of my head — and when I got down, the sled came after me and hit my legs and made my legs weak, and it made my legs joint down.   III, 59

HENHOUSE, BELOW STONE STEPS

(*see* note to II, 41, 16–18)

When we went in the yard, the snow was thick on the henhouse [roof].   II, 41

We went down the stone steps to see papa feed the hens, then we went to see if there were any eggs...   II, 37–38

GARDEN, BEHIND THE HOUSE

Papa was washing the milk pail by the sink window that looks out toward the corn...   V, 1

ORCHARD BEHIND BARN

Somebody's cow got into our orchard.   IV, 23

I saw quite a big flock of snowbirds in the orchard.   III, 5

On the fruit trees, the petals are all coming off the flowers. The ground is white with them — it looks like snow.   I, 42

I can see papa up that biggest tree ...reaching for apples.   IV, 66

(*see also*, note to I, 54, 1)

HAYFIELD BEYOND ORCHARD

One day, quite a long time ago, papa and Lesley and Irma and Carol went to walk...We went out [through the orchard] to the little field and [through the gate and] down the little road...Then we went home to the [gate and the] little field, and home back to the

house from the gate...As we got over the gate, the sun was just going down...   III, 80–81

Carol got scratched on a [chestnut] burr, and fussed about it till he got to the gate and just as he came out of the little field, on his way home, he found a pink cartridge — and that satisfied him till he got the rest of the way home.   IV, 20

GATE BEYOND HAYFIELD

(*see* notes to I, 38–39; I, 54, 1)

Yesterday, papa and I and Carol went out to our big chestnut tree. You go out [through the orchard and through the hayfield] to the gate, climb over the gate, and go...   IV, 19

OLD SOUTH ROAD, BEYOND GATE

(*see* notes to I, 38–39; I, 54, 1)

You go out to the gate, climb over the gate, and go out one of the little woodsy roads that used to be a road that teams rode on and a few scattering houses were along it.   IV, 19

CRANBERRY BOG

(*see* note to I, 54, 1)

...we went out to the gate and [just beyond it, turned to the right on the old South Road and] went down the hill [as far as Hyla Brook, and turned left, following the brook] into the cranberry bog. We took off our shoes and stockings and waded in. We found a lot of flowers.   I, 54

The pogonias grow out in our cranberry bog.   IV, 3

Some time in June the cranberry bog is all spotted over with little pink flowers...   VI, 1

...the cranberry bog was all frozen over...We had great fun sliding back and forth.   III, 76

HYLA BROOK

(*see* notes to I, 36, 2–3, I, 38–39; I, 54, 1; IV, 10, 12–17)

One day, papa and I took a long

INDEX

walk. We went to the gate and ... turned the corner by the gate and went down the path [the old South Road] till we came to the brook [Hyla Brook]. We crossed the brook and I got my foot a little bit wet, but we went on. We went clear up on Klein's hill... I, 38–39

My hoop beat me down to the brook... I, 45

... there came a bull tearing down the hill [toward Hyla Brook] by the back [of the] barn. IV, 23

The peepers sing and the bells do ring... IV, 10

THE ALDERS, ALONG HYLA BROOK

(*see* note to V, 101, 2–4)

The alders is one of my favorite places to go.... But we only go out in the alders once in three or four days. V, 78–79

There is one path out in the alders that we children have been afraid to go down ever since we have been home [from the White Mountains]. VI, 47

Then we took the hobble bush and some other things out in our alders to plant. V, 102

... I jumped up, said goodbye, and ran for the alders. VI, 74

FALLS BRIDGE PARK

(*see* note to V, 101, 2–4)

One day papa set out to find things to put in our park named Falls Bridge. V, 101

KLEIN'S HILL (SOUTH OF HYLA BROOK)

(*see* notes to I, 19, 4–5; I, 38–39)

There is a little hill just in front of [the piazza on] our house. We call it Klein's hill. It isn't our land. V, 39

One morning we came down [stairs] very early. The sun had not come up yet. In December it peeks over Klein's hill at about twenty-five minutes past seven... V, 39

If Klein's hill didn't have so many stones and [sweet-] fern bushes on it, but had a few more big trees on it, it would look a good deal prettier when the sun shone on it. But now it looks rough and bare. V, 41

KLEIN'S WOODS

(*see* note to I, 30, 5)

One day Carol, I, Irma, and papa went way out in Klein's woods and picked a lot of long-stemmed violets. I, 30

I went up on the hill and ... there was a pretty brown rabbit running away into the woods. I walked on and came to the little old garden on top of the further knoll. VI, 74

CELLARHOLE, ON KLEIN'S HILL

(*see* note to I, 19, 4–5)

There was an old house halfway down Klein's hill, on the other side [of the Turnpike, from our house] which was burned down. It was a kind of an old-fashioned house. There were old-fashioned flowers around it. III, 128

GUAY'S WOODS AND FARM

(*see* notes to I, 30, 5; I, 34; I, 38–39; II, 2, 3–4)

We went to walk, yesterday. Papa and I like to go to walk. We went in Guay's woods. II, 2

... we went for a walk, way out in Guay's. III, 80

LONDONDERRY TURNPIKE

(*see* notes to I, 1, 10–11; I, 14, 7; I, 19, 4–5)

TWO PASTURES (ACROSS TURNPIKE)

(*see* notes to I, 19, 4–5; I, 33, 2–3; I, 37)

... went up from the little pasture ... I, 19

... went out in the big pasture. I, 23

You know that wire [barbed-wire fence] in the little pasture with no

M

N

O

P

our things right on and go along out in the yard to play. Then when we get tired of playing there, we go over across the road to play on the bars that lead into the pasture. But soon we want to do something else, and somebody asks, "What shall we play, now?" And then someone else says, "Let's go get a few checker-berries in the field." So away we go down the hill as fast as we can . . . V, 72–73

I love to roll my hoop. I have two places to roll it. I do roll it most all the time. It rolls better on the hill by the barn. It rolls farther there and it's better than ever on the big, big hill. I could hardly keep up with it and I did not keep up with it and the hoop beat me down to the brook . . . I, 45

I do have a nice little store in the grove. I do have a little counter. I like to play in it. I do sell all different kinds of dirt to Carol and Irma. I, 47

I am going to haul stones out of the big pasture with Carol's hay cart, and clean it up and make grass grow there. . . . I am going to bring them over here and . . . make little stone walls . . . II, 22–23

Day before yesterday, I was playing in the little pasture, and I was leaning over a little ledge of rocks . . . when, splash, I went into the water. I pulled myself out again, and I looked like a scarecrow . . . II, 14

. . . we play the woodpecker tree is a store, or something, and buy things there. III, 88

. . . then Lena Guay wanted to look at toys and I gave her some, and by and by I put them away and [we] played in the barn with the swing. II, 37

Today we went out doors to play. . . . We were at playing in a minute or two, and how we did play all the forenoon. We played mud pies. . . . We put dirt in the pans and covers we found, and then put snow on top of the dirt. III, 111

Sometimes Carol and Irma are good to Marjorie, but sometimes they like to tease her. . . . Sometimes they play she's sick and pour all sorts of stuff down her. IV, 44

. . . and play they are bulls and knock them to pieces with other sticks. We have great fun, and Carol and Irma play with me most all day. But they stop when I stop, generally. IV, 46

More than once a day the sitting room gets into a terrible mess, for there are so many playthings. And so when the room gets so thick with them that there isn't any more room to play, then we begin to ask to go out-doors. But mama never lets us, till we have cleaned it all up. V, 66

We have so many playthings, it would cover the floor of two of these rooms put together. V, 66–67

POULTRYMAN

(see, as subhead under FROST, ROBERT LEE)

"Prayer in Spring, A"

(see note to III, 27)

Prophecy

"What I Prophesied" V, 9–10

(see also note to V, 9–10)

PUNISHMENTS

Carol and Irma are so mischievous that we don't know what to do. But we have to stop them, and when they don't stop we have to spank them. And [then] they cry, they break dishes and cups, and bend spoons, and get hold of the sugar bowl and take a spoon and eat every bit of sugar . . . I, 17

We took the cow home and gave her a good spanking, and she never ran away again. III, 2

Marjorie is awfully funny, some-times. But sometimes she's naughty and we scold her. But generally she laughs [at the scoldings] and we have to slap her to make her stop, and that makes her cry. III, 96

Papa generally pinches us where it hurts, but mama where it doesn't. III, 108

Q

"Quest of the Purple-fringed, The"
(see note to II, 7, 7–8)
"Quince Blossoms, The" III, 27–28

R

RELIGIOUS BELIEF
(see note to V, 52, 2)
Yesterday I went to church the first time. . . . The first thing we did was to have all in church stand up and sing something out of the Bible all at once. But mama and I didn't sing. V, 52–53

. . . and the men that were immortals were called gods and some believe that there are [such], and some don't. IV, 58

. . . all her life she believed religious things from the Bible that weren't true and at last became a nun. VI, 51
"Rose Pogonias"
(see note to I, 54, 16–17)
Roy
The next horse we had was a red horse, too, named Roy. IV, 55
Russell, Mr. Lester
(see note preliminary to VI)

S

Salem, New Hampshire
When papa was a little boy . . . in Salem, he lived in a tent with no fly to it. IV, 36
(see notes to I, 35, 4; II, 5–6)
"Servant to Servants, A"
(see note preliminary to VI)
Shakespeare, William
I like Wordsworth and Shakespeare best. III, 78

(first line of song from *The Tempest* by, quoted, III, 58, 1; first line of song from *As You Like It* by, quoted, III, 78, 10–11)
SLIDING
I go sliding down the hills and around . . . I, 7

. . . and there will be no more sliding . . . I, 9

Helen Wilson gave me a ride on her sled. I, 16

"Getting up the Hill after Sliding down" III, 59–60
Snider, the Collie dog
(see note to I, 6, 16; see also the subhead, DOGS, under ANIMALS)
South Road
(see notes to I, 34; I, 38–39)
Stars
(see subhead, ASTRONOMER, under FROST, ROBERT LEE)

T

Telephone
Sometimes Irma plays that her doll is sick, and plays that the doorknobs are telephones, and [she] telephones up to the play doctor . . . III, 96

. . . if Marjorie sees Irma telephoning, she first tries the knob to telephone on, but that is a little too high for her. Then she runs back and forth from one corner to another, and telephones in the corners — puts her head right in them. And it looks so funny that we all burst out laughing. And Marjorie, when she hears it, jumps out of her corner and scuts across to another corner, laughing. III, 96–97

. . . I heard the buzzing in the telephone pole, and I thought just for the fun of it I would go in the bushes and listen to the buzzing a minute. V, 49

About every day, a long long ring rings on the telephone, and if you want to hear what the weather is going to be,

INDEX

just go and listen. Friday, the weather report said that "it was going to be warmer and rain in the afternoon . . ." Well, she didn't get it exactly right . . . V, 55

Tennyson, Alfred, Lord

(*see* notes to III, 123; V, 86–88)
. . . because it reminds me of the brook that said, "I sparkle out among the fern to bicker down the valley." V, 79; note to I, 54, 1

The poem I like best is Sir Richard Grenville ["The Revenge"] . . . III, 123

"My Favorite Books": First there is Tennyson's book. . . . Why I like Tennyson is because all his poems are about things that happened a long time ago, and he made up lovely pictures of castles and old ruins that were made a long time ago. And then he told about the kings that lived in them. My favorite one is King Arthur, now, but of course I haven't read them all yet. V, 86–87

Theriault, Mr. and Mrs. J. A. G.

(*see* note preliminary to I)

THINKING

One day I was out strolling about, up and down the road, thinking. Pretty soon, after I got through thinking about that, I looked around for something else to think about. V, 49

When you are walking along half thinking about something, have you not seen it right in front of you? But when you are walking along, not thinking about it, it is probably right in front of you, but you don't see it. IV, 33

"A Thought": In the night, something came after me, and in the morning I tried to make it come again, but it would not. III, 53

I have noticed when being out alone in a mild winter day like today, when you are walking along thinking, with nothing to hear but the tramp of your feet on the snow, with your head down and not tending to much, you're quite startled if you hear a sleigh coming in front of you. And if you get out [of the way] all right, you generally can't get the thing you were thinking about back and how unhappy you feel. III, 106

Thompson, Lawrance

Robert Frost, The Early Years
cited in notes to I, 2, 6–12; I, 19, 4–5; I, 26; I, 54, 1; II, 2, 3–4; II, 7, 7–8; II, 31–33; III, 72–75; III, 116, 2–3; IV, 5, 6; IV, 47, 11; IV, 53, 8–9; V, 43, 9–10; V, 59, 7; V, 94, 2–3

and Edward Connery Lathem

Robert Frost: Farm-Poultryman
cited in notes to I, 46, 1 and 4; IV, 53, 8–9

TREES, ON OR NEAR THE FROST FARM

APPLE (*see*, as subhead under FRUITS, AND FRUIT TREES)

BIRCH

. . . and now they're building a nest behind the house, in a birch tree. I, 51

A crow flew out of the birch tree by the [kitchen] sink window. V, 8

. . . a birch tree down in the field behind the house. . . . The wind blew it back and forth and made it look as if it was walking. V, 83

When it blew hard in gales like that, the leaves would come off the birch trees back of the house, in swarms, and we would try to catch them. V, 10–11

(*see also* the topical heading, BIRCHES, BENDING)

CHESTNUT

It has been very good chestnutting this year. Papa and we children have got seventeen or eighteen quarts. . . . There is one tree out in Guay's that we got most of them on, but it isn't the great big tree that we generally get most on. VI, 58

INDEX

Yesterday, papa and I and Carol went out to our big chestnut tree....
There were piles on the tree but hardly any on the ground. IV, 19–20

MAPLE

(*see*, on six maples in the Frost farmyard, note to I, 19, 4–5)

...a nest in one of the maple trees here in the yard. I, 51

...and our big maple tree ["the woodpecker tree"] and the other maples haven't quite turned. II, 12

One day we got papa to tap the woodpecker tree. He bored a round hole in it... IV, 91

Most of the leaves came off the woodpecker tree that day and it looked as if winter would be here in a few days. V, 11

OAK

... and the little oaks have turned, but the big oaks haven't... II, 12

... the little oak tree at the corner of the [pasture] bars. III, 29

You go up to the bars, go through them into the little pasture, then through another gate, then up through the lane to the little grove and then it's only a few steps to the lightning-struck oak. IV, 11

PEACH AND PEAR, (*see,* as subheads under FRUITS, AND FRUIT TREES

PINE

... and our big maple tree has all turned and the other maples haven't quite turned and the pines don't ever turn and I am glad because I like to look at green things. II, 12

...and the walnut leaves are dark yellow and the quince leaves don't have any color at all and the pine trees leave their needles on all winter and the needles stay green too. IV, 28

(*see also,* under LANDMARKS, THE BIG PINE GROVE and THE LITTLE PINE GROVE)

POPLAR

Popple leaves yet are green... IV, 28, 1

SPRUCE

The innocence we soon got tired of, because the farm was just white with them. We found the first of them on the woodroad to my little spruce tree. That was in March on Sunday. III, 23

... and then you go up in a little field [in Guay's woods] where my little spruce tree is growing... IV, 19

WALNUT

It is good walnutting, too, but we have been too lazy to get very many, so the squirrels got most of them. VI, 59

... and the walnut leaves are dark yellow... IV, 28

We have a nut tree near our house ... and yesterday papa took us up the lane to see if there were any up there and we found a very nice tree — a good deal better than any of the [other] trees — very thin shelled and easy to get out [of the shell]. II, 9–10

We took the cow and tied her down by the nut tree to eat grass — the grass is long down there — and so she got loose... I, 49

I and Irma [and] Carol went down by the nut tree to play. I, 23

Then we went down by the nut tree and played on the rocks. Then I hammered her some more nuts and she went home and carried them with her. II, 38

"WOODPECKER TREE"

(*see*, for location, I, 19, 4–5; *see also,* FARMYARD, under LANDMARKS

"Tuft of Flowers, The"

(a line from, quoted in the note to III, 27)

U

Upton, Sarah J. (Mrs. George E. Upton) (*see* notes to I, 19, 4–5; I, 34; I, 54, 1)

V

"Vantage Point, The"
(*see* note to V, 110, 7–14)

VEHICLES

AIRPLANE. Now the flying machine that is just begun to be thought of. . . . Only one man can ride on it. . . . They cost more than the automobiles, but people will want to travel in the air for a while and let the autos alone. VI, 35–36

AUTOMOBILE. . . . and just when we turned the corner to go in and see it, right behind us an automobile came chugging up behind us and came in, too. II, 26

A few nights ago, I dreamed that we were out driving and an automobile came and stopped beside us. . . . III, 38

BATTLESHIP. Well, after that, on the brightest sunniest morning — on Sunday — one of them gave a toot and we looked out and there were five or six of the Spanish ships coming out . . . But we beat them easily. III, 104

BICYCLE. Carol and I and Marjorie were going down by Berry's bars and two bicycles came along and I backed into the bushes out of their way. . . . and turned and watched the bicycles go along. VI, 29

BOAT. In the [Fall River Line] boat [to New York City] we had two little rooms of our own, one a bedroom and the other a kitchen. We had berths to sleep in, instead of beds . . . VI, 40

Then they walked down to the edge of the water and hired a boat and rowed out on the lake. V, 75

We had noticed that there was a steamship on the lake. Papa had to go and see what time the ship went. We got on our best clothes and went down to the wharf. It was ick-strodnery icksiting. (Quoted from a journal fragment, in the note preliminary to VI)

CARRIAGE. Sunday we took our walk, all of us. . . . We all went out in the big grove. Marjorie liked it very much. . . . She is a good deal bigger than she was when she just came, and she is more interested in things. Well, when we got there, we left her in the carriage. II, 13

DEMOCRAT WAGON. One day we went to see Mrs. Wilson and we took the democrat wagon and mama and Irma sat in the back seat and papa, Carol, and me sat in the front. I, 16; *see also* note to I, 16

ELEVATED TRAIN. The place where we lived [in New York City] was right in front of the elevated trains, where you could see them from the window. They build the tracks up high now, so as to give the wagons and people more room to pass below. VI, 39

GIG. Carol, Irma, and I were over across the road, picking up little quartz stones, and we looked in the barn and there was papa cleaning up the gig. We ran over there and asked him if he was going to Derry, and he said no he wasn't, that he was going to send it over to Derry by Mr. Perkins so that he could *walk* over and *ride back* with the gig [and the new horse]. IV, 47; (*see also* the note to IV, 47)

HAY CART. I am going to haul stones out of the big pasture with Carol's hay cart . . . II, 22

. . . Carol and Irma were playing on the hay cart . . . IV, 7

We didn't have such a nice time haying, this year, because the haying men put on [the hayrack] so much hay that we couldn't [get up on top of the load and] ride. IV, 85

SLED. Helen Wilson gave me a ride on her sled. I, 16

And when I got to the hill, I slid down and the sled went sideways. I was a little afraid, but when I got down and looked up the hill I thought it would be hard getting up, and so it was. III, 59

(*see also,* topical heading, SLIDING)

SLEIGH

"Jingle bells, jingle bells,
Jingle all the way,
Oh what fun it is to ride
In a one-horse open sleigh."

(II, 50; *see* note to II, 50)

STEAM-ROLLER. Carol thought it was a dragon and I thought it was a train, and Irma ran for the house, and Marjorie began to cry. VI, 7

This morning we were all woken up by the noise of rain on the tin [piazza] roof outside our bedroom window. It was coming down terribly hard, and making a noise like a steam-roller. VI, 19

TRAIN. We all enjoy the ride on the train very much, but Marjorie generally goes to sleep in mama's lap on the way. V, 94

W

WAR

War is a good thing, if you have a good reason for it. III, 124

The war between Japan and Russia didn't interest me very much, for I was too young. VI, 69

There was a war between us and the Spaniards for Cuba. III, 102

Papa and I have a game of the Civil War. IV, 80

I stepped into the bushes and put

my ear to the telephone pole and I began to think what that buzzing meant. I thought a minute, and then said, "It's saying that we are going to have a war with Japan in three weeks." ... When I heard this, I ran home to [tell] papa and mama about it, for I knew that we couldn't get enough battleships and coal and wood in order while they were fighting. For we weren't in fighting order at all, and we all were very much excited. V, 51

The other turtle was asleep because he thought the other turtle would sleep *that* night, in peace or war, just like Mr. Dooley in peace and war. When he got there he was tickled to find him asleep. He lifted his club and let it come down on the turtle's shell and the shell broke ... III, 93–94

These animals are now growing very much more numerous than ever, and I am afraid they will conquer Russia and drive the people out, and that will mean war, too, because nobody will want to take the Russians in. VI, 68

Webster, Mr. George A.

(*see* note to I, 14, 12–13)

... and I went down to Mr. Webster's bars and the cow wouldn't come ... I, 14

We went home a pretty way, and we came out by Webster's. I, 46–47

West-running Brook

(*see* notes to I, 54, 1; II, 20, 4–6)

"West-running Brook"

(*see* note to I, 54, 1)

White, Mr. Edwin

(*see* note to IV, 5, 6)

... and by and by grandpa began to get chilly and wanted to go home, so we went home. IV, 5

... grandpa came in from out in the orchard. He had been piling up brush for a bonfire ... IV, 7

White Mountains

(*see* note to V, 94, 2–3)

INDEX

Wilson, Mr. and Mrs. John

    (*see* note to II, 17–18)

Yesterday, papa went over to Derry [Depot] and he took me with him. We went to Wilson's, on the way over, but he wasn't there, so we went along over to Derry and stopped on the way back. . . . Then we went to the Wilsons' again to get some meat. He was there this time.   II, 17–18

    One day we went to see Mrs. Wilson . . . and we went into Mrs. Wilson's house and Carol and Irma cried and I stayed in a little while and then I went out to play with Helen and she gave me a ride on her sled.   I, 16

Windham, New Hampshire

    (*see* note to I, 35)

We went to Windham, and we turned the corner by the store in Windham. We went past Clyde's and down where the gobbling turkey is. He went, "Like-like, gobul-gobul."   I, 35

Windham Road

    (*see* note to I, 14, 7)

"WOODPECKER TREE"

    (*see,* for location, I, 19, 4–5; *see also,* FARMYARD, under LANDMARKS)

Wordsworth, William

    (*see* note to III, 78)

Poems are very pretty sometimes. I like Wordsworth and Shakespeare's best. . . . "Lucy Gray" is a little too sad . . .   III, 78

    I like Wordsworth's poems about best of all. He makes them so pretty and gives you such a picture that he sees, and he likes to have something in his poems that carries something in his mind.   III, 85

    (poems by, quoted in part: "I Wandered Lonely as a Cloud," III, 85; "My Heart Leaps Up," III, 86; "The Solitary Reaper," III, 85; "To Sleep," III, 86)

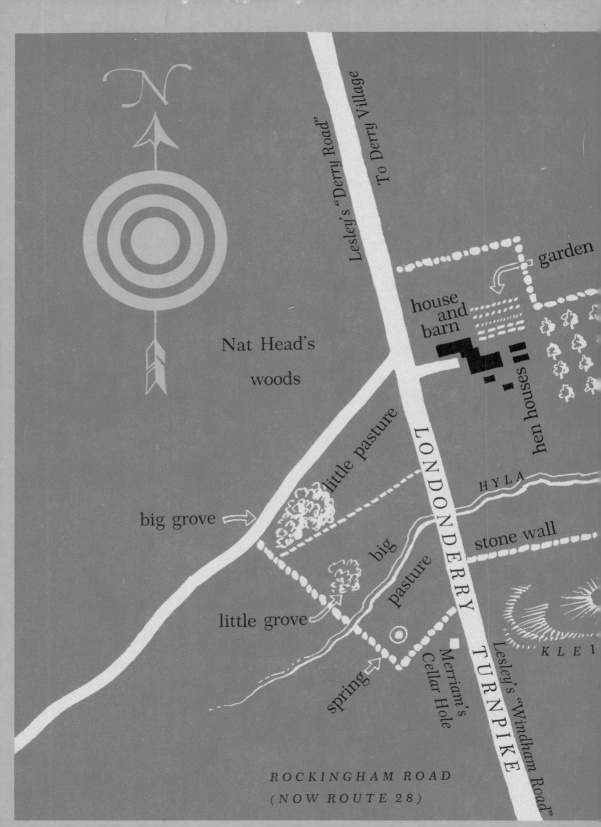